C000120395

CRY ARGENTINA

CRY ARGENTINA

Saving South Georgia
The Terrifying Prelude to the Falklands War

Ian A. Sykes

Book Guild Publishing
Sussex, England

First published in Great Britain in 2013 by
The Book Guild Ltd
Pavilion View
19 New Road
Brighton, BN1 1UF

Typesetting in Garamond by
Keyboard Services, Luton, Bedfordshire

Printed in Great Britain by
CPI Group (UK) Ltd, Croydon, CR0 4YY

A catalogue record for this book is available from
The British Library

ISBN 978 1 84624 871 9

Author's Note

My first visit to South Georgia was in 1967, forty years ago. I was twenty-four and had signed on for a two and a half year contract with British Antarctic Survey as a dog driver and guide and I became known as a fid. We stopped off at Grytviken on South Georgia and shot two hundred elephant seals for dog food. King Edward Cove was literally red with blood. I watched the Falkland Islander crew of the RRS *Shackleton* creating carnage on the beaches; it must have been very similar to the days of the whaling when the huge beasts were hauled ashore onto the flensing platforms and dissected. Perhaps all this bloodletting was the precursor to future events.

I spent most of my time working from Stonington Island on the Antarctic Peninsula but on the way home in 1970 visited a number of Argentinian bases where we had a wonderfully friendly reception and had a second call into South Georgia. No one could have dreamed that this beautiful island could become a place of conflict. For all of us fids who knew the place, when it came, the Falkland Island War was a total shock, a war between two friendly countries that should never have happened.

I left the ship in Punta Arenas in Patagonia and hitchhiked up through Argentina; this was during the early stages of the dirty war. In Buenos Aires bombs were going off as an everyday occurrence and on one occasion a group of us were arrested as suspected *Montanero* terrorists and spent a frightening few days in the local gaol. It was only in the researching of this book that I realised how close we came to becoming some of the 'Missing'.

An army officer called Hugo (I never knew his surname) realised we were not *Montanero* and had us released. To him I am deeply grateful.

In the year 2000 I had a spell in hospital and to pass the time I began to write a history of the island and the reasons behind the invasion and found that although the British side was well documented the military junta in Argentina had given little away other than in propaganda. In 2004 a group of us, now middle-aged fids, managed to get together and sail down to Antarctica, revisiting our old and now derelict bases. We returned via South Georgia and I was lucky enough to walk over part of Shackleton's route across the island from Fortuna Bay to Stromness. The sheer enormity of his undertaking was breathtaking and this was the experience that motivated me into telling this story.

I have tried to write an unbiased account of events from both sides but there is no doubt in my own mind that the military junta in Argentina was a vicious dictatorship covering its back from the atrocities of the dirty war against its own people. Many of the Argentinian servicemen fought as true professionals with great courage. The events are accurate. The actions taking place at Grytviken when the marines took on the frigate *Guerrico* and the helicopter attack on the submarine *Santa Fe* are well documented from the British side but Argentina has never admitted what happened. I have tried to reconstruct the action from their side as accurately as possible. There is only rumour and no evidence that the captain of the *Guerrico* died as the ship escaped from King Edward Cove and the number of soldiers killed in the crashed Puma helicopter are unknown. The extraordinary series of helicopter crashes on the Fortuna Glacier are as it happened.

When writing this story it was hard not to put my own words into the mouths of politicians; as far as possible I have used known text and I have tried to portray events accurately as they occurred.

Ian A. Sykes

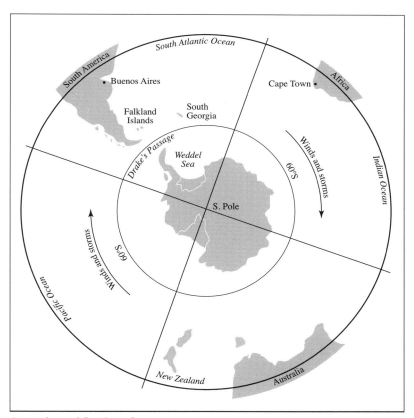

Antarctica and Southern Ocean

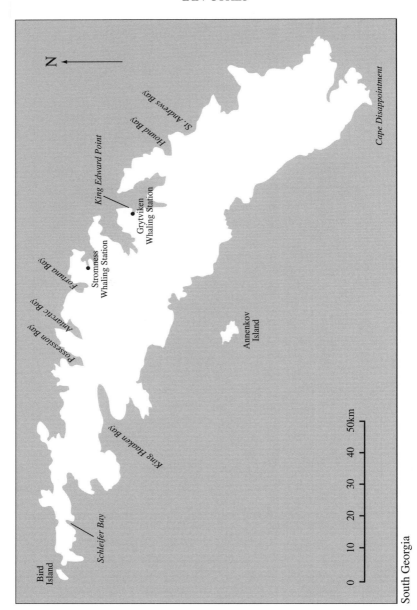

Bird
Island

Schleifer Bay

King Haaken Bay

Possession Bay

Antarctic Bay

Fortuna Bay

Stromness
Whaling Station

King Edward Point

Hound Bay

St. Andrews Bay

Grytviken
Whaling Station

Annenkov
Island

Cape Disappointment

| 0 | 10 | 20 | 30 | 40 | 50km |

South Georgia

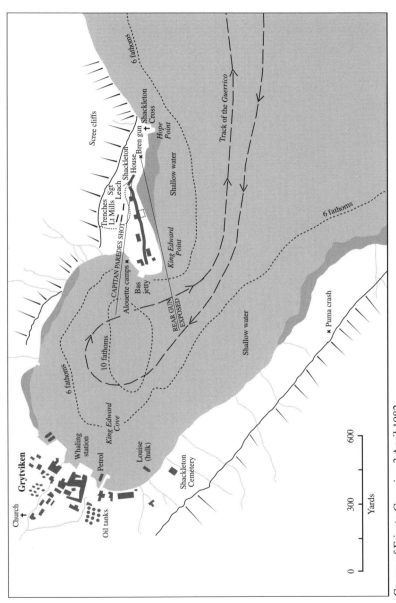

Course of Frigate *Guerrico*, 3 April 1982

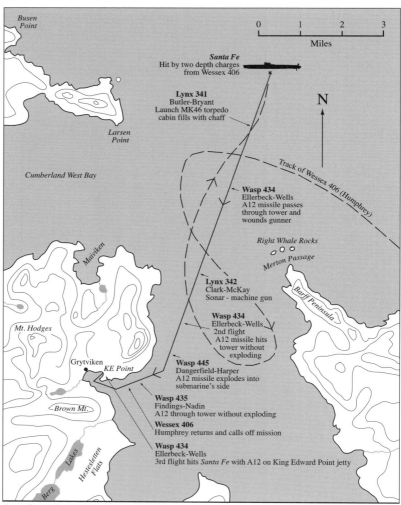

Attack on *Santa Fe*, 25 April 1982

Part 1

An Uneasy Calm

1

Buenos Aires, 1973

Lieutenant de Navio Hugo Corti stood uneasily watching the dock. The gas lamps surrounding the waterfront had recently been electrified and, like so many things in Argentina these days, only about half were working. The moorings along the waterfront and many of the roads around Puerto Madero, the dock area of Buenos Aires, were paved with old-fashioned cobbles brought in by English sailing clippers as ballast during the previous century. The waterfront had an eerie texture of age and decay. The darkness over the water seemed solid and impenetrable. He could see no sign of the naval military police also waiting in the shadows. They, like him, were well out of view and settled in for a long night's wait. His mouth was dry from too many cigarettes but he lit another under the cover of his jacket almost without thinking.

He was a small man, smart in his officer's uniform, with deep-set eyes that made him look serious and older than his thirty years but he laughed easily and was popular among his colleagues. He had joined the navy as a cadet and trained at the Naval Mechanics College in Buenos Aires where he had been singled out as a clever thinker and had gone on to study naval strategy. He had made rapid promotion onto a planning group set up by Admiral Massera and had become aide to Captain Jorge Anaya, one of the navy's senior strategists. He loved this part of his work.

However, these were trying times for young naval officers and Hugo knew that what he might witness tonight could very well affect his future career. He was a navy man; a sailor and a strategist, not a policeman. He knew that, like many other young officers, he

3

was being sent out to become involved in the new tough strategy that the navy was taking against the *Montanero* terrorist organisation. The business of rooting out dissidents was not his job and the viciousness with which the military was tackling this problem concerned him – he felt he was being drawn into something in which he did not wish to be implicated. The last three months had been some of the most dramatic and worrying of his life.

Standing waiting with hunched shoulders, dragging quietly, the cigarette hidden as much as possible in his gloved hand, he watched the dock. A gentle touch on his shoulder made him start suddenly. The young officer at his side had appeared soundlessly from the darkness. Lieutenant Alfredo Astiz was remarkably handsome with a boyish face and, unusually for an Argentinian, golden blond hair, which was cut slightly too long. His naval uniform was immaculate. There was something about his eyes that made Hugo feel uneasy.

'They're coming,' hissed the younger man, almost inaudibly. Hugo, peering into the gloom, could see nothing. Astiz vanished into the night. For what seemed an interminable time, nothing was to be seen. Then, quite clearly, he could hear the quiet, low thump of a motor. A small fishing boat was inching into the dock, showing no lights.

The trap was almost complete. The boat touched the edge of the dock; Hugo could hear the crunch of wood against the quayside. A shadowy figure slipped into the light at the water's edge and began tying up the boat. At that moment, all hell broke loose. Lights flashed on; from all around the dock men came running. The figure on the waterside leapt back into the boat; there was the metallic rattle of automatic fire. Two men from the boat had flung themselves overboard and were swimming frantically away, sitting ducks for the military police now staring down from above on the quay. Hugo, still paralysed at his vantage point, suddenly pulled himself together.

'No, no,' he screamed, 'they're just boys!' It was too late. Men were spraying the water with automatic fire. The swimmers had no chance. On board the fishing boat several young people were standing waving their hands wildly in the air. Looking very pale and terrified, and blinking blindly into lights above, were four boys and two girls, none of whom could have been over eighteen or nineteen years old. In the water the two swimmers were clearly dead, floating face down almost alongside. Military police were swarming onto the fishing boat.

Astiz stepped lightly onto the deck.

'Well, amigos, what have we here?' he asked, in his quiet, cultured voice.

'We were fishing,' said one of the boys, shaking with fright.

'You are *Montanero* – why do you come in with no lights?'

The boy repeated, terrified, 'We were fishing, our lights do not work.'

Hugo clambered onto the boat just as Astiz raised his pistol and hit the boy in the teeth. 'For God's sake, Alfredo,' he said, 'that's enough – they may be innocent.'

The smaller of the boys was crouching down, helping his friend on the deck, who was spitting blood and teeth. Astiz's face was contorted with anger. He turned on Hugo. 'This is a police operation, Teniente. These *Montanero* filth are the scourge of Argentina,' he said, kicking the smaller of the boys. 'You do your job and I'll do mine.'

By now the rest of the group were handcuffed. All the cuffs had a tightening winder twisted to maximum and were so tight that the boys' hands were white and bloodless. They were in obvious pain and very frightened. The military police seemed casual and unconcerned.

Several vehicles had arrived at the scene and the small group was pushed up onto the cobbled waterfront and unceremoniously bundled into a police van. The bodies of the two boys in the water were retrieved and thrown in alongside them.

'Where are you taking them?' Hugo asked.

'They're going to the Military Technical College for questioning; if they are innocent they will be free to go.'

5

'Once in that place you know they will never get out,' Hugo protested. He knew that recently his old college had become a detention centre for dissidents and suspected terrorists and rumour was rife about what went on behind its closed gates. 'I intend to speak to Capitan Anaya about this. Two kids are dead and you haven't a shred of evidence that they're *Montanero* terrorists. For all we know they were just out fishing.'

'As you will,' Astiz snarled. 'It's my job to rid the country of these scum. Now get out of my way!' He slammed the van doors shut and waving the driver away climbed into the waiting police car and indicated Hugo into the back seat. They followed the van into the dark back streets of Buenos Aires in silence, Hugo furiously trying to control his anger.

This has all happened since Peron's return from exile, he thought. The old dictator had sacked the entire naval high command and made Admiral Massera supreme commander. Hugo knew that the purge had helped his own speedy promotion as aide to Captain Anaya who was now one of the navy's senior strategists and a rising star in the new command, but many good men had been forced to leave the Service.

Back at the Academy, Hugo, still shocked and angry, went immediately to see the capitan who, surprisingly, was expecting him. Hugo assumed that Astiz had already informed him of what had happened. Anaya was a thin-faced man with greased black hair combed straight back, and his keen, analytical eyes gave little away. Hugo knew him to be one of Admiral Massera's right-hand men, ruthlessly ambitious for the navy.

He gave a brief account of the night's operation.

'It's our orders to stop this terrorism, Teniente,' Anaya said. 'From what I hear the military police were acting under a reliable tip-off: it's no use getting squeamish about these things.'

'But, sir, there was no evidence; they shot two unarmed youngsters trying to swim away. It's what anyone would have done. It was cold-blooded murder! Surely it will bring the navy into disrepute if this goes on.'

'Teniente Corti, you know full well that President Peron has ordered Admiral Massera to stamp out the *Montanero*. These communists and socialists are wrecking the country. Bombings and murder are an everyday occurrence in Argentina and it's got to be stopped.'

'But surely we need some evidence; there was no sign of anything illegal that I could see.'

'Please sit down, Teniente. You have an outstanding career ahead of you. You have recently been promoted to the new strategy committee; there are great expansion plans for the navy in which you have a part. Don't spoil all this by causing trouble.'

Hugo began to speak but was silenced by the capitan. 'Your father-in-law, Capitan Emilio Vildoza, wasn't he a supporter of Peron in the overthrow of President Irigoyen when the president first came to power?'

'Yes, sir, he always believed that Peron would return and restore some order to the country. Our family has supported him throughout his eighteen-year exile. I can't believe that the president would sanction this kind of behaviour in the navy. Never!'

A vein began to throb in Anaya's neck and his face hardened. Rising from his seat, he looked the younger man straight in the eye. 'I repeat: you have an outstanding career ahead of you, Teniente Corti. My advice to you is that you forget tonight's operation and concentrate on the task ahead.'

'But, sir, what will happen to these youngsters now?'

'There were guns and ammunition on the boat, Teniente, so they will be dealt with in due course.' Anaya answered with a cold smile that terminated the meeting and told Hugo that the capitan was lying. There had been no sign of weapons in the boat.

He left the office feeling sick; Astiz was waiting for him with a triumphant smile on his face and Hugo found himself looking into cold, grey, remorseless eyes. He prodded Hugo with a long, pointed finger.

'You're wasting your time, Corti. You're soft,' he snarled. 'We're going to rid Argentina of these communist scum. Remember,

Teniente, you were there and just as involved as I was. You just haven't the guts to see it through.'

Hugo furiously thrust the hand away. 'You're crazy, you know damn well that those kids were innocent and there were no guns on that boat. This was a free country until you and your bunch of thugs stirred things up.'

A look of blind hatred crossed Astiz's face and then he controlled himself and his features relaxed. 'There's nothing you can do, Corti. This is police business. You have no authority over us so keep out of my way.' He turned contemptuously and left, leaving Hugo standing alone feeling frustrated, angry and impotent.

This man is mad and out of control, he thought. There was not a thing he could do. Deep in thought, he drove home through the dark streets. What on earth was happening in the navy? What had happened tonight could have happened to any youngsters who happened to be in the wrong place at the wrong time. In a year or two's time it might be his own son who was out fishing. He shuddered to think what was happening to the prisoners in the Mechanics College.

He knew that he was in a privileged position. He lived with his wife, Maria, and eleven-year-old son, Raul, in a navy compound in Lomas Del Mirador, a suburb on the outskirts of the city, well away from the trouble spots. Perhaps it was better to keep quiet. There seemed little point in worrying his wife and he didn't want to damage his career. He decided to say nothing.

Hugo's fears were not unfounded. The remaining six students were tortured and beaten mercilessly. Astiz got his confession; by the time he had finished, all were willing to admit to anything that was asked of them. In the early hours of the morning the group, along with three other prisoners, were drugged with Pentothal and, in their confused state, thrown into a truck and driven through the night.

Twenty-five miles away at Lomas military airbase a slight brightening of dawn tinged the eastern horizon. All was still, and a light morning haze hung over the airstrip. Captain Adolfo Scilingo completed the checks in the cockpit of the Hastings. It was 4.30 a.m.; Adolfo could just make out the controller in the tower and the ground crew smoking at the side of the hangar. He shuddered at the thought of the grisly task ahead of him. The rest of the base still slept. The engine hummed smoothly with the normal shaky rattle of tappets as the propeller idled gently. Adolfo hated this job but could see no way out of it. He looked over to Ernesto, his co-pilot, who acknowledged his gaze without speaking. Neither man had anything to say.

The military truck pulled up alongside the aircraft. The pilots watched, fascinated at the ease with which the guards ushered the prisoners up the steps into the hold. They stumbled and reeled but were still walking – not as bad as some of the groups they had taken. Some of this party seemed no more than children and, unusually, there were two women. He knew that they were drugged. The airmen had refused to fly if there was any likelihood of trouble on the aircraft. There were eleven prisoners altogether and six military police, well-armed thugs who also loaded two body bags onto the plane. The young officer in charge squeezed into the rear seat of the cockpit. Adolfo knew him by sight and shuddered. 'El Rubio', the blond one, was as immaculate as ever. Ernesto, the co-pilot, kept his gaze studiously forward.

'All set, Capitan, this shouldn't take long,' Astiz said in his cultured voice.

Adolfo nodded. He moved the throttle forward, released the brakes and the aircraft moved slowly out onto the runway.

They flew south down the coast for a hundred miles or so into a cloudless morning. There was little to see, just the coast road and then the flat pampas, dry and orange at this time of year, with rolling hills in the far distance. After a while they turned out to sea. Still nobody had spoken.

'We're a hundred miles out from Mar Del Plata, Teniente, no shipping in sight.' Adolfo broke the long silence.

The blond officer nodded smiling; he had an air of anticipation as he eased himself out of the cockpit and went back into the hold. The aircraft descended and levelled out at eight thousand feet. The pilot felt the slight lurch and change in pressure as the rear cargo door opened. He banked in a gentle turn and felt a small shudder through the aircraft as the weight changed. Looking out of his side window he could clearly see the falling bodies. They were spread out in a line, falling in slow motion, twisting and turning in their endless drop to oblivion. The sun began to rise out of the sea.

2

Buenos Aires, November 1976

The American Embassy in Buenos Aires is an ugly, bunker-like fortress on Cervino Street. With all the bombings and the political unrest, the occupants were taking no chances; security was nerve-wracking and thorough. Within easy walking distance were many other embassies: the Russians on Rodriguez Penar Street and the Cubans, Chinese, East Germans, Nicaraguans and Czechs all with embassies on Villanueva Street. From their front windows the Americans overlooked the Secretariat Intelligence del Estado, the feared Argentinian Secret Service, best known by its acronym SIDE.

The rooftop of the American Embassy was festooned with a glittering array of aerials and dishes and nobody, least of all SIDE, was under any illusion that these were for high-quality television. They knew for sure that almost all of the so-called friendly embassies also acted as secret intelligence-gathering agencies.

SIDE's own building at 10 Plaza de Mayo was alongside the Casa Rosada, the tallest building in Buenos Aires Central Square, overlooking the presidential palace. The aerial array on its rooftop was, unsurprisingly, similar to that on the American Embassy, since the electrical wire-tapping system they use had been purchased from the United States some five years previously. They would, however, have been very surprised and annoyed had they realised the amount of electronic gadgetry and personnel their friendly northern neighbour housed within its top three floors. In fact, about a quarter of the embassy staff came under the command of the CIA. Hidden in the embassy was a section of the Drug

Enforcement Agency and a secret intercept facility managed by the National Security Agency (NSA). The existence of an NSA listening post was a closely guarded secret and clear breach of diplomatic protocol.

The ambassador, Harry Schlaudemann, was one of the White House's most experienced diplomats, and he knew the continent and its politics well, having previously served as the US assistant secretary for the whole of Latin America. The head of the CIA in the embassy was Arnie Schwartz. Arnie was openly declared as CIA to his Argentinian hosts. A larger-than-life American with a loud voice, huge stomach, receding hairline and cheerful disposition, he ran a major part of his information-gathering business from either the Olivos or Mar del Plata golf clubs, where he played host to his opposite numbers with a cheery disregard for convention. Behind the affable exterior lay a shrewd mind and a clear understanding of US policy in South America. First and foremost, it was to keep the Soviets out of South America.

His opposite number was Arnold Mossolov, who operated from the Soviet Consulate on Rodriguez Pena Street. Russia was a huge customer of Argentina, buying millions of tons of grain and beef. It was easy to see who the next most likely ally might be.

Arnie kept a wary eye on Mossolov, whom he liked and played a regular round of golf with. Both operatives had a high regard for each other.

Arnie was happily unmarried, a career CIA man whose opinion was respected at headquarters in Langley, where he was a personal friend of Bill Casey, one of the CIA's most senior intelligence executives. A lifelong Republican, he had little time for Jimmy Carter, who had been elected to the White House only two weeks earlier. Like many CIA men, Arnie was determined that Ronald Reagan would become president at the next term of office, come what may.

That morning the ambassador, Harry Shlaudeman, asked Arnie to come down to his office. Arnie ambled in without knocking. He liked the ambassador: the two had been working together for a long time and were old friends who understood each other's ability.

'We have a problem, Arnie: the Carter administration has put an arms embargo on Argentina. The junta are taking it badly and are threatening all kind of trade reprisals.' He sighed, 'It couldn't have come at a worse moment. Since Peron's death the country has been in chaos, the economy is in tatters and inflation is running at over a hundred percent.'

'Yeah, since this General Videla guy took over they seem more interested in saving their own necks than sorting out the economy. I see they have Peron's wife, Isabella, under house arrest and are trying to put the blame on her. She should never have tried to hold on to power after he died.'

The ambassador grimaced distastefully. 'The generals are making damned sure that everyone in the armed services is implicated one way or another in war crimes: they're all watching their backs. There's every possibility of a popular uprising, they spend more time trying to restore their tarnished reputations than running the country. The latest estimate is that thirty thousand people are missing since Peron started the "dirty war" to stamp out the opposition, and the *Montanero* are still active.'

'The arms embargo is going to be impossible to administer,' Arnie muttered. 'I'm trying to negotiate with General Martinez, at SIDE, to help us in our operations against the Sandinistas in Nicaragua. We want the Argies to supply the Contra rebels with arms. How the hell am I supposed to fix that if we have an arms embargo?'

The ambassador looked at him questioningly but Arnie continued, thinking aloud. 'At least their military thinkers are on our side. Admiral Massera's group seem to be thinking the same way and General Sotera, the head of the army's intelligence, is on our side. As long as they don't get kicked out of power I think we will have their support, but trust them I don't.'

'How do you know all this, Arnie?' the ambassador asked, puzzled.

'It's easy, Harry – we have a tap on almost every phone line in their security service. The more work that SIDE does the less we have to do.' He laughed. 'It's a funny country. You know the city rats in Buenos Aires have a real liking for telephone cable insulation and it causes the phone system to fail during wet weather. There's no state security in Argentina on a rainy day!'

'We had a strange tap last night,' Arnie continued. 'It sounds as if Generals Belusa Martinez and Freddie Sotera are reactivating *Operation Goa.*'

'What's that?' Shlaudeman asked.

'We've been listening to Admiral Massera's strategy group for some time now. They have this crazy scheme to invade the Falkland Islands, "Ilas Malvinas" they call them. "*Goa*" is the code name for the plan. They've been watching the Europeans giving up and losing their colonies. The Indians took over the Portuguese colony of Goa without a shot being fired. The action hardly attracted international attention or condemnation of any kind and so Massera's think tank conceived *Operation Goa.* I guess they think the Brits will do the same.'

The ambassador nodded, 'They didn't do much to stop Ian Smith declaring independence in Rhodesia. The difference is that the Falkland Islanders don't want independence, they consider themselves British, I guess. Costa Mendez, the foreign minister, has been in the process of negotiating a leaseback arrangement with the British but it's been going on for years. They are supposed to be having talks at the UN at the moment but it's going nowhere. Both sides have been stalling. Each time they just about have an agreement their governments change.' He settled back in his chair. 'Have you seen the fuss in the newspapers about Lord Shackleton? I see *La Presenta* is billing him as a pirate.'

'Yeah, isn't he the son of Ernest Shackleton, the explorer? The British Government sent him down to see if there is any way to improve the Falklands economy. The newspapers are full of it. *La Presenta* has been calling him a pirate as you say. They wouldn't let him fly via Buenos Aires so he flew to Montevideo and was taken to Port Stanley by their ice patrol ship *Endurance.*

The ambassador nodded. 'Last week they thought he was on board the research ship *Shackleton* and the generals ordered their warship *Admiral Storni* to fire a salvo across her bows. The Argie press is wild with approval.'

'The British haven't done a bloody thing about it. If that had been one of our ships I hope Uncle Sam would have blown them out of the water!' Arnie muttered. 'Years of negotiation ruined with one bang. Argentina has severed ambassadorial links with them. Relations can't be worse. A bit of gunboat diplomacy would sort this lot out in five minutes.'

The ambassador grinned, shaking his head.

'You know, the big mistake the British are making is scrapping their ice patrol ship *Endurance*. The Argie papers are having a field day. *La Presenta* had a long article yesterday arguing that once the ship goes the British will have no further interest in the South Atlantic.'

'So, tell me what you know about this *Operation Goa*, Arnie?'

'The idea's a quick invasion of the Falklands. They have a tiny population of less than two thousand people, so remove the lot to Montevideo and immediately replace them with Argentinian settlers – the whole thing'd be a *fait accompli* by the time the British cotton on. The assumption is that Britain's too far away to be able to react and that world opinion will go with Argentina.'

'The generals aren't worried about the Falklands, Arnie,' Shlaudeman said thoughtfully. 'It's to take the heat off their home problems. These riots are getting to them. What a mess! Have you informed Langley about *Operation Goa* yet?'

Arnie pulled a Cuban cigar out of his pocket and wandered around the ambassador's office puffing large volumes of smoke. 'Yes, I spoke to Bill Casey over the satellite this morning. He's going to warn the British Secret Service in London but won't pass on our knowledge of *Goa* or they'll know we're able to tap the military phone system. I'll speak to Simon Sloan; he's their agent in Buenos Aires, working out of the Swiss Embassy. Simon's a good man and you'd be surprised at how much he knows. There are about seventy thousand Brits living in Argentina and there isn't a lot that doesn't get passed on to him.'

'I hope the British have the good sense to do something about this, Arnie; this could blow up into something nasty. Six thousand miles is a long way from home for them. What would you do?'

'Dunno, it's hard to believe that the generals would invade a bunch of crummy islands that nobody has heard of. It doesn't make sense, but they do need some kind of military success to save their necks. If it were my call I'd send in the whole darn British navy.'

3

London, November 1977

Britain's Secret Intelligence Service (SIS) is an odd kind of set-up. The Friends, as they like to be called, have developed over two world wars into the world's third-largest intelligence-gathering service. The CIA and the Russian KGB are larger but, in 1966, prior to the fall of the Berlin Wall, Russia spent most of its budget looking inwards onto its own people. Spying is a curious kind of business and, like its competitors, the SIS has had its failures and successes. Its most publicised failures were when Klaus Fuchs passed on to the Soviets almost all Britain's and America's knowledge of the atom bomb, totally altering the balance of world power, and later when Kim Philby passed on information that just about wrecked the entire Secret Service network. MI6 shook to its roots. For a long time after these events the Americans were very wary of sharing their knowledge with Britain and watched the SIS with grave suspicion.

The Secret Service is roughly split into three: MI5, covering home domestic problems; MI6, the overseas agency; and GCHQ, the government communications headquarters in Cheltenham, which monitors home and overseas signals and intelligence. God only knows what happens to all this information, but a simplified version is worked down into two intelligence committees called Sigs, one for the eastern and another for the western hemisphere. They sift through the data and give an opinion on what should be done either by clandestine or political strategy. In turn, these two groups report weekly to the Joint Intelligence Committee (JIC), which is held every Wednesday morning in London.

17

Traditionally, the JIC is chaired by the deputy head of the Foreign Office and includes the heads of the government intelligence agencies. By the weekend, this committee pulls together a short, top-secret red pamphlet, which is sent under great security to the prime minister and, on a need to know basis, to members of the Cabinet: usually the foreign secretary and the defence secretary. This, along with a huge amount of other national material, is part of the Prime Minister's bedtime reading for the weekend.

Harold Wilson had been an avid reader of the JIC pamphlet. He loved spy stories and here was the real-life thing. On his resignation, his successor, James Callaghan, was even more enthusiastic. He had a large globe placed in his office and watched the world's dangerous hot spots with interest. He loved to drop items from the red pamphlet on his Cabinet colleagues: war games of eastern bloc countries, rebel training camps in Honduras or Chad or Libya, positions of hostile submarines, American excursions into Central America.

That week the JIC pamphlet was as varied as ever: Israel was high on the list of trouble spots, as President Jimmy Carter attempted to woo Anwar Sadat of Egypt and Israel's Menachem Begin into some kind of peace accord. The Baader-Meinhof German terrorist organisation had just murdered the director of Mercedes-Benz and secret services the world over were searching for the culprits. In Pakistan, General Zia had just ousted Prime Minister Ali Bhutto. Almost unnoticed at the bottom of the list was a reference to the Falkland Islands. The diplomatic problems with Argentina seemed to be worsening. A friendly note had come in from the head of the CIA at Langley indicating that trouble was brewing in Argentina. More information had come in from Simon Sloan in Buenos Aires. Argentina had cut the fuel supplies to the Falkland Islands yet again and there was a growing anti-British attitude in the Argentinian press. The JIC recommended that two frigates be sent to the Islands in the hope of warding off trouble.

Callaghan spotted it over the weekend's reading. Like most

people in Britain, he wasn't that sure where the Falkland Islands were. However, on Monday morning he called a meeting in his office at No. 10 Downing Street. Around the table were David Owen, his new foreign secretary, and Ted Rowlands, the minister who headed the Falklands negotiations, along with Fred Mullen, the defence secretary. The discussion that took place was heated: Callaghan was in his element and loving it.

'I think we should send a nuclear submarine to the Falklands as well as the frigates,' he said, enjoying the idea of controlling Britain's war machine.

Fred Mullen, the defence secretary, turned pale. 'My God, Prime Minister, the cost to send a nuclear submarine to the other side of the world will be enormous. The pressure from the Treasury is intense at the moment and I have the navy on a reduced fuel budget.'

Ted Rowlands was the minister who had taken over the job of trying to broker an acceptable deal over the Falklands and was heartily sick of the junta. 'In my view, Prime Minister, a bit of gunboat diplomacy might help the way forward. It's bad enough that HMS *Endurance* is being taken out of service, the Argentinians just don't take us seriously.'

Callaghan turned to the foreign secretary. 'What do you think, David?'

'I agree with you, sir. I don't believe the Argentinians are seriously contemplating more than a political gesture but they have already put a base on Southern Thule in the South Sandwich Islands, at the north end of the Antarctic Peninsula. That's been a British possession since it was discovered by Captain Cook. We decided to ignore them as it didn't seem much harm; my guess is that they will try another island, South Georgia or the likes, to see what we do about it.'

'The chancellor will have a fit!' Fred Mullen murmured, still sticking to his lost cause. 'Surely it's a submarine's job not to have its position known. It will be a pretty poor deterrent if nobody knows it's there!'

'Well, we'll have to let them know. Send the submarine and two frigates,' insisted Callaghan with a grin, overruling his defence secretary and loving every minute of it.

And so it was that, in 1977, the Cabinet and the intelligence system were working smoothly together, as they should be, responding to a possible threat even if it was slightly at the prime minister's whim. That evening, Callaghan phoned Sir Maurice Oldfield, the head of MI6, and quietly told him of his action. Oldfield was astonished that he had even looked at the pamphlet but managed to sound unsurprised at the scale of response.

In GCHQ Peter Bacon-Smith, who ran the South American office, found himself suddenly in the middle of a flap. Ministerial interference always caused trouble but when it was the prime minister the shit really hit the fan. Peter was just back from a comfortable pub lunch when Sir Maurice Oldfield stalked into his office.

'Peter, the Americans have tipped us off that there's trouble brewing in Argentina. The PM has decided to send a nuclear submarine into the Falkland area to act as a deterrent. Two navy frigates are making a courtesy call into Port Stanley and we should make it damned clear why they are there. Somehow we need to leak that we have a sub operating off their coast.'

Peter was an old hand who knew the guiles of the Service well. Three pints of beer at lunchtime had little effect on his thought processes; he was already way ahead of the ministers. 'That's easy, sir,' he mused. 'We'll ask the Yanks to tell them. Who are we dealing with?'

'It came from the top – Bill Casey, CIA at Langley. Their embassy staff passed it on to us and we also have a warning from our own man, Simon Sloan. We have to take this seriously; these problems with Argentina are getting worse. Can you deal with it?'

'Bloody hell, sir, half the Argentinian navy is at Portsmouth doing military training with our mob; we should put a stop to that right away.'

Sir Maurice nodded in agreement. 'See what you can do, Peter.' Both men hated the amount of military expertise that the British passed on to friendly foreign governments. In their view, they weren't always that friendly once they got the know-how.

By that afternoon, memos were flying thick and fast from Peter's office, removing Argentinians from military colleges and keeping a careful eye on them. That evening Peter put a call through to CIA HQ at Langley and spoke to Bill Casey.

'Thanks for the tip-off about the Argies, sir. Just to let you know that our government is taking it very seriously.'

'Glad to be of assistance. I hope you guys are doing something about it.' Casey's strong Texan accent came clearly down the line.

'The prime minister is sending a couple of frigates into Port Stanley and a nuclear sub into the area. Can I ask another favour of you? Will you tip off the junta that we have a sub operating off their coast?'

Casey laughed. 'Good idea – I'll get Arnie Schwartz to tip off General Belusa Martinez at SIDE. They'll have a fit and think we're doing them a favour!'

The small battle group duly headed south under the command of Admiral Henry Leach, a submariner and one of the most able seamen in the navy. As an atomic submarine commander, he was one of the navy's elite. The rules of engagement that he suggested – to set up a twenty-five mile exclusion zone around the Falkland Islands – were quietly approved by the War Office. Any Argentinian warship entering this zone would be blown out of the water. It seemed unlikely but, if necessary, then, by God, he was prepared to do it. Little did he realise that within a short span of five years he would be giving the orders for a huge Task Force to do just that.

4

SIDE HQ, Buenos Aires, December 1977

It was midsummer in Buenos Aires, intensely hot and humid and it didn't help that the air-conditioning wasn't working. All the windows of SIDE's main conference room were open and a couple of electric fans had been hastily rigged in an attempt to freshen the sultry atmosphere. A faint hum of traffic could be heard rising from the Plaza de Mayo.

All the men sitting around the long board table were in military uniform. The table was headed by the President, Lieutenant-General Jorge Videla, a thin-faced army officer who had taken power after the overthrow of Isabella Peron a few months earlier. At his side were Admiral Massera and Capitan Anaya and opposite sat General Freddy Sotera, head of military intelligence, and General 'Belusa' Martinez, the feared head of SIDE state security. Further down the table were senior staff officers of the army and airforce. At a separate table at the end of the room a group of younger officers, aides to their various commanders, were taking notes. Among them sat Lieutenant Hugo Corti, acting for Capitan Anaya.

'We are here to discuss *Operation Goa*.' President Videla's clipped voice brought the meeting to order. 'General Martinez has some urgent information.'

Martinez sprang to his feet. He was a short, thickset man with bulldog jowls and grey, receding hair. Deep-set piercing eyes flashed across the faces of the officers facing him. 'I have heard from my contact with the Americans that a British nuclear submarine is operating off the Malvinas Islands. Yesterday two frigates arrived at Port Stanley, supposedly on a courtesy visit, and today it has been declared in their Parliament that HMS *Endurance* is not to be taken out of service this year.'

There was an uneasy stir around the table. 'This can't be a coincidence. *Operation Goa* is top secret – somebody has compromised us!' He thumped the table with his fist. 'Only the people in this room know our plans.'

Admiral Massera rose angrily to his feet; he was a younger man than Martinez, smart in his naval uniform with dark, wavy hair, broad shoulders and an air of confidence and determination. A highly ambitious man, in the years that he had headed the navy it had more than doubled in size. 'The fleet is on exercise in the Scotia Sea off the Malvinas. *Operation Goa* is absolutely ready. Within the next twenty-four hours the Islands can be in our hands and the army in occupation. What can three British ships do against the new Argentinian navy?'

General Sotera broke in, 'This is supposed to be a secret operation that will gain us the approval of the Argentinian people. We can't risk open warfare with the British – world opinion might go against us. Too many people are in the know and somebody has leaked our plans. The operation should be delayed until we have a total advantage.'

There was an awkward silence around the table before Capitan Anaya broke in. 'I was military attaché in our embassy in London. The British are slow to make a decision and painstakingly bureaucratic: in my opinion they will do nothing. The operation should proceed.'

Hugo could almost feel his anger and frustration.

President Videla stared uncomfortably around the table. There was a clear split between the navy, led by Admiral Massera, and the army generals, who were taking the cautious view. Videla took the army view. 'For the time being the Malvinas operation will be shelved; the risk is too great. We will increase diplomatic pressure against the British, but for the time being there will be no invasion.' He closed the file in front of him.

Admiral Massera, followed by Capitan Anaya and his aides, stormed out of the meeting. Anaya had worked for months on the strategy of *Operation Goa* and was convinced that it would work. Hugo had never seen him so angry. Back at the Naval Mechanics College he was still blazing mad. He had marked the dissenting officers and the lack of confidence of President Videla. Someone had tipped off the British, but who? He swore under his breath that one day he would find a way to remove the enemy from the Islands, and President Videla while he was at it.

5

Ritz Hotel, London, November 1979

A deal to start a war

Oxford Street, London, on a cold November afternoon. A hazy, freezing mist enveloped the streets; cold, creeping damp was everywhere, the distance fading into murky invisibility. Traffic was crawling, headlights barely penetrating the lunchtime gloom. On days like this the city still throbs with life. Lights and decorations already swing across the streets. The pavements are crammed with people and the overcrowded roads burst with traffic. This was the winter of discontent: over four million workers on strike, an unhappy government trying to enforce a three-day working week. Even in the midst of this disastrous national crisis there is an air of jollity – the Christmas rush has begun.

Sir Gerald Elliot walked briskly from Baker Street underground station avoiding the shoppers: a small, dark, dapper man comfortably dressed in a tweed suit. A Scottish gentleman, he is the great-great-grandson of Christian Salvesen, managing director of the family company, Salvesen, which was once the world's largest whaling company. Competition and over-hunting between the two world wars had brought the whale stocks to near extinction and the industry almost to its end. Salvesen had successfully moved its business into fish-freezing factory ships and then into frozen transport, and was now a conglomerate of many companies.

So, here he was, walking down Oxford Street, dodging across the traffic and entering the imposing entrance to the Ritz Hotel. He was here to meet an Argentinian scrap dealer, Constantino

Davidoff, who had offered to purchase the scrap metal from the old disused whaling stations on South Georgia. It seemed a strange place for a meeting to sell scrap metal but on this grand scale possibly very lucrative. He smiled to the smartly dressed attendant who opened the door for him and entered the relaxed, deeply carpeted splendour of the foyer. Although he had never met the man, he recognised Davidoff immediately and walked over to where he was sitting.

'Signor Davidoff?' The Argentinian danced to his feet and shook Elliot's hand enthusiastically. Dressed immaculately, he was a dark, swarthy man, tough looking and self-made.

'Constantino, please, Sir Gerald,' he smiled, speaking good English with a strong Latin accent. 'Thank you for seeing me; please sit down. Can I order you a drink?'

'Just tea, please.' Elliot settled down, smiling. 'Have you considered my offer?'

'Yes, but the price is too high. The difficulty of demolishing the whaling station and transporting the metal across the roughest sea in the world is considerable and very expensive.'

'How are you going to do it, Constantino? The Governor of the Falkland Islands will not be keen on large numbers of Argentinian workers there and they would have to be under the jurisdiction of the British Government and obey our laws. The island is at present run by the British Antarctic Survey.'

'Of course, of course, my son and I will oversee the whole operation. We are used to this work and will leave Leith whaling station in a very good state.'

What Davidoff omitted to say was that he had done a deal with the cash-strapped Argentinian navy to transport the scrap for a small fee and ship it as a military exercise. He knew that the Falkland Island Government would be very unlikely to allow the Argentinian navy anywhere near the island and hoped that once the metal was removed it would be a *fait accompli*.

Sir Gerald nodded. 'I think we can persuade the Foreign Office to sanction this as long as you're prepared to sign a contract agreeing to all our legal terms.' He too had a hidden agenda. The whaling stations were now huge, rotting and unwanted ghost towns. Spillage from old oil tanks had been reported to the Governor of the Falkland Islands. Elliot realised that government pressure was bound to come to clean up the sites. He shuddered at the enormity of such an operation. This sale at any price could save his company millions.

The two men chatted amicably for a while, Davidoff about Argentina's difficulty with the Pinochet regime in neighbouring Chile since president Salvador Allende's assassination. Sir Gerald kept the subject on a lighter note: Sebastian Coe was now holding the world records for the 800 metres, the 1500 metres and the mile. There wasn't a lot else positive in Britain at this critical time.

'Half a million pounds is too much, Sir Gerald.' Davidoff opened up the serious negotiations. 'You have no further use for the whaling station and the cost of shipping it back to Argentina is enormous. How about one hundred thousand pounds? If this works we can try a better deal for the other stations.'

Elliot loathed the idea of breaking up the whaling stations but knew that the industry was finished and that this was a profitable way of clearing up what was becoming a growing and expensive problem for Salvesen. The millions of tons of scrap metal on South Georgia would pay handsomely if it could be shipped to Argentina, but this would be no easy task. To move this amount of steel across the worst sea in the world would be an extraordinary undertaking.

'I'd never get that through my board, Constantino. Let's call it one hundred and fifty thousand pounds, paid in advance. Our lawyers can draw up a contract.'

Davidoff smiled in agreement and the two men shook hands.

What neither realised was that their private and friendly deal would spark off the extraordinary series of events that would lead to two friendly countries eight thousand miles apart and on opposite sides of the world entering into a particularly vicious war with the loss of hundreds of lives and causing crippling economic problems for both nations. In later years Sir Gerald was to ruefully claim that he had started the Falklands War in the lounge of the Ritz.

6

South Georgia, Monday 15 March 1982

The continent of Antarctica sits almost centrally over the South Pole. Surrounding this vast icy landmass lies the Southern Ocean, which itself merges into the three great oceans of the world: the Pacific, the South Atlantic and the Indian. On a map, there is no real line separating these great masses of water but anyone who has sailed south will tell you that once crossing the Antarctic convergence, where freezing seas meet the more northerly oceans, one enters instantly into a different world. There is a distinct line: an instant drop in temperature and almost immediately the first icebergs are in sight – great towering cathedrals, flat tabular bergs from the ice shelves and smaller growlers spinning noisily in the waves with the ever-possible danger of pack ice. Life is abundant with shoals of penguins, killer whales, petrels, skuas and albatrosses.

Between latitudes 55 degrees south and the Antarctic Circle at 67 degrees south, a great circle of water a thousand miles wide spans the globe, uninterrupted by any land. Around the Antarctic Circle an immense area of low pressure circulates the continent, drawing high pressure from the northerly oceans and katabatic winds from the frozen continent. This acts as a huge pump where virtually ceaseless westerly gales blow, at times with hurricane intensity, sometimes attaining speeds of two hundred miles an hour. Such winds are unheard of elsewhere in the world except perhaps within a tropical cyclone. Unstopped by any land, for aeons these winds have driven great waves remorselessly around the globe in a great oscillation. Here, below the fortieth parallel,

29

in what sailors call the *Roaring Forties*, the wind increases and the temperature drops as one heads south, first reaching the *Raving Fifties* and then, for the few who have ventured further south below the sixtieth parallel to the Antarctic sea, the *Screaming Sixties*.

There is one exception to this great circle: where the Antarctic Peninsula reaches north towards Cape Horn, the southern tip of South America. This is Drake's Passage, where the circle narrows to about five hundred miles. Enormous seas spilling through this gap and the waves produced have been the peril of seafarers since the first sailing ships risked all and rounded the Horn.

'Cape Horn rollers' or 'Greybeards' have been the stuff of legend: huge waves the size of six-storey buildings careering unstoppably along; billions of tons of water propelled by colossal winds. Add to this great cauldron icebergs, growlers, pack ice and the Cape Horn westerly current and the nightmare is almost complete.

Having passed through Drake's Passage, the Greybeards accelerate out into the Scotia Sea where, eight hundred miles west on the fifty-fifth parallel, slap bang in line with this great westerly flow, is the tiny isolated island of South Georgia. Surrounded by enormous seas and blasted by wind, this sub-Antarctic island, sixty miles long by twelve miles wide, suffers the worst weather in the world.

At the head of Cumberland Bay at Grytviken on South Georgia, Alison Shackleton photographed the great rollers roaring in over Sappho Point. Riding in and leaping from the breakers were dozens of macaroni penguins. These tough little birds were struggling several hundred feet up the cliffs on well-worn tracks to reach their colony. They are about twenty inches high with a long yellow head feather that gives them their name from the nursery song 'Yankee Doodle': 'Put a feather in his cap and call him Macaroni'.

Earlier Alison had filmed them at their nesting sites and found them very aggressive. Close together on the bare gravel mountainside without any real nest, each pair of birds guarded chicks or eggs in a little space cleared of stones. Protecting their small territories, they pecked viciously at her legs and battered her with their flipper-like wings, seemingly oblivious to her size. A hundred yards further up along the cliffs Alison could see Anna Cinderford doing a similar silly dancing walk of her own, avoiding the penguins' beaks as she tried to set up the camera to film the colony. Alison laughed inwardly at her friend's discomfort. Never had she been more truly happy or content. This was her big break, working for the BBC as an assistant to Anna and acting as a photographer in her own right on a major TV series, *This Cruel Earth*.

The BBC had been trying to get permission for Anna to film on South Georgia for some time but they had always been turned down. The excuse was that British Antarctic bases were not organised for women and that if they got into difficulty while working away from base it would be expensive and hold up scientific programmes.

Anna, however, had played a trump card. She had known Alison Shackleton from her student days at Oxford. Alison, she knew, was a distant relative of Ernest Shackleton, the polar explorer; she was also an enthusiastic mountaineer and had a number of Alpine and Himalayan peaks under her belt. Anna had approached her and suggested the trip to South Georgia and Alison had jumped at the chance – the possibility of a trip to South Georgia was just too much to miss. The whole of her childhood had been steeped in the history of her famous relative.

She and Anna approached her uncle, Lord Shackleton, the Labour peer and son of the polar explorer, explaining their problem, and a few days later her uncle invited the two women round to his house.

'I've spoken to Doctor Laws, the head of the Antarctic Survey. He's old school and not keen on women in the Antarctic,' he said. 'I told him that times are changing and it will be easier to get government funding if women are involved. He squirmed a bit but finally gave in. You're on your way!'

Alison whooped and hugged her uncle, who was grinning from ear to ear.

The old man continued, 'I visited South Georgia in 1976 when I went on my fact-finding trip for the government. I went down on HMS *Endurance* and visited father's grave at Grytviken and had a good look around the island. It's a remarkable place; I wish I was coming with you. Did you know that the Argies called me a pirate; they fired a shot over the RRS *Shackleton's* bow thinking I was on board. It was great fun! Jim Callaghan sent a nuclear submarine and a couple of warships to Stanley and they backed off.'

'What happened to your report on the Falkland Islands?' Anna asked.

Shackleton's face fell. 'I believe that with very little investment the Islands could become economically viable – the islanders are getting a raw deal from the government and the Falkland Island Company, which owns most of the land. If they were given ownership of their farms and the communications were improved they would become self-sustaining. Nothing much happened and my recommendations were ignored. Anthony Crosland, the foreign secretary at the time, misrepresented it in Parliament and used it as a cover for the government's inaction. I guess the report is gathering dust somewhere in the bowels of the Colonial Office.

'Unless we sort the Falklands out there will always be trouble with Argentina. They have constantly claimed them as theirs although they were a British colony before Argentina existed. Did you know that an Argentinian businessman tried to buy the Falkland Island Company recently? At least the governor managed to put a stop to that.'

'What are the Islands like?' Alison asked.

Her uncle thought for a moment. 'The Falklands are very like the Scottish island of Lewis in the Hebrides and, I suppose, Port Stanley is a bit like Stornoway. Most of the buildings are of corrugated iron. Inland, the camp as they call it, are low-lying hills with very few trees; it's sheep country, with a few very isolated farms.'

'What about South Georgia?'

'It's a very remote place and probably has the worst weather on earth. It has high mountains and is mostly glaciated. The Antarctic Survey base is in King Edward Cove, just a few hundred yards up the coast from the old disused whaling station at Grytviken where my father's buried. It's wonderful that another member of the family is going there. You'll find the base very comfortable; all mod cons compared with what it must have been like in father's day. You'll love it!'

And so it had turned out. Once having been given BBC approval, the Antarctic Survey couldn't have been more helpful. The women flew to Montevideo, where they joined the research ship *John Biscoe* and called in at the Falkland Islands for a few days on their way south before a rough five-day passage through the Scotia Sea to South Georgia.

Standing here on this snowy, windswept cliff-side, Alison couldn't imagine being more content. She was a small, wiry woman, with boyish, short-cropped curly hair and a slightly oriental face, which burst easily into a dazzling smile. At times she had a short-lived but fiery temper, which was put down to the Irish ancestry of her family. Here, she was in her element. The job of looking after Anna seemed perfect: the culmination of all she had learned on her climbing expeditions and a way of putting her mountaineering abilities to more serious use.

In the short time that she and Anna had been together they had become friends. For her part Anna was no amateur. She had filmed wildlife all over the world but never in a climate like this where the temperature seldom rose more than two or three degrees above zero. She had the good sense to realise that in this terrain Alison was the expert. They were very different: she was tall with long fair hair, classic features and clear blue eyes. Normally a quiet person, she was very determined and professional in her film work, though at times childishly demanding with the odd burst of anger if things weren't going her way.

Having finished filming for the day the two women packed their equipment and set out on the long walk along the coast back to the base. Anna admired the easy way that Alison heaved the heavy rucksack onto her back and how, with almost twice the load of her own, she picked her way along the steep hillside with her easy mountaineer's gait.

'Look at that!' Alison had stopped and was watching a group of king penguins standing on the rocks above the sea with the obvious intention of diving in, but something was stopping them. The birds were hanging about peering nervously into the water.

To her amazement, an extraordinary occurrence took place. A group of penguins suddenly pushed one of their unfortunate companions off the rocks into the sea. She was certain it was done on purpose. There was a sudden commotion in the water as a giant leopard seal dived upon the unfortunate bird and in a second it was all over. The watching penguins on the shore fussed about unhappily then turned guiltily and waddled away. Both women burst into laughter; it was hilariously funny and impossible not to laugh at this macabre comedy.

'We've got to get that on film somehow,' Anna said. 'I wonder what the chances of seeing that happen again are?'

The two women headed back along the coast towards King Edward Cove base. The weather had improved; in the distance Alison could see Mount Paget, the highest of South Georgia's peaks, gleaming in the evening sun. In the crystal clear light everything stood to attention, with shining snow-covered mountains as far as the eye could see. As she rounded Hope Point, Alison saw the cross.

So, that's it, she thought. Here, facing the huge rolling breakers, the white-painted cross gleamed in the evening sunshine; overlooking West Cumberland Bay, filled with icebergs, with the backdrop of mountains, pink in the evening afterglow. This was his true memorial. She had already visited her great-uncle's grave at the little cemetery at Grytviken. It had been easy to find. The whalers had raised a great block of granite and, chiselled roughly and almost amateurishly, were three words: 'Ernest Shackleton. Explorer', but here at the entrance to this beautiful harbour was a more fitting monument.

Alison stood before the cross, her mind reeling. For a while they stood quietly, looking out to sea, deep in thought, before she and Anna turned and headed back into King Edward Cove.

7

Argentina, March 1982

In Argentina, the political situation had changed since 1973. The military government, headed by Lieutenant-General Jorge Videla, had collapsed and been replaced by a regime led by the former army commander, Roberto Viola. His presidency, too, was short lived and he had been forcibly retired, ostensibly on grounds of bad health. In the upward struggle for power, three new men had taken control. The new president was General Leopoldo Galtieri, a handsome extrovert, ambitious and ruthless. He was supported by Brigadier Basilio Lami Dozo, the able and energetic head of the air force, and his good friend Admiral Jorge Anaya, the newly appointed supreme commander of the navy.

Anaya had been quite clear when he agreed to support Galtieri that the build-up of the Argentinian navy to equal status with the army was his paramount goal. As the protégé of Admiral Massera, in the early days of his rise to power he had been sent to London as the naval attaché at the embassy. It had been an unhappy experience; he disliked the British, whom he found pompous, slow and bureaucratic. He left with an undying dislike and resentment for the country as a whole. Those who knew him well believed him to be the one man with the ability and commitment to make the seizure of the Malvinas Islands possible, and this was clearly his intent.

Argentina was now in the fortunate position of being courted by the most powerful country on earth. Forgotten seemed to be the criticism of human rights and torture in prison, which had been America's concern during Jimmy Carter's administration.

Ronald Reagan, the recently elected president, had his own agenda with new problems in Latin America, and needed allies. The military junta in Argentina were seen as fellow fighters in the war against Marxism.

As he climbed the power ladder Galtieri had made a number of visits to the United States, where he became friendly with his opposite number, General Edward Mayer, a hard-drinking soldier not given to subtle politics. He was wined and dined with defence secretary Caspar Weinberger and publicly acclaimed as being 'a majestic and charismatic personality and a great ambassador of his people'. Such accolades would turn the head of many a man and Galtieri was no exception.

From the American point of view he was right wing, un-sophisticated and politically biddable, the perfect partner in their war against communist revolutionary governments in South America. They suggested to him that as president he should remain commander of the army to protect his back. Such support from the all-powerful USA left him bursting with confidence.

When General Galtieri took power, Argentina's economy was in tatters and riots, bombings and national protest were day-to-day events throughout the country. What he needed was a diversion; something to restore Argentina's national pride, and his friend Jorge Anaya knew he had the answer. Anaya's price for his support of Galtieri as president was the taking of the Falkland Islands by the navy within the first two years of his presidency. The two men had shaken hands on it; already a provisional date for the invasion had been set for the autumn of that year. It had to be before January 1983 as that would be the one hundred and fiftieth anniversary of the Falklands seizure by Britain. Only six men knew of the plan, which was code-named *Operation Rosario* (Operation Rosary) and this time Anaya was not going to risk a security leak. The die was cast.

8

Grytviken, South Georgia, Monday 15 March 1982

Shackleton House, Base S, is unlike any other of the survey
stations on the Antarctic continent, which tend to be prefabricated
sheds, which were easy to construct and designed to withstand
bitter cold. It's a large, friendly, wooden, two-storey house surrounded
by a dozen small outbuildings and sheds, and stands about half
a mile up the south shore of King Edward Cove from the derelict
whaling station of Grytviken. The house itself is the comfortable
living quarters of the *fids*, the strange name that all the Antarctic
Survey people go by. It has offices and scientific workrooms; the
surrounding buildings are used for meteorology, radio, carpentry
workshops, food stores and so on. The view across the bay is
stunning: on rare clear days the Allardyce Range of mountains
gleams in the background and the giant Nordenskjold Glacier
pours into Cumberland East Bay with Mount Paget and Mount
Roots soaring above.

The base has always been a hive of activity: scientific programmes
changing from year to year; field parties studying the geology and
geophysics of the island, its plant life, birds and animals. In
previous seasons there had been divers under the ice, geologists,
meteorologists, ionosphericists and map-makers. Because of its
relatively northerly latitude, it is usually the first port of call in
the season for the two Antarctic survey ships, the *John Biscoe* and
the *Bransfield*. The old RRS *Shackleton* had been sold a few years
earlier. Occasional tourists' cruise ships had started to call and
even small, ocean-going yachts were venturing this far south. In
summer the base staff almost doubled.

The previous year a decision had been taken that the South Georgia base was to close and already some of the scientific programmes were shutting down; consequently there were fewer scientists than usual on the island. The British Antarctic Survey (BAS) was strapped for cash and was desperately trying to keep its high-profile projects going on the Antarctic continent. Word of the imminent closure of the base had already been noted in Buenos Aires and, as with the proposed decommisioning of HMS *Endurance*, was seen by the Argentinians as yet another indication of Britain's lack of interest in the South Atlantic.

Alison and Anna had arranged that HMS *Endurance*, which was due to arrive that evening, would take them to Antarctic Bay, about twenty-five miles up the coast the following day. They planned to stay for a month in the small hut there and try to capture the remoteness and wildlife of the island on film. That afternoon they had finished packing for their trip and at last had the chance to take a walk down to the whaling station.

They wandered along the track chatting to two fids, David Asquith and Sebastian Holmes, who were also being dropped off by the ship at Fortuna Bay at the same time.

'Why do they call you fids, David?' Alison asked.

'Aw, it's nothing really,' he said laughing. 'It's the initials of the "Falkland Islands Dependency Survey" but it really means "fucking idiots down south"!'

They all laughed. The two men were clearly good friends and had worked together for a while. David was a New Zealander, tallish and, unusually for a fid, with a tidily trimmed beard with close-cropped brown wavy hair. He was a sailor and a keen mountaineer and was employed as a field assistant looking after scientists, much in the way that Alison was working with Anna. He had an easy confidence about him and spoke in a broad Kiwi drawl.

In contrast, Sebastian Holmes was a larger-than-life character. He was a geophysicist. Like most fids he was not long out of university and had applied to go to the Antarctic for the adventure and to avoid the horrors of office work. He was short, slightly overweight and very scruffy, with greasy black hair touching his shoulders and a bushy unkempt beard. He had decided not to shave for the duration of his stay on the island, and his clothes were in tatters. He had a lazy disposition and a knack of avoiding day-to-day chores. Nonetheless he was a clever man and universally liked. David worked with him on field trips and the two were a good team.

They finally reached Grytviken and walked out onto the giant flensing platforms where in the past millions of whales had been dragged ashore to be flensed, that is cut up and boiled down into oil and animal food. Moored alongside were a number of hulks of old ships, semi-submerged against the rotting piers.

'The whalers left these ships here when they closed the station,' Sebastian said. 'Those two are the whale catchers *Dias* and *Albatross*; the bottoms are rotted out of them but that one over there, *Petrel*, is still afloat. A few years ago a bunch of fids fired her up and she was still working but it would take a lot to make her seaworthy now.'

Alison noticed that the gun in her bow was armed with a harpoon. There was still red, white and blue paint on her funnel flaking into the bay.

'That hulk over there is the old whaler *Louise*, quite a famous ship in her time.'

They wandered through the streets of this once-thriving town; far from empty they were littered with old ironmongery, flensing knives, old harpoon heads and oil drums. These derelict buildings once provided thousands of barrels of oil to light the lamps of a forgotten century, boiled from the carcasses of a million whales. Among all this decaying steel lay hundreds of elephant seals. These ugly creatures wallowed and roared and grunted, their breath steaming in the cold air. If you got too close to them they would rear up, towering menacingly above you, weighing anything up to two tons.

'Watch this!' David walked confidently up to a huge bull

elephant seal, and the enormous creature obliged accordingly, summoning its full height and menace. David lifted his hands above his head so he appeared taller than the bull and it immediately backed off nervously. 'They're pretty harmless once you get used to them,' he laughed.

'This place is much bigger than I thought,' Anna said. 'It's hard to imagine what it was like when the whalers were here.'

'There were over a thousand men working here in its heyday,' Sebastian said. 'There's a power station, hospital, bath houses; these are machine workshops and look at those rows of oil tanks. This is the oil business of the last century before we started pumping it out of the ground. They ruined it by wiping out the whales just like we're wasting our oil now!'

They wandered through the rusting streets along with hundreds of king penguins and the odd macaroni. 'My God, is that a rat?' Anna asked, horrified.

'There are loads of them here – we think they're the descendants of ship rats from the hulks. They're like the reindeer: they've gone native!'

They arrived at a beautiful old church, freshly painted and in perfect condition. 'This is the most southerly church in the world,' David said. 'Everybody does their bit to keep it restored. We still hold services here now and then.'

Alison and David went in. It was simple and very beautiful, hand-carved pews made with loving care by the whalers. Alison found herself very attracted to the New Zealander. He was relaxed and easy to be with, quiet and confident. They had a lot in common. Just my luck, she thought. It's a pity we are away tomorrow, just as I'm getting to know him – this always seems to happen. She knew she would be away from the base for most of the rest of her stay on the island and the opportunity to spend much time with him was unlikely to arise.

Light flakes of snow began to fall. 'Better be getting back to base,' Sebastian said, 'there's been a storm brewing all day. I hope *Endurance* arrives before it gets too rough.'

Back at base, they went straight into the common room, where a group of young scientists sat chatting around the bar. Alison loved this room: it was large, warm and comfortable with a huge, twenty-foot long table that had been built inside the room by a wintering party some years earlier. It was a work of art and Alison reckoned that it would still be there long after the building had gone. The bar was in the corner, the end of which was built into a large coal-burning stove, which glowed cosily; the walls were lined with books and there were a few musical instruments scattered around. Almost everyone smoked and there was a general fug in the room. This was a place of warmth and shelter in an otherwise extreme environment.

There had been some good-natured banter about women invading their privacy but they felt very welcome. To Alison's surprise, she and Anna were not the only women on South Georgia. Cindy Buxton and Annie Price, two well-known wildlife photographers, were working alone at St Andrews Bay, about twenty miles down the coast. They hadn't met but had managed to chat on the radio.

They joined Steve Martin, the base commander, a quiet man in his late thirties who had been to the Antarctic a number of times. A keen sailor and a mountain man, he also acted as magistrate as well as seeing to the day-to-day organisation of the base.

'How many of us are there on the island at the moment, Steve?' Anna asked.

'We only have about thirty just now, maybe a few more by the end of the season. A lot are scattered about the island working but not as many as usual. The Survey's short of money and I guess the programmes down on the Antarctic continent are more important to them,' he replied wryly. 'We're building a small base at Bird Island at the north-west end of the island so the biologists can continue their work but it will be very limited. We have a party of builders over there at the moment.'

'The Survey is operating four other bases in Antarctica,' David said. 'Halley Bay on the south coast of the Weddell Sea, which is a large station on an ice shelf – every few years it floats off as an iceberg and we have to rebuild it. There are two small island bases, Signy and Faraday, at the northern end of the Antarctic peninsula and Rothera, a new base under construction, about halfway down the west coast of the peninsula almost exactly on the Antarctic Circle. That's a big project and I guess what's eating up all the money.'

One of the radio operators, Peter Bayman, came over with a couple of signals for Steve. 'We got one from Captain Barker to say *Endurance* is almost in Cumberland Bay and should be here within the hour. This other looks more serious.'

Steve read and re-read the note. 'It's from Rex Hunt, the Governor of the Falklands,' he said. 'We're expecting a party of Argentinian scrap-metal workers to start dismantling Leith Harbour whaling station any day now. Rex isn't happy about it and I can't say I'm that keen. The strange thing is they set off almost a week ago on the Argentinian navy ship *Bahia Buen Suceso* and since then we haven't heard a peep. They ought to be contacting us by now. The governor wants us to keep an eye on them when they turn up.'

'He's dead right,' David said. 'Last September this bloke Davidoff arrived at Leith on another navy ship, the *Armaralty Irizar*, and they hung about for ages. They had no entry permit and it was a totally illegal landing.'

'Yes, I spoke to him on the radio but he just kept saying that he had permission from the Foreign Office – a load of nonsense,' Steve said. 'Neither he nor the ship's commander, Captain Tombetta, had contacted us, and the landing was contradictory to both the contract with Salvesen's and international law.'

Sebastian lit a cigarette. 'I bet Davidoff's going to make a packet out of the scrap. There must be millions of tons of steel at Leith Harbour and that's before you start on Stromness and Husvik,' he said.

Damian Saunders joined the group. He was a diver working as a marine biologist, and had some knowledge of salvage work.

'It will be a hard way to make a living. I bet Salvesen's are getting a cut of the profit. Just imagine trying to ship all that steel back across the Scotia Sea: it won't be easy.'

'There's trouble in the Falklands as well,' the radio operator said. 'I spoke to Ray Binnie, a *Chay* radio ham, who told me that the Argentinians have cut the islanders' fuel supplies again.'

Alison looked questioningly at David. 'We call the Falkland Islanders Chays,' he said. 'They have a habit of calling friends "Chay", much the way you Brits call a friend "Mate",' he said. 'The Chays think that the governor is trying to keep HMS *Endurance* around to fly the flag but London won't do anything to upset the apple cart while there are talks going on at the UN.

'While we've been trying to calm things down, they've been threatening us for years. Last month one of their Hercules reconnaissance planes flew down the island taking photographs.'

A cheer went up as *Endurance* was spotted entering King Edward Cove. The 'Red Plum', as she was nicknamed, appeared as a cocky little ship and although the fids at times called her the *Encumbrance*, she was a very welcome visitor. Alison, sitting quietly alongside David, had been only half listening to the conversation in the warm and friendly atmosphere. She watched the ship's arrival with mixed feelings. She was looking forward to her trip to Antarctic Bay the following day but this was to be her last evening on the base and she was just getting to know everybody. David and Sebastian were also getting a lift elsewhere from *Endurance* and they would be away for the rest of the season.

Such is life, she thought, as she joined the rest of the crowd walking out to the jetty to watch the ship's arrival.

Steve Martin remained quiet. Although a bunch of Argie scrap-metal dealers didn't seem very alarming, not for the first time he felt an air of unease about the situation. Lots of Argentinian boats had called at Grytviken during his stay and the people had always been friendly and courteous. The sabre rattling could be left up north with the politicians. He had a base to run. In an isolated outpost like this there was little room for squabbling. *Endurance* was coming up the fjord and the extra company would be a pleasant change for a couple of days before she left for the winter. There seemed little reason to worry and he decided not to share his concern with the rest of the base.

9

Buenos Aires, Tuesday 16 March 1982

The sun blazed from a cloudless sky onto the parade ground in front of the Naval Mechanics College, shimmering on the white hats, gloves and spats on the rows of immaculately dressed young sailors standing rigidly at attention. Sitting with his wife on the raised platform with the rest of the military dignitaries was Captain Hugo Corti. He had changed little; he was forty now and his jet-black hair had receded slightly and there was a grey tinge on his temples. The cheerful countenance that had made him popular in his youth was still with him but the years had made him wary. Survival in the Argentinian navy had not been easy, but his lucky star still seemed to be shining. The meteoric rise to power of his commanding officer, Captain Jorge Anaya, first to admiral and then, almost immediately, to one of the three rulers of Argentina, had its compensations. Today was the passing out parade of Hugo's son, Raul, from the military academy, and it was at the admiral's request that he and Maria were in pride of place on the podium. Maria had aged little and today she was looking immaculate and prosperous and was bristling with pride and pleasure at the sight of her son.

Raul was now twenty and, following the family tradition, had joined the navy. How time had flashed past! He was taller than his father but similar in looks and temperament. Both parents were watching him with immense pride. Taking the salute at the head of the parade square stood Admiral Anaya. He too had changed little since Hugo had first met him. There was something cold about him that Hugo had never been able to fathom, even though he had shown him kindness throughout his career. Ramrod straight and a man of few words, Anaya could be a vicious opponent and Hugo was glad to be on the right side of him. General Galtieri, the president, and Anaya were good friends and Hugo had noticed that the few times he had ever seen the admiral smile and let his hair down, were at military functions when the two were together. It was an odd relationship; the navy and the army did not usually fraternise and Hugo wondered what brought about this friendly conspiracy. Both men, he knew, were hardliners determined to keep Argentina under military rule.

The dirty war was still going on; in many ways Hugo approved of the battle against the *Montanero* and union movements but the violent methods used by the military police stuck in his throat. He knew that the Mechanics College, where he had enjoyed his earlier years of training, had become a secret detention centre and shuddered to think what went on behind its doors.

He often wondered what had happened to the bunch of youngsters who had been arrested on the docks. There were always a crowd of women hanging around the academy entrance desperate for news of missing loved ones. It was difficult to look them in the eye.

Alfredo Astiz had become famous. He was known throughout Argentina as 'The Blond Angel' and sometimes 'El Rubio' (Blondie) and seemed to relish the notoriety. His undercover work was legendary; he had been accused of the murder of two nuns, from the convent of 'Mothers of the Plaza de Mayo', which was suspected of harbouring dissidents. This had been emphatically denied by the navy but Hugo knew he was wanted for questioning in a number of countries that were trying to trace missing nationals. Both men met on occasions. Nothing further had been said about the docks incident but Hugo gave him as wide a berth as possible, remembering the psychopathic pleasure he showed as he had beaten the defenceless youngsters.

The drill was coming to an end. Admiral Anaya took the salute, the men stood down and the parade broke up. Hugo and Maria left the platform and walked across the grass to the parade square to greet their son. Raul was beaming and looked very young and smart in his naval officer's uniform. He kissed his mother and shook hands warmly with his father. Admiral Anaya walked over and joined them. Raul shot to attention but the admiral signalled him to relax.

'Congratulations, young man. I hear that you did well at the college.' He turned to Maria, smiling. 'Argentina needs professional sailors; I understand this is the fourth generation of your family to join the navy. I knew your father well: how is Capitan Vildoza?'

'My father's fine. He's enjoying his retirement but still thinks he's in the navy,' she replied.

Turning to Hugo, the admiral said, 'It seems a long time since we were working together with Admiral Massera. I'd like you to come up to my office on Saturday afternoon; there's something I want to discuss with you.'

As Admiral Anaya moved away, Raul breathed a sigh of relief. Hugo's stomach had also lurched – what could the admiral want with him?

'I have my first posting,' his son said, still smiling. 'I'm going to sea at last!'

'That's wonderful! What ship?'

'The battleship *General Belgrano*. I'm to be the second electronics officer.'

10

The Red Plum

For eleven years, the Danish merchant ship *Anita Dan* ploughed the frozen seas of northern Europe. She wasn't an icebreaker but had an ice-strengthened hull and a steep sloping curve to her bow, ideal for the icy passages between Norway, Iceland, Greenland and Spitsbergen in the Svalbard Archipelago. She was slow and reliable, her single screw allowing a maximum speed of only thirteen and a half knots, ideal for carrying passengers and freight to these isolated northern ports. By 1967 she was no longer profitable and her owners retired her to her moorings with an uncertain future. A few months later she was purchased by the Royal Navy at the bargain price of less than three hundred thousand pounds, roughly her scrap value, and taken to the Harland and Wolff shipyard in Belfast for conversion.

On 28 June 1968 she re-emerged, transformed into HMS *Endurance*, possibly the most cost-effective ship ever purchased by the navy. Her renaming ceremony was carried out by Alexandra Shackleton, the granddaughter of Sir Ernest. Standing with her parents, as her aunt smashed a bottle of best-quality Bollinger across the bow, was the eleven-year-old Alison Shackleton. To her the brightly painted new ship was a wonder; little did she realise that in a few short years her life would be inextricably linked to this beautiful ship. The family seriously hoped that this ship wouldn't come to a similar end to Shackleton's original HMS *Endurance*, broken and twisted in the ice somewhere at the bottom of the Weddle Sea.

She had metamorphosed into something unlike any other ship

in the navy. For a start, she was painted bright red to make her clearly visible in the ice-bound Antarctic sea and from day one she was known throughout the fleet as the 'Red Plum'. Behind her bridge was a new hangar and workshop to house her two Wasp helicopters. This made her top heavy with a tendency to roll awkwardly even in moderate seas. She still had the Burmeister & Wain two-stroke diesel engines but larger fuel tanks had been fitted to give her the four-thousand-mile range she needed for her lonely journeys south.

The Antarctic Treaty prohibited the deployment of military weapons within the treaty area, and she was certainly no ship of war; more like a floating workshop, ideal for mapping and charting the seabed of Antarctica, she had a laboratory and an advanced (for the time) satellite communications system.

For all that she had a sting in her tail; in fact two: in her hangar were two tiny Westland Wasp helicopters, mainly used for mapping and transferring materials between ships or helping out moving light loads for the Antarctic bases. They were old and had already been phased out in the rest of the Royal Navy but, like their ageing parent ship, they were simple, reliable and easy to repair. Normally a two-man aircraft, the rear seat carried mountings for a general-purpose machine gun and they had external fittings for the Nord AS12 air-to-surface missiles, sixteen of which were hidden away in *Endurance*'s hold. Also below deck were stowed two obsolete Oerlikon 20mm heavy-duty machine guns that could, at a pinch, be mounted on her bridge superstructure. She would be no match for a one-to-one battle with even the smallest of warships; her guns would be little more than pea-shooters against a well-armed foe. No one ever imagined that this small ship would go to war; her crew were mostly young volunteers looking for adventure away from the humdrum of normal naval life.

And so, for the next fifteen years she was the British navy's Antarctic patrol vessel. In a regular pattern each October she would leave Portsmouth and make the six-thousand-mile journey south to the Falkland Islands in time for the end of the dark Antarctic winter, where for the next eight months she would fly the British flag, making regular calls into South American ports, Montevideo, Buenos Aires, and so on, and making contact with similar ships to herself from the US, Chile, Argentina, Russia and the rest. In Port Stanley she was always welcome; her arrival from the UK heralded the end of winter and the all-important link with the home country. She was a happy ship and ambassador for Britain in the southern oceans until catastrophe struck in the autumn of 1982.

11

HMS *Endurance*, off Fortuna Bay, South Georgia, Tuesday 16 March 1982

Captain Nick Barker was not a happy man. He and his entire crew had been appalled to learn that *Endurance* was to be sold or scrapped on her return to Southampton. Worse still was the fact that they had got the news from the Argentinian press and it had only just been confirmed by the Admiralty. The navy and Lord Carrington, the foreign secretary, had tried desperately to save the ship but John Nott, the defence minister, had stuck rigidly to the radical defence cuts policy the recently elected Conservative Government was pursuing, and it seemed that Barker's ship was doomed. The captain was devastated and trying to make the best of a bad business.

Nick Barker had been the captain since May 1980. He was tough, energetic and fair with a wide smile, and was steeped in navy tradition. His father had been commander of HMS *Ardent*, killed in action when his ship was sunk off Norway by the German battle cruisers *Scharnhorst* and *Gneisenau*. Unconventionally, Nick had joined the navy as a national serviceman, was commissioned two years later and worked his way up from the bottom. He took a keen interest in the politics of the South Atlantic and in some ways acted as a go-between with Governor Rex Hunt in the Falklands and Ambassador Williams in Buenos Aires. He was much more in accordance with Rex Hunt's thinking and felt the British Embassy was more interested in trade and seemed blissfully unaware of the worsening political situation.

That morning, at the same time that Hugo Corti watched his

son Raul parade on the square in Buenos Aires, the *Endurance* had taken on board two parties from the King Edward Point base. The geophysicist and his assistant were about to be taken ashore at Fortuna Bay and the two BBC women were to be dropped at the small field hut in Antarctic Bay, a few miles further up the coast. Standing with him on the bridge, David Asquith was pointing out the features of the huge Fortuna Glacier as it poured into the sea. The beach was clear of ice and steep grassy hills rose from the coast at either side of the ice front. On the beach they could see thousands of penguins and in the distance a small group of reindeer was grazing. The glacier was at least five miles wide and heavily crevassed.

'This is the way that Shackleton descended with Frank Worsley and Tom Crean in 1916,' he said. 'The glacier is receding so these days you can more or less get along the beach but I reckon that seventy years ago the ice front was out in the sea. They must have crossed higher up.'

'Good grief,' Nick Barker said. 'It's miles wide – how did they do it?'

'As far as I know it was just bitter determination!' David said. 'They were totally unequipped and suffering from exposure and exhaustion. Over there you can see the pass they climbed to reach Stromness whaling station. That doesn't look too bad but further back across the island it must have been very tough going.'

Alison had been staring intently up the glacier. 'They crossed the island in thirty-six hours with hardly a stop,' she said. 'They had a rough chart of the coast and the island had never been explored. And all after crossing the Scotia Sea in an open ship's lifeboat – it's a miracle they found a way.'

Captain Barker sighed, looking out across this huge glacier. It was easy to imagine the hardships of these extraordinary men and he wondered what he would have done in the same situation. 'Come on,' he said. 'I'll get Tony Ellerbeck to fly you ashore with your equipment in one of the Wasps.'

'It's much more crevassed than I expected,' Sebastian said

anxiously. 'We're doing a magnetic and gravity survey and I was hoping to do a lot of work up on the glacier.'

'No worries, Seb,' David said, smiling. 'The glacier's much flatter further up: it'll be fine.' He turned to the captain, 'Thanks for the lift, sir. We're here for three weeks and have loads of food. Steve will send the base cutter round to pick us up and if there's any problem it's an easy walk over the pass to Leith Harbour and we have loads of stuff dumped there.'

Captain Barker's face clouded. 'Be careful, we're expecting these Argentinian scrap men any time now at Leith, keep away from them if you can.'

There was something odd about the *Bahia Buen Suceso*'s non-arrival. He knew she had left Buenos Aires a week earlier – plenty of time to get here – but since then there had been neither sight nor sound. For some reason she seemed to be keeping radio silence. He had sent one of his Wasp helicopters over to check Leith Harbour but the place was deserted. He would like to hang around to make contact with Davidoff's ship and see that the work was done according to the agreement with Salvesen but could hardly stay if nothing had happened.

This was likely to be his last day in South Georgia. He was anxious about the situation in Argentina and had been reporting his concern back to his superiors in Britain and to the British Embassy in Buenos Aires but had the awful feeling that they thought he was exaggerating the situation to save his ship. The only ally he had was Rex Hunt, the Governor of the Falklands, and nobody was taking any notice of him either.

He watched the Wasp fly the two men ashore. The enormous glacier dwarfed the two tiny specks waving below the massive ice front as the ship pulled away.

He envied the two fids on the beach; theirs would be a tough but simple existence for the next few weeks. He had one more party to drop off and then the six-thousand-mile trip home, taking his ship to the knacker's yard and an uncertain future for himself and his crew. His beautiful ship – since the day he first came aboard he had loved her, the strange un-navy like plum red colour and her awkward pitch and roll in heavy seas caused by the unwieldy hangar on her afterdeck, and the men, so different from the rest of the navy, young and enthusiastic. How would he be able to bear the endless journey home? Sighing, he went below.

The mess deck on *Endurance* still boasted the elegant splendour of her earlier incarnation as the *Anita Dan*, with oak panelling and comfortable seats, and Captain Barker joined his guests, who were discussing the situation in Argentina. He had an unusually large contingent of passengers on board. Three VIPs: Lord Buxton, the chairman of Anglia television, and his wife who had visited their daughter, Cindy, who was filming wildlife down the coast at St Andrews Bay; and Commander Mario Fontanot of the Uruguayan navy on a good-will visit to the Antarctic. Also on board was a returning joint services climbing expedition led by Lieutenant Bob Veal.

The previous year Lord Buxton had spoken out in Parliament, alongside Lord Shackleton, outraged at the possibility that *Endurance* might be withdrawn from service. He had already telexed a report to his friend Lord Carrington stating his concerns about the anti-British feeling he had come across in Buenos Aires on his journey south, and he was very worried about the exposed position of the people living in the Falkland Islands.

'The situation in Argentina is very grave,' said Commander Fontanot, in his impeccable English. 'They are having strikes all the time and Argentinian currency is valueless, bombs are going off in the streets every day and the government is very unpopular. It's affecting us in Uruguay: we have enough troubles of our own without a bad neighbour,' he said, shrugging his shoulders expressively.

Lord Buxton nodded. 'Nobody at home is taking this seriously, and when I was in Buenos Aires they openly claimed the Falklands as their property, non-negotiable. I understood that talks at the UN were going well but that's not the feeling I got in Buenos Aires. I had lunch with the Argentinian foreign minister, Costa

Mendez, who said quite openly that the junta might make landings on our territory and he was certain that such incursions would not be opposed.'

The captain voiced his own anxiety. 'Last November we called in at the naval base at Bahia Blanca on our way south, and we couldn't have been treated better. We moored up alongside the cruiser *General Belgrano* for a week and had barbecues and folk dancing with its crew. We were welcome in their homes and some of the lads made some really good friends. On our way back from the Antarctic a couple of months later we called in at the Argie port of Ushuaia in their southern province of Tierra del Fuego. We've always been welcome there, but this time we were dumped at the end of the jetty with a slop bucket and were told we were in a war zone and to leave as soon as possible. At first I thought that it was trouble with Chile but then somebody said we were in the Malvinas zone. When I asked what that was all about they shut up like clams and would say no more. The local people were as friendly as ever and seemed embarrassed about the whole thing.'

Nick shrugged his shoulders and continued: 'A few days later we called in at their navy base at Mar del Plata, and there was no trouble at all. The Whitbread round-the-world yacht race came in while we were there and it was great fun. We were moored alongside one of their submarines, the *Santa Fe*, and her captain, Horacio Bicain, was very friendly and we had him round for drinks most evenings. There was none of the trouble we had down in the south but I'm sure that something's going on.'

An hour later *Endurance* sailed into Antarctic Bay. It was well named, with glaciers falling into the sea on all sides and not so much greenery. It was a well-chosen spot for filming. Millions of king penguins covered the beaches and there was wildlife in abundance and spectacular scenery whichever way you looked.

The ship's boat was lowered into the sea and began to ferry the food and belongings to the shore. Alison and Anna were lifted out to the hut in one of the Wasps by the pilot Tony Ellerbeck and then the captain flew out himself for a look. It was tiny, about eight by ten feet. There were two bunks at one end and a small table by the window. It was filled with emergency rations and there was hardly room to move inside. A Tilley lamp hung from a beam over the table. The last occupants had left a bottle of Scotch and a note of welcome on the table. The pilot helped carry the sledge boxes filled with stores and their camera equipment up to the hut. Tony was very helpful; he had dropped off many field parties all over the Antarctic and was always anxious about their safety. He helped set up the radio and Anna's small solar panel to charge her camera batteries. The radio checked out with Peter Bayman, the operator at Grytviken.

'The *Endurance*'s next port of call is Port Stanley,' the captain explained. 'We'll be in radio range for the next couple of days. *The Goon Show* is at seven each evening, that's when all the Antarctic sledge parties relay their positions to us and formal information is passed between the bases, and there's usually a bit of a chat afterwards. I don't think you'll be able to hear the southern bases or the sledges at this range but you should be able to speak to Signy Island, which is at the north end of the Antarctic Peninsula.'

Both women realised that Captain Barker was being careful to let them know all the options in case they got into difficulty.

'Don't worry about us, Nick,' Alison said. 'We'll be extraordinarily careful. The last thing we want to do is call for help. There's enough food for two months, more if we're careful, and in an emergency there's plenty of seal and penguin about.'

The women gave both ship's officers a big farewell hug and the Wasp buzzed into the air and rejoined the ship. Captain Barker would have liked to have hung around longer in the hope of contacting the Argentinian scrap men but could hardly wait indefinitely for a problem that hadn't happened. For all he knew Captain Briatore of the *Bahia Buen Suceso* might turn up and register on the island quite legitimately.

Feeling very much alone, Alison and Anna stood waving on

the beach as *Endurance* hooted for the last time and headed north on what she expected was to be the start of her final journey home.

12

Leith Harbour, South Georgia, Friday 19 March 1982

The *Bahia Buen Suceso* slipped quietly into Leith Harbour and moored up alongside the old jetty at the whaling station. For the last two days they had been in a holding position fifteen miles off the northern point of South Georgia waiting for HMS *Endurance* to leave. She moored alongside the old flensing platform and within a few hours work was underway unloading the heavy cutting equipment and a small portable crane had been erected.

Two of the houses at the station were in good condition. Captain Briatore took over one of these for the use of the fifteen-man commando unit which was on board – the elite troops of the Buzo Tactico, Argentinian Special Forces. The second house was taken by the scrap men. Briatore was worried when he realised that the building had been locked and was in use by the British scientists. The place was filled with food boxes and fuel. The men kicked in the door and ransacked the food. One of the men climbed up onto the roof of the old power station and ran up the Argentinian flag and a rousing cheer went up from the workers. Captain Briatore grinned but was concerned that things were getting out of hand. He had specific orders not to cause trouble or draw attention to his party.

The commandos were organised and efficient, and set about unloading the weapons and military equipment according to plan, but Briatore had little control over the scrap-metal workers, who set about looting the whaling station with scant regard for authority. Constantino Davidoff had not come south but put his son in charge of the workmen and he seemed to have little control over them. Wildlife was abundant at Leith – fur and elephant seals lined the beaches and a large herd of reindeer grazed the hillside behind the harbour. The soldiers shot two of these, a welcome addition to the evening meal, and the captain asked that they should be butchered carefully and the skins saved for him.

About mid-afternoon a small commotion took place as four Britons walked into the whaling station. Anticipating the arrival of the scrap men they had come over to shore-up the buildings that were being used by the Survey. Briatore had been expecting this but had hoped that their arrival would not have been noticed quite so soon. The men walked up to the house where their food and equipment was normally stored and found a group of Argentinians sitting down to a meal of reindeer steaks. A bunch of workers formed outside the hut staring curiously at them. In the corner of the room the 'No entry' sign leaned against the wall and the 'British Antarctic Survey' sign over the door was scribbled out and replaced with 'Argentina'. The scientists felt quite nervous but put on a bold face. Nobody could speak Spanish but their reception was quite friendly.

Two of the men, Trefor Edwards and Neil Shaw, walked nervously down to the ship and were taken aboard, where they were met by Captain Briatore. Much to their relief he spoke excellent English.

'Welcome, welcome! We are pleased you have come to visit us.'

'This is not your port of entry,' Trefor said. 'We have been expecting you: the ship should go first to King Edward Cove for documentation.'

'This is not necessary; we have permission from the British Foreign Office in London. I spoke to them only yesterday, there is absolutely no need,' the captain lied.

'I'm sorry,' said Neil angrily, 'but these are the rules of the island. The house where our equipment is stored has been broken into and ransacked. This is British territory and you are flying the Argentinian flag. The reindeer are protected and must not be shot.'

The captain shrugged despairingly. 'I'm sorry, these scrap men can't be trusted, but don't worry, we will put everything right. I have a gift of fresh fruit from Constantino Davidoff for you to take back to your base. You are most welcome to stay on board for the night if you wish.'

'No thanks, we'll stay in one of the houses,' Trefor answered. 'I must ask you again to contact the base commander at King Edward Point.'

Captain Briatore was friendly and relaxed but his reference to London was so preposterous that the men knew that something was amiss. There was little else they could do so they politely refused the gift and left the ship to rejoin their friends.

Briatore grinned as they left. There was nothing that they could do that would affect his plan at this stage.

'Leave them alone but don't let them anywhere near the soldiers or the weapons,' he ordered, as he watched them leave.

The two fids walked nervously back through a hive of activity. Nobody seemed to be taking any notice of them and they joined their two friends, Brian Lockwood and Bob Banner, who had moved their rucksacks into the old villa that had once been the home of the whaling station manager.

'I've got Steve Martin on the radio, Trefor,' Brian said. 'Bob's upstairs taking photographs. There are military personnel all over the place.'

Trefor took over the radio and quickly told Steve what had been said on the ship.

'Can you stay there for the night, Trefor?' Steve's voice crackled over the air. 'I'll speak to the governor in the Falklands and get some advice on what we should do. Keep the radio on but we'll keep transmissions to the minimum. And be careful.'

Bob Banner came down the stairs looking shaken. 'There are blokes in white uniform unloading guns and ammunition. They've unloaded hundreds of oil drums; there's enough fuel to tank up the entire navy! I've got plenty of pictures; I don't think they've seen me.'

'We'd better keep watch through the night,' Trefor said uneasily. 'This whole thing stinks. What the hell are they doing with all these guns?' There was an uneasy silence. It wasn't difficult to figure out. The only people on the island were about thirty fids and they were totally defenceless.

In the early hours of the morning Steve Martin came back on the radio. 'Trefor, can you take this message down carefully and pass it on to the captain. After that I suggest you get out of there.'

Once again Trefor and Neil walked uneasily down to the ship; Captain Briatore was as jovial as before. Trefor passed him the message from Rex Hunt, the Governor of the Falkland Islands. It was a careful piece of diplomacy, unambiguous and non-threatening.

> *You have landed illegally at Leith without obtaining proper clearance. You and your party must go back on board the* Bahia Buen Suceso *immediately and report to the Base Commander at Grytviken for further instructions. You must remove the Argentinian flag from Leith. You must not interfere with the British Antarctic depot at Leith. You must not alter or deface the notices at Leith. No military personnel are allowed to land on South Georgia. No firearms are to be taken ashore. Ends.*

Captain Briatore smiled cheerfully and accepted the note but indicated that he would do no such thing. As the men left his ship he tore it up and threw it overboard grinning. The four fids then left Leith and walked up the coast back to their boat and within a few hours were back at the base giving an account of their adventure to Steve Martin. An air of uncertainty had come over the base and the peace and tranquillity of the island had changed. This was no place for men with guns.

13

Port Stanley, Falkland Islands, Saturday 20 March 1982

As Trefor Edwards' party settled down to an uneasy night's watch from the old villa at Leith they were not the only people to suffer a sleepless night. Governor Rex Hunt and Captain Nick Barker didn't get much sleep either. *Endurance* had arrived in Port Stanley Harbour the previous afternoon and disembarked her passengers. It was a relief to be back to having a normal ship's crew. That evening Captain Barker joined Governor Rex Hunt, Lord Buxton and their wives for dinner at Government House. During the meal a message arrived from the ship that trouble was afoot in South Georgia. A pleasant evening turned into a long, eventful night.

Steve Martin had been frantically trying to contact the Falkland Islands, but late on Friday evening nobody could be raised. It took a full two hours of anxious calling until he was finally heard by HMS *Endurance*'s radio operator. Worse still, having decided to transmit in code, it was ages before the governor had the full story. The scientists were not used to working with codes and it took some time to realise that they were using one code while the staff in Rex Hunt's office were transmitting another.

Between them Rex Hunt and Nick Barker concocted a response message to Captain Briatore, which was signalled to Steve Martin at King Edward Point who in turn passed it on to Trefor Edwards.

'I knew there was something fishy about the non-arrival of the *Bahia Buen Suceso*,' Captain Barker muttered.

'We'd better get on to the Foreign Office,' the governor said. 'This looks as if they are trying it on with another incursion like Southern Thule in the South Sandwich Islands.'

'I think I should take *Endurance* back to South Georgia and kick them off,' Nick said. 'There's a new bunch of forty marines due in Montevideo to change the garrison. I'm supposed to be bringing them here before I head for home.'

The governor thought for a moment. 'The British Antarctic Survey could help us out; I'll speak to their director, Dick Laws. Their ship, the *John Biscoe*, could bring the marines over, and we should hang on to the old garrison as well. We could probably let you have a small contingent of marines to take down to act as guards at King Edward Point.'

By the early hours of the morning, Rex had sent a long signal to the Foreign Office reporting the situation, suggesting a course of action and asking for advice. He and Captain Barker talked late into the night. To their amazement a signal from London arrived back almost immediately with approval, ordering *Endurance* south and giving permission to use the *John Biscoe* to transfer the marines.

Unknown to either of them the signal had been passed on to Lord Carrington, the foreign secretary, who had in turn spoken to the prime minister, who had instantly approved and told them to get on with it. Dr Laws had been contacted on the radio. He was at sea on board the RRS *Bransfield* off the coast of Chile and he readily agreed that the Survey would help out.

Rex Hunt then contacted Steve Martin at King Edward Point. 'Can your people keep an eye on Leith Harbour, Steve?' he asked.

The base commander sounded concerned. 'Bloody hell, Rex, my guys are already acting as emissaries and now you want us to do something that could be construed as spying. This is a scientific base: if there's trouble we're supposed to be neutral!'

'Needs must, Steve. *Endurance* will be down in a few days with a detachment of marines to take over from you. If we act quickly this will all be over in a day or two.'

'OK,' Steve agreed reluctantly. 'As long as Dick Laws gives me the authority. Try to remember that I have a scientific programme to run.'

The Falkland Island Garrison is stationed at Moody Brook Barracks, about a mile down the road from Port Stanley. It's an assortment of wooden and corrugated-iron huts that house the small detachment of forty or so Royal Marines whose job it is to fly the British flag and theoretically guard the Islands against invasion. A dull posting where nothing much happens.

Acting lieutenant Keith Mills was shaken from his bed in the early hours of Saturday morning and asked to report immediately to Captain Barker on *Endurance*. As one of the most junior officers on the base he guessed that he was probably the most easily spared. He arrived on board to find the ship in a high state of alert, frantically loading fuel and stores.

'I'm sorry for the short notice, Lieutenant,' the captain said. 'I want you to take a small detachment of men to South Georgia with us, to act as guard at the base.'

'What's up, sir?' he asked, grinning. The chance to visit an Antarctic island sounded like an interesting break.

Captain Barker briefly filled him in about the situation at Leith Harbour. 'You are to maintain a British military presence on the island, protect the scientists at King Edward Point and take over the surveillance of Leith Harbour from the fids. We sail as soon as I get enough fuel on board. Can you get your men together?'

Mills readily assented and rushed off to sort out his men and equipment. He was given a contingent of twenty marines and a senior NCO, Sergeant Peter Leach, an old hand with twenty-two years' experience and plenty of action under his belt. He had served as a scout in Borneo, witnessed the Turkish invasion of Cyprus and served on the streets of Northern Ireland. No one thought that there was any serious likelihood of armed combat. The idea that the Argies would mount a frontal naval attack on Grytviken was so outlandish that it was never mentioned during the planning stages. They did, however, draw a significant amount of weapons from the armoury just in case.

For all his inexperience, Mills was an ideal candidate for the job. He was twenty-two years old, tall and thin, a keen skier and diving instructor, a boxer and judo black belt. Boisterous and bursting with confidence, he could be mildly irritating in his enthusiasm. He was nonetheless well aware that he was going into a situation where any action he took would reflect on his status in the regiment. As it turned out, rarely had a small British force been so lucky in its choice of officer. At this point in the proceedings there was not the slightest indication that the landing at Leith Harbour was anything but a small Argentinian incursion onto South Georgia. There was no hint of the grand plan for the invasion of the Falkland Islands.

The air link with the mainland was run by LADEAir Service, which was at that time a branch of the Argentinian air force. Their office overlooked the harbour, not one hundred yards from where *Endurance* was moored. The airport manager had returned to Port Stanley a few days earlier, with a large group of helpers, ostensibly to conduct an office audit. He was in fact Vice Comodoro Hector Gilbert, an air force Secret Service officer reporting on the state of alertness of the garrison at Moody Brook barracks to General Sotera at J2 Military Intelligence. From his window it was easy to watch the hectic activity on-board *Endurance* and the Royal Marines loading weapons and equipment. There was no secret that she was returning to South Georgia. He immediately reported the news to Argentina. His transmissions were monitored by the American listening post in Buenos Aires and were read thoughtfully by Arnie Schwartz.

As HMS *Endurance* lifted her anchor and turned south on her unexpected return to South Georgia, armed only with a large machine gun, two small helicopters and twenty-two marines, she was, at that moment, the only British warship in the whole of the earth's southern hemisphere. Meanwhile, the Argentinian navy was on full alert, its military rulers preparing for war.

14

London, Saturday 20 March 1982

Looking down from the walls of the Foreign Office are the portraits of foreign secretaries and their advisers who would not, at a moment's notice, have given a second thought to military action when it was deemed necessary. The tradition was: if in doubt send a gunboat!

To many of his admirers, the present incumbent of that comfortable office in Whitehall was just such a man. Lord Peter Carrington was a nobleman: confident, wealthy and immensely popular amongst the Tory hierarchy. A war veteran from the tank regiments, he was highly decorated. Margaret Thatcher, Britain's first female prime minister, was halfway through her first term of office; these were difficult times and she was unpopular. She knew that many of her Cabinet colleagues had not supported her leadership bid and that Carrington was one of these. However, his experience and ability as a statesman seemed beyond question and, in the interest of party unity, she had made him her foreign secretary when she came to power in 1979. He did not have her bullish, right-wing approach to foreign policy. His aristocratic self-assurance and the fact that as a hereditary peer he had not been elected to Parliament put him into a class of Tory that Mrs Thatcher found difficult to stomach. In short, the prime minister and her foreign minister were not bosom friends but they did have a polite working relationship.

That morning word had come from Rex Hunt, the Governor of the Falkland Islands, about the scrap-metal dealers raising the Argentinian flag on South Georgia. Eyebrows were raised, but it hardly seemed to be an international incident. Nevertheless, Carrington's parliamentary secretary had passed him a curt memo from the prime minister, asking for a paper on the Falkland Islands situation. Somebody had tipped her off that there was a problem. This, at last, was the Foreign Office's big chance. For months now, they had been quibbling with the Ministry of Defence about the withdrawal from service of HMS *Endurance*. Carrington had been arguing the case that her removal from the South Atlantic would complicate the negotiations with Argentina, which were taking place at present at the United Nations in New York.

It was hard to interpret what the junta was thinking. The talks were cordial enough, but what Enrique Ros, the Argentinian negotiator at the UN, was saying, and the threatening hard-line his superior, Nicanor Costa Mendez, was issuing from Buenos Aires, were very different. Costa Mendez, after ten years, was once again Argentina's foreign minister, now acting for the generals and one of the instigators of *Operation Rosario*. Neither Carrington nor Enrique Ros had the faintest notion that *Operation Rosary* existed and was already committed by the junta for the autumn invasion of the Islands. Ros was as mystified as everyone else about his leader's intent.

Correctly interpreting that Davidoff's scrap-metal workers were cover for yet another Southern Thule-like military incursion, and having read Rex Hunt's anxious signal, Carrington approached the prime minister who, with remarkable promptness, agreed with him to send HMS *Endurance*, and a group of marines from the Falkland Island Garrison, to Grytviken as a deterrent. At the same time, Mrs Thatcher asked John Nott, the defence minister, to submit a minute on what options were open to her in the event of escalation of the problem. This did not make good reading: it stressed the huge distances involved and the difficulties in taking on the Argentinian navy, let alone retaking the Islands if they were occupied. It was pointed out that this was all hypothetical as the Argentinian leadership had plenty of its own problems at home. Also, negotiations at the UN were friendly and seemed to be going well.

Nott went off to a NATO meeting in Colorado and gave the matter no further thought. Carrington's problems on the world stage seemed more important – he was off again to Brussels for yet another Common Market budget dispute and then going on to the Middle East where, after President Sadat's assassination, the Israelis were threatening to invade the Lebanon. The prime minister's hands were full of the Irish troubles – Bobby Sands and nine others in Belfast's Maze prison had died on hunger strike and the nation was in shock.

There was something comical about a bunch of Argentinian scrap-metal workers invading South Georgia and the British press was treating it as a joke. The foreign secretary asked to be kept briefed on events (it surely wasn't that serious), and problems at home seemed much more imminent. He put the Falklands situation to the back of his mind and got on with the rest of his portfolio.

15

Buenos Aires, Admiralty HQ, Saturday 20 March 1982

From the moment that President Galtieri made Nicanor Costa Mendez foreign minister, the stage had been set for the Falkland Islands' invasion. It seemed ridiculous to Costa Mendez that, in the ten years that had passed since he and Lord George Brown had come to cordial agreement, more or less wrapping up the Malvinas problem, nothing had happened. He knew that at that time Britain had been keen to clean up the Falkland Islands' situation and that the Foreign Office was not, in principle, against Argentinian sovereignty.

The situation in Argentina was precarious. In an attempt to patch up the ailing economy, the junta had made Dr Roberto Alemain minister of the economy. Under the banner *Deflate, Deregulate, Nationalise,* he set about the most devastatingly severe economic measures that Argentina had ever seen. Taxes rose, he floated the exchange rate on the world market and froze public sector wages. He even attempted to reduce defence spending, to which the junta paid scant or no attention.

All three of the new military leaders of Argentina knew they walked a precarious tightrope. Public unrest was at its worst for years: inflation was running at a hundred and fifty per cent, there were daily demonstrations and riots in the streets. The dirty war of the seventies had left thirty thousand people missing; all their hands were bloody. Lesser men than they had come to a very sticky end.

From his office in Naval Headquarters overlooking the waterfront, Admiral George Anaya looked down over the city's main centre of commerce with its modern high-rise buildings. From here you could see the port, with a number of ships moving up the Rio de la Plata estuary. In the docks was a large military presence and he looked with pride at the two new German-built frigates moored alongside the aircraft carrier, *Veinticinco de Mayo*. There were two missile corvettes, the *Granville* and the *Drummond*, with their strangely British names, and a number of smaller military ships.

Preparations were going ahead for the annual naval exercise with Uruguay. Away from the military area the docks were as shabby as ever, the buildings decayed and unprepared, with a mass of people thronging the littered streets. Little had changed in the sixty years since Ernest Shackleton had joined the original *Endurance* here on its fateful voyage. The age of sail had passed to steam and then to diesel and now nuclear warships and submarines patrolled the oceans. Military hardware had changed dramatically but in essence the port was much as it had been half a century earlier.

Anaya paced his comfortable office deep in thought, poured himself a large Scotch whisky from a silver decanter and drank slowly. He had been drinking more than usual lately but the excitement and adrenaline from the planning of *Operation Rosario* was keeping his head clear. His neck was rigid with tension and mounting anger. Word had just reached him from General Freddie Sotera's intelligence service that HMS *Endurance* was leaving Port Stanley for South Georgia with a detachment of Royal Marines on board. Surely he was not going to be outplayed by the British again!

There was a gentle tap on his door and Captain Hugo Corti entered. He was in civilian clothes but still walked smartly up to the admiral's desk and stood at attention.

'You wish to see me, sir?' he said, the usual pleasant smile on his face masking the uneasiness he felt inside.

'Sit down, Hugo; it's good to see you. I have a job which I think will interest you.'

The admiral poured himself another whisky and one for Hugo and sat down behind his ornate desk. Hugo could not help noticing that the admiral's hand was shaking. Without more ado, Anaya briefly outlined *Operation Rosario* to the younger man. Hugo was flabbergasted; it was years since he had been involved in *Operation Goa* and he remembered the bitter disappointment they had felt when President Videla had scrapped the operation. However, times had changed and his understanding was that the negotiations over the sovereignty of the Malvinas were going well with the British.

'My problem is this, Hugo,' Anaya said. 'We've just learned that Mrs Thatcher has sent the frigate *Endurance* to South Georgia with a company of marines. If they reinforce the garrison in the Malvinas Islands before we liberate them, the whole operation will be in serious jeopardy. I am convinced that the British will do nothing once we take control of the Islands. What we don't want is to give them the time or the opportunity to be prepared. It must be done quickly with minimal force and loss of life.'

'But, sir,' said Hugo anxiously, 'surely they will retaliate and won't world opinion be against us as the aggressor? What if the Americans side with the British?'

'We are certain that America will support us. Britain has no interest in the South Atlantic; this is our part of the world. They're closing their base in South Georgia and only last week our embassy staff in London reported that Lord Carrington had confirmed in Parliament that their ice patrol ship *Endurance* is to be withdrawn.'

'What about the talks at the United Nations, sir, I thought they were going well?'

Anaya shrugged in exasperation. 'The talks have been going on for years, Costa Mendez made an agreement with Lord George Brown ten years ago that we could have sovereignty, and nothing has happened. They were going to improve the airport and have never done it. The joint communications treaty we made with them has never been honoured. Who can blame us – it's time to take action.'

Hugo nodded in assent: the Malvinas situation was a running sore to Argentina's national pride; perhaps the admiral was right.

'All our information tells us that the British will do nothing,' Anaya continued. 'They have their own problems at home and, as I say, have little interest in the South Atlantic. The whole thing will be a weekend crisis. We shall be very magnanimous with the Falkland Islands people. President Galtieri and Costa Mendez have both assured me that the Americans will remain neutral. Remember what happened in Goa.' The admiral spread his hands expansively. 'As the British say: a storm in a teacup!'

Briefly, the admiral explained the situation on South Georgia. 'The newspapers are full of the story about the idiot scrap-metal workers raising our flag over South Georgia. *La Presenta* has it as front-page news. Capitan Tombetta was a fool to let them do it; it's hard for us to back off without losing face. If we do, the press will crucify us.'

Hugo felt the sweat on his forehead – this was an understatement. Everywhere he looked there were signs of national unrest: there were daily demonstrations against the military rulers and who could blame the people? The armed services themselves, whose pay had been frozen for almost a year as prices soared, were beginning to be rebellious. All the signs of yet another military coup were evident. Perhaps the admiral was right: the retaking of the Malvinas would give Argentina back its pride and perhaps buy the time needed to get the country back on its feet.

'What would you like me to do, sir?' he asked.

'I'm sending you to South Georgia. We'll move the scrap-metal workmen out of the way and replace them with a commando unit. The British have only the one small frigate, *Endurance*, in the area and are unlikely to retaliate. Costa Mendez can keep up the pressure at the United Nations and we'll stall for time. I'd like you to keep an eye on things and report directly back to me. Make sure that everything is played as quietly as possible and avoid trouble. I'm sending you south on the *Bahia Paraiso*; she's well armed and ice strengthened and will be more than a match for *Endurance*. Make sure you avoid conflict at all costs. I'll also put the submarine, the *Santa Fe*, into the area so you'll have plenty of protection. We'll bring the workmen out on the *Bahia Buen Suceso*, which is with them on South Georgia at the moment.'

Hugo asked anxiously, 'Does anyone else know about *Operation Rosario*?'

'Only the captain in charge of the marine commando detachment. He's very reliable and will be in control in the event of any military action. He's Teniente Alfredo Astiz. I'm sure you remember him.'

Hugo tried to hide his shock. 'Sir, surely Teniente Astiz is not the right man for this kind of operation. If we are trying to make this low-key, Astiz's reputation will draw attention to it.'

Anaya's face grew angry, a muscle twitching in his neck. 'The success of *Operation Rosario* is paramount, Capitan. When we occupy the Malvinas Islands it will be a great victory for the navy. People will realise that the hard line we had to take was in Argentina's best interest. Teniente Astiz has been a hero and will be seen as such. Our military services are under a great deal of criticism and we now have the opportunity to set the record straight. He's a capable and experienced officer and I have every confidence in his ability.'

There was no argument. 'When do you want me to go, sir?' Hugo asked, resignedly.

'The *Bahia Paraiso* is at Puerto Santa Cruz and preparing to sail for South Georgia tomorrow. I want a daily report on the situation – particularly any sign of increased military activity by the British. I'll have a plane fly you down in the morning so you have plenty of time to pack.'

Hugo stood up and clicked his heels. He had the distinct feeling that events were happening that they were not quite in control of. The thought of a prolonged stay in the close company of Alfredo Astiz made him shudder; his name had become synonymous with everything that brought the military into disrepute during the dirty war. This was something that could go horribly wrong. The week had started with such promise: his son's passing-out parade in the glorious morning sunshine.

He left the Admiralty with the impression that nothing would stop Admiral Anaya. There was no doubt in his mind that the liberation of the Malvinas would be hugely popular in Argentina but it seemed highly unlikely to him that the British would do nothing about it. The first splashes of rain began to pound the pavement as an afternoon storm raced in from the South Atlantic.

16

Antarctic Bay, South Georgia, Thursday 25 March 1982

Alison lay in the tussock grass in warm sunshine looking out over Antarctic Bay, watching Anna filming a fur seal with a bunch of pups playing in a pool on the beach. One of the cubs was albino and was being attacked by the others, and Alison feared for its long-term survival. The hut above the beach was warm and comfortable and they had settled into an easy way of life. This beautiful place suited both of them. There was plenty of food and fuel and since the ship had left the weather had been excellent..

They had a portable radio and listened in the evening to the BBC World Service and pop music from RSA (Radio South Africa) and lots of South American stations. The evening radio conversation with the base at Grytviken was a great distraction. They chatted with other scientists working on different parts of the island.

The arrival of the scrap-metal workers at Leith Harbour was causing some concern but nobody was taking it too seriously. To everybody's relief *Endurance* had arrived back that morning and the general feeling was that everything would be sorted out relatively quickly.

Alison managed to speak to David Asquith most evenings. Nothing much had been said on the radio but she knew that he had climbed over Coronda Peak to spy out Leith Harbour and that he and Sebastian felt very exposed where they were. David told her that they had moved their campsite further up the coast, away from the Argentinians. It all seemed rather exciting and not the kind of thing you would expect in such an isolated place.

'Just in case, you never know with these jokers! They mostly stay around Leith but now and then they come poking about. We're a bit too close to them for my liking,' he said.

On the other side of the fjord two other fids had been keeping watch from Jason Peak, a small mountain with a clear view of the Argentinians. Initially, Bob Headland and Peter Stark had kept a cold and lonely vigil, tucked in the rocks below the skyline, watching through powerful binoculars. Bob, a botanist, who had lived in Spain and spoke good Spanish, was able to monitor radio traffic from the ship and understood that they were unloading large quantities of fuel. They soon found out that the *Bahia Buen Suceso* would be leaving and replaced by another warship. Bob headed back to base to help Steve and was replaced by Neil Shaw, and the two men heard the ship leave during the night.

The following day *Endurance* arrived back at Grytviken and, much to Steve Martin's relief, the Royal Marines took over the watching from the fids at Jason Peak. Lieutenant Commander Tony Ellerbeck managed to fly another group of marines to Grass Island, less than three miles offshore from Leith Harbour with a much clearer view of the goings on. He was an expert in covert flying and managed to slip the helicopter in at low level behind the island, hoping that the engine noise would be drowned out by the noise of the Argentinian generators.

Alison and Anna were walking back along the gravel-strewn beach when they spotted a large ship flying the Argentinian flag rounding the point of Cape Constance and crossing the mouth of Antarctic Bay. By the time they had run to the hut and made contact with Steve at King Edward Point, the marines were already watching the *Bahia Paraiso* as she slipped into Leith Harbour.

17

Leith Harbour, South Georgia, Thursday 25 March 1982

Captain Tombetta, commander of the Argentinian warship *Bahia Paraiso*, sailed into Leith Harbour for the second time: it was he who had made the illegal entry with Constantino Davidoff the previous December. He was now flying the flag of 'Commodore of Antarctica'. A burly, cheerful and expressive man with a clear idea of what he was doing, he was a close friend of Admiral Anaya's and one of the few men totally aware of the junta's invasion plans. He knew Captain Nick Barker quite well and had wined and dined with him on the odd occasion. The two ships had been sailing south almost in tandem. In fact, Tombetta knew that *Endurance* had arrived a few hours before him on the previous evening. Prudently, he had signalled the *Bahia Buen Suceso* to get clear of the island and she had sailed the previous day leaving all but a dozen workmen and a small military detachment awaiting his arrival.

Three Argentinian navy officers stood on the bridge of the warship: Tombetta, effectively admiral of the Antarctic fleet; Lieutenant Alfredo Astiz, to be in charge of the military overthrow and occupation of the island; and Captain Hugo Corti, strategist and planner and Admiral Anaya's man on the spot. There was an air of excitement on board. A coded message had been received from the admiral that *Operation Rosario* was under way and *Operation Azul* was now going to be implemented. These three men knew the full implications of the message. *Azul* was the code for the attack. Anticipating that the British might reinforce the Falkland Islands, the generals had decided to bring the invasion forward by a few months. The decision had been taken and the die was cast. Their orders were to take over South Georgia at the same moment that the Malvinas invasion took place.

Hugo's dislike of Alfredo Astiz had if anything increased. He found him a loose cannon – very affable and sure of himself, but Hugo wondered how he would react if the chips were down. Astiz had worked as an undercover agent at the height of the dirty war and had gained a notorious reputation; his treatment of the soldiers under his command was appalling. Hugo felt that he lacked any normal humanity and wondered why on earth he was to be given the task of military governor of South Georgia. What could the military planners be thinking? Strings were being pulled, he was certain.

18

American Embassy, Buenos Aires, Thursday 25 March 1982

Arnie Schwartz sat in his office, thinking quietly. He was almost packed up to leave for home after the longest posting of his career. Actually the job had finished three years earlier and his official position had been taken over by another CIA man, 'Vinx' Blocker, but Arnie had stayed as advisor to the ambassador during the changeover of administration. He and Vinx got on fine.

His old boss at Langley, Bill Casey, was now the head of the CIA and liked to have his own men in the hot spots so Arnie had stayed on. Rumour had it that during the presidential elections Jimmy Carter's briefing notes had mysteriously fallen into Ronald Reagan's hands just before the national TV debate, courtesy of the CIA, and Bill Casey, the man responsible, had been rewarded in the time-honoured way with promotion to the top job.

Casey was an Anglophile. As a young US navy lieutenant he had been in London during the Blitz in the OSS (Office of Strategic Service), which had been a formative influence on the rest of his life and given him a zest for risky covert operations. He and Arnie had been friends for years.

All day reports had been coming in of greatly increased military activity. This was not unusual in this part of the world and the CIA had been monitoring the joint naval exercise between Argentina and Uruguay. However, the whole series of events during the last few hours had put the listening station onto full alert. This was clearly no ordinary exercise.

Vinx bounced into his office, looking slightly shaken. 'Arnie, we just picked up on military activity in Puerto Belgrano. They're loading twenty US Amtrak armoured personnel carriers and about a thousand troops onto half a dozen of their ships. The soldiers think they are on some kind of anti-submarine exercise but why the hell would they need all these troops?'

Arnie was perplexed. Normally they got plenty of warning through their phone taps but nothing of any great significance had been heard. 'I don't get it, Vinx, but there's one hell of a flap going on.'

The clear phone on his desk began to flash. 'I have Mark Heathcoat on the line,' his secretary told him.

The two agents looked at each other questioningly. Mark Heathcoat was the SIS operative in the British Embassy. Well known to both men, he was a larger than life character. A tall, lanky, red-haired man, he was the son of a baronet, which astonished and impressed his American counterparts. He was a real aristocrat, with a plummy English accent, and he gave off an air of self-deprecating, confused amusement. Arnie liked him a lot.

'Hi Mark, what's the trouble?' Arnie asked, half expecting what was coming.

Mark came straight to the point. 'I take it you've picked up the troop movements at Puerto Belgrano, Arnie. We've just monitored a signal from Admiral Anaya, ordering the frigates *Granville* and *Drummond* to break off and head south. We think that it's to reinforce the *Bahia Paraiso* in South Georgia.'

'Shit,' said Arnie. He knew that the Brits would never divulge that they had a listening post unless they were getting extremely anxious. The Americans guessed that New Zealand was probably monitoring the airwaves and suspected that the British had a listening post somewhere on the Chile border.

'The ambassador has started to shred sensitive documents in the embassy and things are getting very touchy with the junta, and we may be slung out at any time. Can you let us know if you pick anything up? I'd like to ask a favour.'

'Sure, Mark, anything,' he lied, raising his eyes to Vinx, who was listening.

'We were wondering if you're monitoring the exercise with Uruguay by satellite. If you could give us some kind of warning of ship movements if anything strange happens, we would be most obliged.'

'I can't do that without authority from on high, but you'll get it for sure,' Arnie said, looking at Vinx.

Heathcoat thanked him and rang off. The two Americans stared at each other.

'I think we have a crisis on our hands,' said Vinx.

'Not as much as the Brits. You know, the Argie navy is at sea and the army is getting all set to go and we're here sitting on our asses watching the world go by. I don't know how the junta have kept this quiet but if it's what I think it is we are either facing an invasion or a trial run. This is like old times back in 1973, Vinx. I guess we've got work to do.'

19

Leith Harbour, South Georgia, Friday 26 March 1982

On board the *Bahia Paraiso*, Hugo stood with Captain Tombetta watching the activity on shore. The ship was moored alongside the main jetty, where the remaining dozen or so workmen were half-heartedly demolishing one of the corrugated-iron buildings and moving the metal onto the flensing platform ready for loading onto the ship. Astiz was supervising the marines, who were using the small mobile crane to move crates of armaments and ammunition into the old power station behind the jetty. The rest of the troops were organising their billeting in various buildings around the whaling station.

Hugo was aghast at the state of some of these soldiers. Unlike the marines, these were conscripts, unruly, disorganised and poorly equipped. They were short of cold-weather clothing and much of their time had been spent looting for anything of value they could find. Most of them were country boys from the pampas and there were a number of Andean Indians among them. They were used to a warm climate and he reckoned that few, if any, had been away from Argentina before. The navy men were used to discipline and had reasonably good equipment but these troops were a poor lot who he guessed had been dumped on South Georgia to put them out of harm's way.

Lieutenant Astiz came back on board and joined them on the bridge. He was as immaculate as ever and greeted Hugo politely, but there was an atmosphere and tension between them that both men tried to hide.

The older Captain, Tombetta, was jovial and confident. 'You seem to be getting organised, Alfredo; how's it going?'

The younger man rubbed his chin. 'I can't see that much will happen here – any attack will have to come from the sea and we're well positioned to defend the bay. There's plenty of cover in the whaling station and I've protected the harbour entrance with a machine gun and rocket site on the hillside over there.' He indicated the high ground at the side of the beach.

'The rest of the troops aren't up to much,' said Hugo, watching a group of men wandering around the old oil tanks in search of loot.

Alfredo smiled. 'They should be all right. We can use them to dig trenches and keep watch. The scrap men are still working and we can use them to help if necessary. The scientists at Grytviken are unarmed and I can't imagine there will be any problem from them.'

Hugo watched the Alouette helicopter as it took a short flight along the coast. The pilot was Lieutenant Remo Busson and the observer Lieutenant Gullermo Guerra, both of whom he had come to like and respect. The helicopter was mainly helping to unload the ship but was also keeping an eye out for any unwelcome visitors. The area around the old whaling station was not very glaciated; a green valley ran out behind them with low, snow-free hills on both sides and a meandering river through the moraines and into the tussock grass above the beach. There were small herds of reindeer grazing close by and the beaches were teeming with king penguins, fur and elephant seals and all kinds of birds. The rusting sheds and oil tanks of a once-thriving whale industry were a stark contrast to the beauty and peace of the island. He wondered if Astiz should be sending out patrols but all seemed so remote and quiet there seemed little point. They were well away from the British scientists at Grytviken and it seemed a waste of manpower.

Tombetta and Astiz had been planning the takeover at Grytviken. *Endurance* seemed to be the only problem and she was hardly a match for the *Bahia Paraiso*. By the time of the Malvinas invasion they would have significant reinforcements: they expected the frigate *Guerrico* at any moment and there would be plenty of others. The submarine *Santa Fe* should also be on hand. The easiest thing would be to blockade *Endurance* into King Edward Cove. She would have no means of using her troops and little chance of defending herself. It would be suicide to come out and the logical thing for them to do would be to surrender. War had not yet been declared and their intention was to take the island at the same time as the Malvinas invasion. For the moment the best thing was to ignore the British.

Six hundred yards away, hidden in the tussock grass behind the rise in the ground that Astiz had indicated as a suitable machine gun site, Lieutenant Keith Mills and Sergeant-Major Peter Leech watched the Argentinians with interest. Mills tried to imagine what the three officers on the bridge were talking about. There was little doubt that the crates being lifted ashore were ammunition, and numerous fuel drums were being stacked on the beach. The Alouette helicopter was a constant worry but didn't seem to be searching and there was plenty of cover. They could see the workmen breaking up the building and many of the soldiers sitting around. More of a concern was a group of white-suited men who they took to be Special Forces and who were clearly much better organised than the rest.

Both marines were well trained and experienced. That morning they had been taken by launch to Carlita Bay, crossed the foot of the Neumayer Glacier and walked the ten miles along the shore through the old abandoned whaling stations of Husvik and Stromness. A five hundred-foot climb up the slopes of Harbour Point above Leith had got them to a perfect vantage point where for an hour they watched and took photographs. Leech muttered his disgust at the lack of any form of watch by the Argentinians as they slipped away and started the long walk back to their boat.

After about a mile's walk they spotted two figures hiding behind a small hill and they crawled in to investigate. To their amazement it turned out to be Captain Nick Barker and the pilot, Tony Ellerbeck. The brightly painted Wasp helicopter stood out of sight behind a small bluff.

The two marines slipped out of the grass to the surprise of the naval officers. 'Hello, sir, didn't expect to find you here,' Mills said.

Captain Barker grinned, feeling like a schoolboy caught playing truant. 'Just here for a look, Lieutenant, didn't expect you either. We're just about to leave: do you want a lift?'

The Argentinian helicopter buzzed close along the beach, before suddenly peeling off and heading back towards the whaling station.

'I think we should get the hell out of here,' Tony Ellerbeck said. 'That Alouette may have seen us.'

Back on the bridge of the *Bahia Paraiso* the captains were still planning their campaign when an urgent radio call came from the crew of the Alouette helicopter as it landed on the deck. The animated voice of the pilot, Lieutenant Remo Busson, came on air.

'Capitan, we have visitors!' His voice sounded excitedly staccato over the intercom. 'We've seen a helicopter hidden behind the hill – there are people watching us.'

'Blast,' muttered Tombetta. 'All right, Remo, let's go and have a look.' He turned to Hugo and Astiz. 'Would you like to come?'

The three officers ran out on deck and ducked in under the circling blades of the waiting helicopter, and the aircraft lifted instantly off the ship and headed directly towards Harbour Hill. As they soared over the top the little Wasp was clearly visible in its bright red colours. A group of four men stood, visibly aghast, as the helicopter flew and hovered directly above them.

Captain Tombetta found himself looking face-to-face into the eyes of Nick Barker. Both men recognised each other in the same instant. There was a commotion at his side, and he saw Hugo Corti grab the wrist of Astiz, who was holding a grenade in his hand.

'Don't be a fool, Alfredo,' shouted Tombetta angrily. 'We're not at war yet.' He smiled down and waved expansively to Nick Barker, who saluted back politely as the Alouette peeled off and flew slowly back to the ship.

'They know exactly what we're doing. We could have finished them off here and now and nobody would be any the wiser,' Astiz said, turning angrily from Hugo, who was still holding his wrist. For the first time, Tombetta recognised the violent animosity between the two younger men.

'You might be right but we're to keep a low profile until we're ready,' he said. It was clearly a setback that they were being watched. The cat was out of the bag but there wasn't much that the British could do.

'Our orders are for minimal casualties, Alfredo,' Hugo murmured. 'Argentina is a civilised country.' He gently released the younger man's wrist.

20

Whitehall, London, Monday 29 March 1982

Peter Bacon-Smith always said that the weeks leading up to the Falklands War were the most interesting of his life. During the five years since his previous involvement he had paid scant interest to the Islands. His promotion had been steady and, he liked to think, inevitable. As a senior executive in MI6 he still had the Falkland Islands on his patch. He had aged somewhat over the years: almost bald now and a little heavier, he was still fit and alert; surprisingly so as his consumption of alcohol had remained the same as ever. He ran his own small section of the Service with methodical and rather belligerent efficiency. He was considered a loose cannon by his superiors but his clarity of thinking and knowledge of how things worked in the Service had always been in his favour. He had never married but had a number of affairs over the years, none of which had come to anything. Some women found him attractive but his real love was the Service and the intrigue that it involved. The name that agents and operators of MI6 are known by is '*the Friends*' but it would be hard to imagine Peter Bacon-Smith being anybody's close friend. A typical senior MI6 executive, he wore his pinstriped suit as a badge of office.

Signals from Buenos Aires had been increasing for weeks as discussions over the sovereignty of the Islands took place in the United Nations, but nothing of significance had attracted MI6 attention until the problem in South Georgia with the scrap-metal dealers had occurred. By the time that Ambassador Anthony Williams had started to shred his papers at the embassy in Buenos

Aires, the Secret Service had begun to stir from its lethargy and move into operations mode.

On Friday 26 March Peter received a report on his desk with a curt note from Colin Figures, the new head of MI6, asking him to study it over the weekend and give him an opinion in time for the weekly JIC meeting. Peter was in full flight long before Monday morning. The realisation of impending crisis hit him like a bombshell. By Sunday afternoon he had been round to Figures' private residence and raised the alarm. He had not slept in the last forty-eight hours and his staff was sending out for sandwiches and coffee.

As Captains Tombetta and Barker were having their confrontation on the hills behind Leith Harbour and the Argentinian fleet was making its final preparations for war, a state of apathy seemed to have overcome the government. Although warnings had been flashing, nobody had taken the possibility of invasion seriously. The British, in exactly the same way as the Americans, had taken the view that even the junta would not be so stupid as to risk an outright war. Peter realised immediately that the security services, and MI6 in particular, had failed to comprehend what was staring them in the face.

At this precise moment, as Mrs Thatcher and her foreign secretary, Lord Carrington, were preparing to fly to Brussels for yet another Common Market budget meeting, the secretary of state for defence, John Nott, was out of contact in Colorado Springs at a NATO conference and the chief of defence staff was in New Zealand. Meanwhile, units of the armed services were leaving their bases and standing down for the Easter bank holiday break, and the majority of what remained of the British navy was on exercise in the mid-Atlantic.

In Parliament that afternoon the Commons was debating whether Britain should go ahead and purchase the Trident submarine nuclear deterrent system from the Americans. The decision to spend eight billion pounds was being fought loud and acrimoniously, with Michael Foot, the Labour leader shouting his opposition to a house in uproar.

'I am a peacemonger!' he yelled – a situation soon to change.

During a lull in the debate, Keith Speed, a former navy minister, rose to his feet and asked: 'With these enormous sums of money being made available for defence, would it not be prudent to keep HMS *Endurance* in service?'

John Nott, the defence secretary, retorted angrily, 'I do not intend to get involved in a debate about the Falkland Islands now. These issues are too important to be diverted into a discussion about HMS *Endurance*.'

So, in these few words *Endurance* was written off only twenty-four hours before the crisis really blew.

Peter Bacon-Smith was way ahead of the game. His first phone call was to Mark Heathcoat, the MI6 operative in Buenos Aires. Heathcoat sounded anxious.

'There's definitely something happening here, Peter,' he said. 'This is much bigger than the usual exercise with Uruguay. There are a lot of troop movements and they've ordered two of their frigates, *Granville* and *Drummond* south, I suspect to South Georgia to reinforce their ship at Leith, presumably to confront HMS *Endurance*.'

'The talks are still going on at the UN. Our ambassador thinks it's just a bit of sabre rattling to put us under pressure and will die down in a day or two,' Peter said.

'Well it doesn't look like that from where I'm standing. Some idiot in the Falkland Islands broke into the Argentinian Airways office and draped a Union Jack over their flag. The newspapers here are having a field day; they say it's an insult to their national pride; the ambassador's having the devil of a time trying to eat humble pie and apologise.'

'I'm not sure that backing down and appeasing them is the right attitude at this stage,' Peter muttered angrily.

'It looks as if they are going to kick us out of the embassy. We've tipped off a lot of the British nationals here to have a suitcase packed and ready and the ambassador's started to shred sensitive documents.'

'What do you think's going on, Mark?'

'I thought it was just an incursion onto South Georgia using the scrap-metal men as a cover but now I'm not so sure: a full scale attack on the Falklands seems unlikely but possible. The New Zealanders are monitoring their signals for us and we have a listening post at Puerto Natales in Chile. I've asked the Americans if they'll tip us off if they pick anything up and I think they will. There's not much that we won't pick up.'

'Okay, Mark, keep me posted.' As Peter put down the phone the picture was becoming very clear. Everything he heard was sending out alarm signals.

Late on Monday evening Peter made a phone call to the Ministry of Defence in Whitehall to get some background on any possible show of strength Britain might make in the South Atlantic. The operator asked him to wait a moment and much to his surprise Admiral Sir Henry Leach, the First Sea Lord, came on the line.

The admiral sounded both angry and frustrated and questioned him for some minutes on the intelligence situation. Admiral Leach was the nuclear submariner who, five years previously, had commanded the small naval force sent to the Falklands to act as a deterrent to *Operation Goa.*

'Nobody is taking this seriously,' the admiral said. 'The government seems to think that the only real threat is the Soviet Union. They want to scrap our carriers within the next eighteen months and rely on American air cover. This situation is exactly what we've been warning them about – what the hell are we supposed to do when the unexpected happens in other parts of the world?'

'What are you doing at the moment, sir?' Peter asked.

'The fleet is in the mid-Atlantic on exercise "Springtrane" but I've ordered three nuclear submarines south and the fleet auxiliary *Fort Austin* is heading down with fuel and stores to replenish

Endurance. There'll be hell to pay; the government has us on limited fuel usage at the moment.'

'How long will it take?' Peter asked, feeling relieved that at least somebody was taking the threat seriously.

'*Spartan*'s the only nuclear submarine ready to go: she's at Gibraltar right now swapping her dummy torpedoes for real with one of our conventional subs, HMS *Oracle*. The other two, *Splendid* and *Conqueror*, will follow as soon as we turn them around.'

'What kind of a force might we need to face the Argentinian navy?' Peter asked.

There was a long pause. Leach had clearly been thinking about this for some time. 'This isn't some tinpot country,' he said thoughtfully. 'They have a substantial navy with surface, underwater and air capacity. They have at least six ships with Exocet sea-skimming missiles, six submarines and at least two hundred aircraft. It's not so much their firepower that bothers me; it's the fact that we would be facing them in their own back yard with our line of communications six thousand miles long. How seriously is MI6 taking this?'

'Nobody seems certain that this is a serious invasion threat. Nothing has been declared and the general opinion is that it's some kind of incursion onto South Georgia,' Peter replied, 'but it seems to me that they have gone a long way if it's just to make a gesture. Their whole fleet is mobilised.'

'A token show of strength might make the junta think again before making an irreversible move. It's sticking my head right above the parapet but I'm putting the entire fleet on standby,' the admiral confided. 'We've been trying to explain to the politicians that the reason we have a navy is for just such an unexpected event as this. All eyes are on the Russians and they seem to forget that there's a whole world out there. The Ministry of Defence has little stomach for confrontation.'

Leach seemed relieved that MI6 had begun to take the matter seriously. Peter promised to phone him as things progressed or if any major policy decisions were taken. They rang off on good terms.

Breathing a sigh of relief, Peter finally wrapped things up in his office. It was raining in London and he took a taxi instead of his usual walk home. The navy at least seemed to have the matter in hand. Picking up an evening paper, he scanned the pages; there was no mention of the Falkland Islands. The headlines were on the escalating trouble between Israel and the Lebanon and the fact that Britain was to spend eight billion replacing Polaris with Trident nuclear submarines. A small item caught his attention.

> **Riots in Argentina.** *Massive anti-government demonstrations in Mendoza by the trade unions spreading to other cities throughout the country. Police and army clashing with demonstrators with fatal results.* La Presenta, *the national newspaper's headline was tonight saying 'The only thing that can save this government is war.'*

That should keep the bastards occupied, he thought, as he trudged wearily up the steps to his flat.

21

Grytviken, South Georgia, Wednesday 31 March 1982

There had been a sigh of relief among the scientists at King Edward Point base on Monday evening when the marines, watching from Jason Peak, reported that the *Bahia Paraiso* had weighed anchor and put to sea. There was still a party of scrap-metal workers half-heartedly dismantling some buildings and a detachment of soldiers remained with them.

The weather, which had remained relatively fine, had begun to deteriorate. Summer was ending and the Antarctic autumn was setting in as the first flurries of snow began appearing on the hills along with sleet and rising winds in the fjords. The same rising storm that was hampering the Argentinian navy off the Falklands began to hit the island. In London, the daffodils sprang to life as winter turned gently into spring.

Since his unexpected return, Captain Nick Barker had kept a low profile. His marines had kept a close watch on Leith Harbour but his orders, against his own best judgement, were not to escalate the situation and this made it hard to decide what strategy to take. On base it was business as usual, and scientists were all over the island working on their projects.

That morning, Wednesday, *Endurance* slipped out of King Edward Cove and searched the ocean to the north with her sonar and radar. With little difficulty she found the *Bahia Paraiso* in a holding position about fifteen miles off Cumberland Bay. The two ships passed within a mile and politely acknowledged each other's presence over the radio. Nick couldn't see much point in hanging about and headed back into King Edward Cove, acutely aware that his every move was being watched by the *Bahia Paraiso*.

At lunchtime, a signal was received from Navy HQ Northwood ordering him to return urgently to Port Stanley. His marines were to be put ashore at King Edward Point to protect the scientists and act as a military presence on the island. It indicated that the invasion of the Falklands was a serious threat.

The base commander was not a happy man. Up until now, none of the scientists had taken the situation too seriously: there is little room in the polar regions for political disputes. Visitors, whoever they may be, are rare and welcome, signalling a time for celebration and storytelling. *Endurance*'s presence was a relief from the usual quiet of the island.

Steve Martin was an experienced fid, having worked for the Survey for a number of years. A university graduate, he was a sailor and a boatman and took his job as commander and magistrate very seriously. At half an hour's notice twenty-two marine commandos had landed on his base. Anywhere else it would have been understandable, and he had no doubt in his own mind that the Argentinians were in the wrong, but here in this beautiful place the polar peace was being disturbed.

He wasn't a soldier or a diplomat and had been unable to contact either of his directors, Doctors Steven Laws or Ray Adie, both of whom were at sea somewhere off the coast of Chile. The new arrivals brought a host of problems: accommodation was short and, although the marines had brought a few food packs, with twenty-two extra hungry mouths to feed some kind of rationing was sure to be needed. His main concern, however, was how the military presence on his base would affect the scientists' neutral status. Within minutes of the signal's arrival he was heading the Survey cutter out to join Captain Barker and Keith Mills on board *Endurance*.

*   *   *

For the second time in a week, Nick Barker found himself trying to find the Wisdom of Solomon as he faced two young men frantically attempting to solve their own problems.

Lieutenant Keith Mills asked anxiously, 'What are my orders if trouble breaks out? What are my rules of engagement?'

'Who's in charge of the island? I'm supposed to be the government representative – and what about my scientists' neutrality?' Steve asked.

Nick gave the best instructions he could think of. 'Yellow card rules,' he told Keith. 'It's not totally appropriate here but you'll have to use your own discretion.'

Yellow card rules are the guidelines to determine the conduct of troops embroiled in dangerous situations in dozens of trouble spots throughout the world. They are the engagement instructions developed by the army over the years to protect servicemen caught up in conflict mainly between unarmed civilians. Northern Ireland, Cyprus, Aden. Very simply the instructions are:

You are responsible for the safety of personnel, property and equipment of the area you are ordered to guard. At any time you may fire against a foe who you think is going to attack you and there is no other way of stopping him. You are to continue acting independently only until the situation is in the command of someone senior to you.

Keith Mills nodded. He was an experienced soldier, having done a tour in Northern Ireland, and knew the rules.

'In the meantime, you remain in command, Steve; and it stays that way unless there's any trouble, in which case Keith takes over. You should try to keep your staff out of the way and do your best to remain non-combatants.'

And so it was that a commonsense agreement was reached between the three of them. There would be no change in administration. In the meantime, the tranquillity of Shackleton House base at King Edward Point was shattered with the arrival of twenty-two rowdy marines. The scientists needed peace and quiet to get on with their work. Steve Martin made the best of a bad job; it was a relief that many of his people were working away from the base on different parts of the island.

Nick Barker's next problem was to escape from King Edward Cove without the Argentinians knowing. The *Bahia Paraiso*, outside the entrance to the fjord, was effectively blocking off the whole of Cumberland Bay, and he felt trapped and vulnerable and realised that if more ships arrived he would be totally blocked in.

Cumberland East Bay is protected at its north-east end by Right Whale Rocks. These sharks' teeth are a continuation out to sea of the Barff Peninsula, which is at the east shore of the fjord. A narrow gap between these rocks and the main cliff is known as the Merton Passage and had been navigated by the fids in their small cutters in calm weather, but no ship of any size had ever passed through, or even contemplated such a thing. The seabed had never been surveyed and there were grounded icebergs all around the point. It was through this treacherous gap that Captain Barker proposed to take his ship clear without being spotted by the waiting Argentinians.

All day the weather had been deteriorating. At 7 p.m., in growing darkness with a westerly gale blowing, *Endurance* slipped out of King Edward Cove and across to the eastern side of the fjord. She had never been in action before and all afternoon the crew had made preparations. Her lights were blacked out and they maintained strict radio silence. The radar was switched off but they had decided to risk brief squirts occasionally to check her position and the whereabouts of icebergs. They used the echo sounder in a limited way but in this uncharted sea it would not be of much use. Nick reckoned that there was a good chance that the large number of icebergs drifting around the fjord would mask his movements from the *Bahia Paraiso*'s radar.

On the bridge, Nick handed over to Lieutenant-Commander Bill Hurst, the navigation officer, to con them through. It was vital that the ship's silhouette did not show against the sky as she slipped tightly under the cliffs of the Barff Peninsula. Apart from the dull thump of her old Burmeister engines you could have heard a pin drop. The gale increased in velocity as she edged her way out of the shelter of the fjord and into the mouth of the Merton Passage. In all her years of sailing in the Antarctic Ocean, she had never been in a more terrifying position than this. Everyone knew what a touch and go situation they were in as she took the full brunt of the gale on her beam. On the starboard side huge cliffs rose above them and to port there was the crash and roar of spray bursting over Right Whale Rocks.

Ping ... the echo sounder registered the bottom rising towards them. *Ping* ... twenty feet. One rock would spell disaster. The gale catching the ship broadside against her hangar and superstructure was causing her to reel about drastically and drift towards the cliffs. *Ping* ... rocks below her keel. Everyone stopped breathing. *Ping* ... the bottom began to drop away: they were out!

Hugging the coast and keeping herself among the icebergs she slipped away, avoiding the *Bahia Paraiso* radar. Hound Bay, St Andrews Bay, Cape Harcourt. Suddenly, just off the coast from Royal Bay, they spotted the lights of a ship. Hurst slipped *Endurance* even closer to the shore. It couldn't be the *Bahia Paraiso* but may well have been another Argentinian warship coming to reinforce her. Nick had been warned that there was a submarine lurking and that the frigates *Drummond* and *Granville* were on their way.

By dawn she had passed Cape Disappointment, the southernmost tip of South Georgia, and the captain felt he was far enough away to turn north. In the teeth of a force-ten gale she set course for Port Stanley just as fast as her old engines could take her.

As the Argentinian fleet approached the Falkland Islands the sum total of British defence consisted of the Red Plum, wallowing about in a gale in the Scotia Sea, a contingent of seventy-three marines at Port Stanley, and Keith Mills and twenty-two marines sleeping on the floor at Shackleton House base on South Georgia.

22

Houses of Parliament, London, Wednesday 31 March 1982

Peter Bacon-Smith left his office at Century House in a rush and hurried along the Embankment to the Houses of Parliament. It was one of those clear mornings when London is at its best. Tourists were disembarking from their buses and staring up at the beautiful old building. The Thames was alive with small boats and the streets were teeming with activity. Spring was in the air.

As promised, he phoned Sir Henry Leach, who he had tracked down at a naval function in Portsmouth, and informed him of the impending meeting with the prime minister in her parliamentary office. Mrs Thatcher had summoned her senior advisers for discussions about the impending crisis and Peter felt that the admiral ought to have his say.

Leach thanked him; he had a Sea King helicopter on standby for just such an occasion and was worried that the Ministry of Defence would capitulate before he could give the navy's opinion. He reckoned that he could be there within the hour.

Peter joined Sir Antony Acland, head of the JIC committee, at the entrance to Parliament; he had his briefing papers and was there to advise him on the intelligence situation. They made their way through police security, along echoing corridors, to the prime minister's office. It was a large room, attractively furnished with a board table, desk and some comfortable armchairs. The meeting was already under way and Sir Antony joined the table. Peter, rather uncertainly, joined a group of parliamentary secretaries at the back of the room. He knew most of them by sight but it was the first time he had seen Mrs Thatcher in the flesh. His immediate impression was how small she looked. She sat in the middle of the table talking to John Nott, the defence minister and the two Foreign Office ministers, Richard Luce and Humphrey Atkins, who were standing in for the foreign secretary, Lord Carrington, in his absence. Peter sat quietly in the background, amazed at the number of people arriving. All over Whitehall that afternoon the word was out of impending disaster. Peter sat with Clive Whitmore, the PM's private secretary, away from the main table, feeling like a schoolboy at his first dance. There was no sign of Sir Henry Leach.

John Nott was giving his impressions to the prime minister. He had recently undertaken a military review and, more or less, rewritten the British naval strategy for the next decade. All immediate threat seemed to come from the Soviet Bloc and he had come to the decision that for the foreseeable future the navy would be unlikely to operate outside the NATO zone. His approach was that the British defence would be the hunting and destruction of Russian submarines. Air cover would be from the giant US carriers and the UK would have little use for its own. The big and expensive carriers such as HMS *Hermes* could be sold or scrapped and the new, small, modern carriers like HMS *Invincible* could be sold off as they were of no use in modern anti-submarine warfare and were far too costly to replace. This was the scenario that the strategic planners had taken. To the horror of the navy, it was to be run down. There was some hypothetical logic to this and the admiral's concern, 'What happens when the unexpected occurs that isn't written into the script?' had not been heeded. Just such a series of events was now happening at breakneck speed and the author of the policy was the current defence secretary, John Nott!

Nott was an able and clever man but nervous and emotional and not a good Cabinet speaker. He found it difficult expressing his views when powerful arguments were coming from all sides. 'All the advice I have at hand, prime minister, indicates that to fight a campaign at six-thousand-miles' distance could be a very difficult operation. We have looked at the possibility of sending a rapid response team in, either via Chile or Uruguay, but that appears to be out of the question. A naval Task Force would take some time to organise and might act as a deterrent or persuade the Argentinians to withdraw but at the same time might develop a momentum of its own and become very difficult to stop.'

'This is a British island that has been attacked by an aggressive military dictatorship,' the prime minister replied. 'We can't just sit here and do nothing.'

Peter could not help but notice that the only person in the room arguing for action was Margaret Thatcher. She was clearly furious but was being beaten down by her advisers. She indicated that she would ask the Americans to intercede with the junta and instructed her secretary to call the president on the hot line immediately after the meeting. It was agreed that any British response should be within international law and they decided to instruct Sir Anthony Parsons, the United Nations Ambassador, to request an urgent meeting of the Security Council. She shared with Ronald Reagan the view that the less they had to do with the UN, the better, but she conceded that in an inevitable propaganda war it would be better to have right on her side.

Ian Gow, the prime minister's parliamentary secretary, slipped into the room and announced that the First Sea Lord was outside the door. Should he be allowed to come in? Margaret Thatcher assented, as there were no other military in the room. As Leach entered, a gasp went round the table: he was in full military uniform, having arrived direct from Portsmouth. Ramrod straight, tall and confident, he was the epitome of a naval admiral.

There is no doubt that the arrival of Sir Henry Leach changed the whole tenor of the meeting. Margaret Thatcher positively simpered and hung on his every word; she had at last found her ally. She questioned Leach extensively on the navy's ability to put a Task Force together. Leach had his chance and was grabbing it with both hands.

The admiral pinpointed the Argentinian strength and made

two specific points: that the operation could and should be under way within seven days; and that it should be a balanced fleet, not a small squadron. To take on the Argentinian navy would require a large force with full logistical support.

Although no final decision was taken, as the meeting broke up, the admiral was instructed to make every endeavour to put the fleet on alert. To a certain extent, John Nott won the day: caution prevailed although he did not oppose the alert.

For the second time, Peter heard the admiral state categorically, 'This is exclusively a navy matter.'

Margaret Thatcher turned to him quickly, her eyes gleaming, and asked, much in the way that Elizabeth I asked Sir Walter Rally what to do about the Spanish Armada: 'Admiral, what would your reaction be if you were General Galtieri and such a force as you suggest were to set out from Britain?'

'Madam,' Leach replied, looking her straight in the eye, 'I would return to harbour immediately.'

23

United Nations, New York, Thursday 1 April 1982

Sir Anthony Parsons' feet had hardly hit the ground since he entered the United Nations building on Thursday morning. Mrs Thatcher's instructions had reached him at 7 p.m. the previous evening. That had been midnight in London and 8 p.m. in South Georgia; the precise time that HMS *Endurance* was making her terrifying run through the Merton Passage.

A quietly spoken, experienced diplomat of the old school, he had been posted to the UN after hurriedly leaving Tehran after the fall of the Shah. He was determined and dogged in his approach, and in the months that followed would become one of the unsung heroes of the Falklands War.

Just after midnight he made an urgent call to Downing Street and spoke to the prime minister.

'We need some hard evidence; it will be easier to get the Security Council's support if we can prove what the Argentinians are planning.'

'That won't be easy, Sir Anthony, it will compromise our intelligence sources,' Mrs Thatcher told him.

'The US Ambassador, Mrs Jean Kirkpatrick, is the chairman of the Security Council this month; it's done on a rotation basis. She's pro-Argentina and trying to improve US relations in the south. She's said openly that no western power should dare to use the Security Council procedure to maintain a colonial stake in South America. Can you speak to President Reagan personally and ask him very specifically to rein her in? If she blocks us we'll have no chance of getting a supporting UN resolution.'

'I'll do what I can,' Mrs Thatcher assented. 'I have a call booked with him in the next few minutes. I'm trying to get him to speak to General Galtieri. Keep me informed; it will be easier if the UN is on our side.' She rang off.

After some hurried diplomatic activity, Sir Anthony managed to reach the new President of the Council, Mr Kamanda wa Kamanda, and delivered him a curt note.

I have the honour, on instruction, to address you urgently about the situation in the South Atlantic. The Government of the United Kingdom has good reason to believe that the armed forces of the Republic of Argentina are about to attempt to invade the Falkland islands. In these circumstances, I request your Excellency to immediately call a meeting of the Security Council.

By evening the note had produced a statement on behalf of the council calling on both sides to exercise restraint. Even before the invasion had taken place, Britain's diplomatic effort had begun to pick up steam.

Through the night a tired Margaret Thatcher spoke with Ronald Reagan and General Haig, got the US support in the Security Council and the president also agreed to speak with the junta. This was no easy task; the last people on earth that General Galtieri wanted to speak to were the Americans. He was keeping a low profile and couldn't be reached. While Reagan was being briefed by his aides, Ambassador Harry Shlaudeman put the pressure on the Argentinian Government and, after some hours of wrangling, Galtieri was finally persuaded to speak to him and dragged to the telephone. Through a translator for over an hour the president told him in no uncertain terms that Argentina was the aggressor and that the invasion would end the US good relations with Argentina. He offered Vice-President George Bush as mediator. The general turned down all the offers.

As he replaced the phone, Galtieri must have been suffering a bad case of cold feet. He contacted Admiral Anaya immediately. The admiral, in exasperation, told him pointedly that it was too late for second thoughts. His ships were already in formation and heading for the Malvinas Islands.

24

Port Stanley, Falkland Islands, Thursday 1 April 1982

As was usual, Governor Rex Hunt rose early on Thursday morning. The previous evening had been a pleasant one. He and his wife, Mavis, had entertained guests at Government House to celebrate one of the staff's fifty years of employment and they had watched a video film about the Islands made by Anglia Television, *More British than British*. It had been a relaxed and cheerful occasion. While Mavis cleared up and made breakfast, he called Steve Martin on the radio. Neither man was aware of the advancing Argentinian fleet or the diplomatic activity taking place around the world. He knew that the Argentinians were at sea but was under the impression that any potential trouble would be a consequence of HMS *Endurance* attempting to evict Davidoff scrap-metal workers from Leith Harbour. He did his best to quell the anxiety of the base commander.

The rest of the morning passed in the usual way with a series of meetings with islanders on government business. He had a pleasant lunch with his wife and had just returned to his office, at 3.30 p.m., when one of his staff rushed in with an urgent telex from the Foreign Office.

> *We have apparently reliable information that an Argentinian Task Force could be assembling off Cape Pembroke by dawn tomorrow (2 April). You will wish to make your dispositions accordingly.*

He read and re-read the paper then sat quietly for a moment, collecting his thoughts, as the bombshell struck. Rex Hunt was a down-to-earth pragmatist who had served in many trouble spots around the world: Uganda, Borneo, Malaya; he had been in Vietnam and witnessed the chaotic scenes at the fall of Saigon.

He immediately sent for the two marine majors commanding the barracks at Moody Brook, Mike Norman and Garry Noott, and showed them the telegram.

'It looks as if the buggers really mean it this time!' he said – a statement that has gone down in Falkland Island folklore.

The marines had received no warning or orders from Britain but immediately set about mobilising their men and planning the defence of the Islands. They knew it could only be a token defence; the small garrison of seventy-three marines could hardly hold off the whole of the Argentinian military, but the raging storm holding up the invading fleet at least gave them some time to prepare. They mobilised the islanders' small defence force, blocked the airfield runway and the racecourse, and arrested twenty-eight Argentinian technicians who had suspiciously arrived to do maintenance work on the oil tanks.

In Government House, the staff began to shred and destroy all the classified documents and codes. It reminded Rex of the chaotic destruction of papers during his last few days in Saigon. At 8 p.m. he walked along the waterfront to the radio station and delivered his first warning to the unsuspecting islanders.

25

Shackleton House base, South Georgia, Thursday 1 April 1982

The marines had settled in comfortably in the twenty-four hours since *Endurance* had slipped away from the base. The storm had continued to rage but a bright spell in the afternoon had allowed them to do the usual tourist walk down to the old whaling station about half a mile down the bay. They wandered around the old corrugated-iron sheds and clambered onto the whale catcher, *Petrol*, still afloat and almost serviceable. Most of them visited Shackleton's grave in the small cemetery on the far side of the cove. By late afternoon wind and sleet was again lashing the island and the mountains were hidden in cloud; everyone headed back to the base.

With twenty-two extra bodies things were a little cramped at Shackleton House but the two groups of men had settled into a reasonable working arrangement. The fids found the squaddies a little crude but generally things were fine. Many of the scientists were away, working on different parts of the island, and in the interest of easing the crush Steve Martin planned to disperse more of his staff away from the base.

Since the *Bahia Paraiso* had left Leith Harbour, the general feeling was that the whole episode would eventually work itself out. Steve's talk with Rex Hunt that morning had been reassuring. The usual evening radio chats with the field working parties around the island were uneventful. Most of them were sitting out the storm in their tents and huts. Steve kept his two radio operators listening out around the clock, but nothing seemed out of the ordinary.

Steve and Keith Mills sat chatting in the bar. Some of the men were playing snooker, and it was a pleasant, relaxed evening with a bunch of young men, mostly in their early twenties, getting to know each other. At about 8 p.m., somebody put on the radio. Pat Watts, the *Chay* radio announcer in Port Stanley, was doing his usual evening music show when he suddenly broke across a record and announced that the governor was about to speak.

With few preliminaries, Rex Hunt came on the air and, speaking quietly, said, '*I have an important announcement to make about the state of affairs between the British and Argentinian governments over the Falkland Island dispute ... There is mounting evidence that the Argentinian armed forces are preparing to invade the Falkland Islands...*' He went on to say that the Royal Marines were on alert and called on the civilian Falkland Island defence force to muster in the drill hall. '*I shall come on the air again as soon as I have anything to report. But in the mean time I would urge you to remain calm, and to keep off the streets. In particular, do not go along the airport road. Stay indoors and please do not add to the troubles of the security services by making demonstrations or damaging Argentinian property. This would play into their hands and simply provide them with the excuse to invade us.*' He asked the islanders to keep their radios on and wait for further information.

There was a stunned silence in the bar as Rex faded off the air, before a clamour of voices rose in consternation. All eyes turned to Steve and Keith, both of whom were as shocked as everybody else.

'Did you know about this, Steve?'

'What happens now?'

There was little they could do. An anxious cluster formed around the two men. In this isolated place it seemed highly unlikely that an Argentinian invasion force would come steaming up the fjord with all guns blazing. Most of the fids had been on board friendly Argentinian vessels as they called into the bases and they had partied with the crews. Steve and Brian Stanwood, one of the radio operators, went into the radio shack and tried to contact Port Stanley but couldn't get through. Stanley Radio continued to play Pat Watts' night show. By the early hours of Friday morning most of the men had turned into their bunks and only a few diehards remained up listening to the wireless.

At 4.30 a.m., Rex Hunt's voice again broke onto the air. '*I have no alternative other than to declare a state of emergency with immediate effect under the Emergency Powers Ordinance of 1939. Under these emergency powers I can detain any person, authorise entry to any premises, acquire any property, and issue any orders I see fit. I must again warn people in Stanley to stay indoors. Anyone seen wandering the streets will be arrested by the security forces.*

'*I have no further news of the Argentinian navy Task Force, but may I say that the morale of the Royal Marines and the defence force is terrific, it makes me proud to be their commander-in-chief.*'

The small group of people at King Edward Point were not alone in their shock. This was the first time that any of the Falklanders had any serious indication that an invasion was imminent. The tiny community of about two thousand people was scattered around the Islands in isolated farms. If ever a group of British subjects was unwarned and unprepared, this was it.

Rex had little time or resources to ready the islanders for the onslaught. The small marine force was deployed around Port Stanley and two of the most likely landing beaches were covered by small detachments of men. Everybody was ordered to retreat for a last stand at Government House. They blocked the runway and had initially called out the small Falkland Islanders' defence force but then sent them home out of harm's way. Rex knew they could only make a gesture against the large force that was approaching and there was little point in putting more of the islanders at risk than necessary.

The Argentinian plan was simple. A force of commandos, landed from the submarine *Santa Fe*, would trek the short distance overland and capture the barracks at Moody Brook, about a mile out of town. They would then join up with a second group of commandos at the governor's house, arrest him, and make the town safe for the full invasion fleet to enter Stanley Harbour. With the element of surprise, there should be minimal use of force and ultimately the invaders would be benevolent to their captives. The world would see a glorious and bloodless takeover of the Islands.

The lack of radio silence between the ships and the junta's need to quell the riots and national unrest at home, plus the great storm that was thrashing the Scotia Sea and holding back the fleet for twenty-four hours, completely scuppered the element of surprise.

Nevertheless, the commandos team landed at Mullet Creek more or less according to plan at 4.30 a.m. and reached Moody Brook an hour later. If they intended a bloodless capture of the barracks, their tactics were anything but restrained. Quietly encircling the building, they hurled phosphorous grenades and sprayed the rooms with automatic fire. Had the marines been in their beds it would have been a massacre. Fortunately, there was nobody there.

Up the coast at Stanley Harbour entrance, Lieutenant Bill Trollop managed to hit a landing craft with an anti-tank missile and then headed back to the governor's house. The marines slowly fell back to the building as more Argentinian reinforcements arrived and encircled them. The siege began.

Long before the Islands had surrendered, news of the invasion was being pumped out on Argentinian radio stations proclaiming their recovery of the Malvinas to the rest of the world. As the British Government reeled in shock, General Galtieri had gone on national television declaring the glorious news that the military government had anticipated the will of the Argentinian people. They'd had no alternative but to do what had been done. Speaking with wild enthusiasm to a jubilant crowd outside the presidential palace, his voice broke with emotion. The people, who for the last week had been protesting violently against the government (only forty-eight hours earlier military police had been shooting at rioters in the Plaza de Mayo), were ecstatically cheering the generals. Not since the days of Peron had the country screamed with such enthusiastic approval. He told them that the lives of the islanders would not be disrupted and hoped that the good relationship between Argentina and Great Britain would not be breached. General Mario Menendez was to be the new Governor of the Malvinas.

Back on South Georgia, by 4.45 a.m. almost everybody was up listening to the radio. Pat Watts had kept his show going through the night. Outside, the storm was at full force ten, battering the island in sheets of spray. At about 8 a.m., Rex Hunt again came on the air, describing the siege that was taking place around his home. The shocked audience in Shackleton House could hear the rattle of automatic fire as Rex described the battle going on around him. Half an hour later, they heard Pat Watts nervously saying that Argentinian soldiers were entering his studio, and a moment later the radio went blank.

Half an hour later *Endurance* broke radio silence: she was halfway to Port Stanley and still heading north. Nick Barker quickly confirmed that the invasion had happened and warned Martin and Mills that they had intercepted radio signals and that more Argentinian ships were heading to the South Georgia area. He wished them luck and went back to radio silence.

In London, all links with Port Stanley were cut. The Foreign Office had no means of checking the Argentinian claims and it was not until 4 p.m. on Friday that a Welsh radio ham managed to confirm with one of the islanders that the governor had surrendered.

* * *

King Edward Point base became the height of activity. Steve Martin, still reeling from shock, discussed with his men what best to do.

'We'll move everybody except the marines into the old church,' he said. 'Take as much as you can, field notes and any other stuff you wish to save. We'll move as much as we can with the tractor.' He looked round. 'I'd like to get as many of you away from here as possible until this thing quietens down. Peter, Tony and Miles, can you grab some kit and go over to St Andrews Bay and keep an eye on Cindy and Annie. One of the boys will take you across the fjord in the launch.'

'What about food?' Peter Stark asked.

'There's plenty with them and you can always raid the other field huts in the area if you get short but I don't think that this will last for long,' Steve said. 'Trefor, can you and Damian Saunders walk over to join Ian Barker and Campbell Gemmell at the Lyell Glacier field hut?'

Trefor Edwards grinned his assent.

'Right, let's get to it; Bob Headland can stay here with me for the time being. He speaks Spanish and might be able to help me on the radio.'

There was pandemonium as the men prepared to move their belongings to the beautiful old church behind Grytviken, about three-quarters of a mile away. Steve then went into the radio shack and contacted the field parties spread about the island and told them to stay out of sight, avoid provocation and keep radio use to the minimum. Everybody had been listening in and knew what was happening. Cindy Buxton and Annie Price were adamant that they were absolutely OK but sounded pleased that they were having visitors. The party of fids builders working on the new hut at Bird Island on the north-west tip of South Georgia were to keep their heads down and not draw attention to themselves.

Steve then spoke to Alison and Anna at Antarctic Bay. 'There's no way we can get a boat to you in this weather, Alison,' he said, 'and anyway it would be right in front of the Argentinians' noses.'

'We're both fine,' Alison said. 'And we've plenty of food, so don't worry about us.'

David Asquith and Sebastian Holmes were a real concern. At Fortuna Bay they were very close to the Argentinians occupying Leith Harbour and were in a tent with only limited provisions. They had seen a number of Argentinian parties moving around the area but were sure that they themselves had not been seen. 'What do you think about moving to join the women at Antarctic Bay?' Steve asked.

'The route looks OK from here,' David said. 'Nobody's been across that way since Shackleton in 1915 but it looks easy enough. I'll hang on for a day or two and see what happens. Seb's no mountaineer so we'll not go unless it's absolutely essential.'

'Use your own judgement, David,' Steve said, 'but don't take any risks.'

And so it was settled. Steve and Bob Headland took it in turns to man the radio. Bob collected confidential documents, government seals, codes and ciphers, which he put into a sack and threw out into the bay. There were a number of rifles and other weapons used to cull reindeer and elephant seals around the island. Steve removed the bolts and locked them in the safe to make doubly certain that none of the civilians could be seen as combatants.

By 9.30 a.m. most of the fids were over at the church with a radio transmitter and had started to move food and valuables across. Peter Stark, Tony North and Miles Plant crossed Cumberland East Bay in the launch *Albatross* to the Sorlings Valley; from there they started the long walk past Hound Bay to join Cindy Buxton and Annie Price at St Andrews Bay. The boat trip across the fjord below the snout of the huge Nordenskjold Glacier in the foul weather was risky but relatively sheltered and the *Albatross* returned unscathed. Trefor Edwards and Damian Saunders, both very fit mountaineers, set off on foot for the field hut on the Lyell Glacier. That left thirteen fids at Grytviken at the old church. Steve and Bob Headland stayed at Shackleton House; Steve decided to remain in his capacity as base commander and as Justice of the Peace until the last minute.

While this was going on, the marines set about preparing the defences of the base. Keith knew that he could not face a superior force for long. His idea was to defend the base for as long as possible and then withdraw over the back of Mount Hodges to Maiviken, where there was a hut and food dump. All his men were fit and had undergone Arctic warfare training. He had every confidence in Sergeant Peter Leach, who was older and more experienced than the rest. He felt sure that they could lose themselves in the island and sustain themselves for weeks if necessary, fighting a guerrilla campaign until relief forces arrived.

In lashing rain and wind, they excavated slit trenches behind the base, which were filling with water as they dug. Marine Les Daniels was an explosives expert and set about making makeshift mines by packing scrap metal around plastic explosives in ammo boxes and burying them on the beach. He also hung a drum of petrol and high explosives under the jetty. All these were wired back to the base. It was a miserable task and they were all soaked to the skin.

Sergeant Leach was anxious about four of his marines, who were manning the observation post at Jason Peak. He needed all the men he could get and there was not much to see in this weather; there was no way a boat could get round the coast in this storm and they were very close to the Argentinian positions.

By 9.30 a.m. the storm was howling at full force, and spray, mist and rain raged around King Edward Point. Suddenly, out of the mist rounding Hope Point at the entrance of the cove, a large ship appeared, her guns directly facing the base.

'Stand to! Stand to!' The marines grabbed their weapons and dived into their soaking trenches. It was the *Bahia Paraiso*.

26

Bahia Paraiso, Cumberland Bay, South Georgia, Friday 2 April 1982

For all her size, the *Bahia Paraiso* was pitching like a cork, with waves breaking over her deck and the spray blanking out any reasonable visibility. In seas like this she had a tendency to screw sideways as she slid into a trough. Like *Endurance* she had a large aircraft hangar on her stern, catching the wind, which made her roll alarmingly. The officers and crew were used to this but the contingent of eighty commandos on board were having an unpleasant time. Nonetheless, there was an air of celebration and excitement. The ship's tannoy system had been running the radio reports as the situation in the Malvinas Islands began to unfurl. When President Galtieri announced Malvinas as the new district of Argentina everybody on board had yelled with enthusiastic approval. The Islands had been a running sore in the national pride for years, and at last a strong government had taken the initiative.

On the bridge, Hugo and Captain Briatore shook hands, grinning. A hundred yards away, on the port side, the frigate *Guerrico* was flashing her lights excitedly, her captain and crew celebrating the moment themselves. All the years of planning seemed to be coming to a perfect fruition. The radio spoke of the glorious welcome that the troops had received from the people of Malvinas, the people at last free from British tyranny. Hugo was not as certain as Admiral Anaya that the British would not retaliate, but what could they could do?

The air of expectancy for the takeover of South Georgia was tinged with concern. The plan had been to take the island at the same time as the Malvinas invasion but in this weather it was clearly impractical to put men ashore to take over the British base. The same storm that had held up the Argentinian fleet was still raging over them. For the last two days they had patrolled the entrance to Cumberland Bay in appalling seas. There was no sign of *Endurance* and both captains were conscious that, although she was poorly armed and no match for either of their ships, her two Wasp helicopters were very capable of launching air-to-sea missiles or torpedoes. They were unsure what weapons she had on board but all the *Bahia Paraiso*'s defence systems were on full alert. Bottled up as she was in the fjord, she was no match for either ship and Captain Briatore hoped that her captain would realise the futility of a fight. He knew that Nick Barker was no fool and would not risk the lives of his men unduly. With luck and diplomacy he might well be able to apprehend the ship with minimal force.

The *Guerrico*'s big 100mm guns could blow *Endurance* out of the sea from five miles away and she was equipped with an Exocet missile system as well as conventional rockets. Briatore decided to leave her guarding the entrance to Cumberland Bay and go in himself to have a look.

Most of the ship's officers had come on to the bridge as the *Bahia Paraiso* moved slowly into the fjord. Hugo stood to one side with Lieutenant Remo Busson, the Alouette helicopter pilot who he had got to know well over the last few days. He had come to like Remo, who was a calm and steady hand. With him were two other airmen who were to fly troops ashore in the large Puma helicopter secured in the hangar. Lieutenant Astiz joined the group and was watching the scene carefully. He and his men had been planning the landing and takeover of the British base and wanted a clear view of his objective. The gale was at full blast, with mountains closing in on both sides of the fjord and only the cliffs at the water's edge visible. The ship's radar guided her slowly in. The gleaming white Shackleton Cross at Hope Point, the entrance to King Edward Cove, came into view, sharp against the murk, as the ship slipped quietly past. All her guns were manned, their crews ready. On the bridge everybody was scanning the cove looking for *Endurance*.

Briatore cursed. 'Damn, she's not here.' There seemed to be no sign of life. The cove looked totally deserted.

The captain gritted his teeth and walked over to the radio. '*Bahia Paraiso* to Antarctic Survey, do you hear me, over?'

'Copy *Bahia Paraiso*, loud and clear, pass your message,' Steve Martin replied. He was clearly waiting at the radio.

'We have important news for you; please stand by for further instructions.' The captain spoke politely in perfect English.

'Standing by,' came the clear reply. No indication on either side was given that anything unusual was happening.

The captain signalled his ship to put about. There had been no sign of anybody on the shore – through the murk and sleet of the storm the place had looked abandoned and desolate. Peering through his binoculars, Hugo was certain that he could see a figure standing on the jetty below the base. It had been tempting to put a boat ashore and speak to the scientists but in these conditions and with the uncertainty of who was there it seemed prudent to wait until the weather cleared.

Captain Briatore studied the chart; he guessed he could see the way that *Endurance* had slipped out. He was a good seaman himself and realised with some admiration that the only way that Captain Barker could have eluded him was through the Merton Passage. How the ship had evaded his radar had been a real conjuring trick. Where is she now? he wondered.

It was of little consequence: two more frigates, *Drummond* and *Granville*, would be with him within the next twenty-four hours. Two destroyers, the *Piedra Buena* and the *Commodoro Py*, were also under way, with the supporting tanker the *Punta Medanos*. The submarine *Santa Fe* was also heading towards them. It would be easy to hunt the *Endurance* when the time was right. He would like to have the operation complete by the time the rest of the ships arrived but in this storm there was little that he could do.

118

'Capitan Corti,' he said, turning to Hugo. 'I would like you to join Capitan Parades on the *Guerrico* once we can get the helicopters flying. It doesn't look as if there will be much resistance and *Guerrico*'s guns should persuade them. Teniente Astiz will stay on board this ship and oversee the troop landings with the Puma helicopter. The weather should be calm in the morning.'

Both officers nodded in assent.

27

Grytviken, South Georgia, Friday 2 April 1982

The Last Supper

The arrival of the *Bahia Paraiso* in King Edward Cove had been a nerve-racking experience for the marines as they prepared themselves for the Argentinians' arrival. Had the great storm not been raging they would have been totally unready. As the ship slipped out of the murk they grabbed their weapons and dived into their soaking, half-dug trenches. Uncertainly, Keith Mills walked down to the jetty and waited, expecting a deputation of some kind. He felt very alone and vulnerable and was unaware of the short radio conversation taking place between Captain Tombetta and Steve Martin. When the *Bahia Paraiso* turned round and headed out of the cove he had breathed a sigh of relief but was both nervous and perplexed. His soaking men scrambled out of their trenches cursing. The whole episode seemed futile and an anticlimax.

They continued to prepare their defences but as the storm increased and darkness fell they returned to Shackleton House. This was the first time that they had been on their own since leaving Port Stanley so, while the fids were settling in at the draughty old church at the whaling station, they had the run of the base. There seemed little point in worrying about rationing or food shortages and Keith ordered Marine John Stonestreet, the cook, to raid the larder and create a banquet, and the lads made full use of the free bar. They took it in turns throughout the night to walk out through the storm to Shackleton's Cross at

Hope Point and stand guard but there seemed little likelihood of trouble while the storm continued. A hilarious party with plenty of booze ensued,a gathering that would go down in the annals of the regiment as 'The Last Supper'. Young men dancing at the brink of battle.

Twelve miles away, up the coast, Corporal Nigel Peters' four-man team, watching the Argentinians at Leith Harbour, was having a miserable time. The observation point was very exposed and as the storm increased there was not much to see. They were soaking wet and in constant fear of being spotted by one of the helicopters. There was a small corrugated-iron hut at Jason Harbour where they took turns to sleep. They gave short radio reports but mainly kept silent to avoid detection. Their position became almost unbearable.

Typical of South Georgia, the storm abated as fast as it had arrived. During the night the wind dropped and the sun rose to a glorious morning, the mountains and glaciers gleaming white against a deep-blue cloudless sky, the sea almost flat calm. The watchers at Jason Peak reported that the *Bahia Paraiso* and another ship, the *Guerrico*, had entered Leith Harbour during the night and were preparing to take on fuel.

Back at Grytviken, Sergeant Peter Leach decided it was time to get Corporal Peters' observation team out and asked Keith Mills if he could take the base launch *Albatross* round the coast to get them. He reckoned he needed all the men he could get. Keith agreed but Steve Martin wasn't happy at all. The boat would have to navigate a six-mile stretch of open water across Cumberland West Bay and in this clear weather it seemed hardly the sensible thing to do with Argentinian ships and helicopters moving around. He was also concerned that Sergeant Leach was unused to the boat and had no knowledge of what to do if the engine broke down. The argument as far as Steve was concerned was a lost cause. Leach, usually a quiet man and father figure in this group, was not to be trifled with. An unarmed combat expert and weapons instructor, he was the only man in the party who had been in action. He informed the base commander in no uncertain terms that he intended to take the *Albatross* with or without his permission. He needed those men, he was going and that was that.

Reluctantly, Steve showed him how to work the controls and Peter left the base at 6 a.m. towing one of the marines' Gemini inflatable assault boats. He planned to abandon *Albatross* if attacked and escape in the faster and more manoeuvrable small boat. Hugging the coast around Sappho Point, he then headed out across the open six-mile stretch of water feeling very isolated and exposed. In his career he had been in some tight places but had never expected to find himself in such an unusual situation. He hoped that the early hour and the refuelling would keep the Argies out of his way. By 7.30 a.m. he was picking up the shivering men from Jason Harbour and running the gauntlet back across the open sea to Grytviken.

By sheer coincidence, one of the watchers with Corporal Peters at Jason Peak was Paddy McCalion, an Irishman from Carrick Fergus, who had served his apprenticeship as a fitter at Harland and Wolff's shipyard in Belfast. He had a keen interest in warships and their armament and had instantly recognised *Guerrico* for what she was and had a good understanding of her weapons and ability. Her 100mm and 40mm guns would be disastrous against them and she was light, fast and manoeuvrable, but at short range her aluminium superstructure could be penetrated by small-arms fire. Paddy realised that her Exocet missile system would not work against a land target and her anti-submarine equipment was irrelevant.

The return journey in *Albatross* was calm and uneventful; by 9 a.m. Nigel Peters and his men were tucking into a hearty breakfast back at the base, although they did wonder whether they had come out of the frying pan into the fire. Paddy's information gave Keith Mills some hope; he knew that the *Bahia Paraiso* had landing craft on board and was expecting a waterborne assault; if they could entice her close in they might just be able to do some damage. Steve had received a short coded message from *Endurance* that she would be in the area by 3 p.m. that day. If they could hold out or stall until then she might just be able to tip the balance.

Time was everybody's enemy and was running out at breakneck speed. Half an hour later most of the marines were pottering about their trenches laying out spare ammunition and chatting. In the radio shack, Steve and Keith talked to the nearest Antarctic base commanders at Signy and Faraday Islands, mostly about the improving weather situation. All seemed calm and peaceful.

Suddenly there were yells from outside: 'Chopper, take cover.' Glancing out of the radio shack window, Steve could see an Argentinian helicopter at low level moving slowly up the fjord.

Again the marines grabbed their weapons and dived into their trenches. Sergeant Leach dropped into a depression just in front of the base. 'Watch your front. Don't point your weapons. Don't shoot. Pass it down the line.'

Everybody watched the helicopter as it moved cautiously up the bay about five hundred yards from them. It didn't come near the base and the marines were sure that they hadn't been seen. For the next ten minutes it circled the cove and then, as quickly as it had arrived, it turned north and headed away. Almost immediately, the *Bahia Paraiso* came into view in the outer fjord.

Captain Tombetta's voice crackled to life on the radio. 'Do you read, Grytviken? Following our successful operation in the Malvinas Islands, the ex-governor has surrendered the Islands and dependencies to Argentina. We suggest you adopt a similar course of action to prevent any further loss of life. A ceasefire is now in force.'

'I read you,' Steve replied. 'I require five minutes to confer with my colleagues.'

Steve and Keith looked at each other. Both knew that, although Rex Hunt had surrendered the Falklands, nothing had been said about South Georgia or any other British protectorates. They had been listening to the BBC World Service and had heard nothing about a ceasefire.

'This is Capitan Tombetta. I am ordering you to bring your people out into the open to be counted, you will be treated well.'

'What now, Keith?' Steve asked, ignoring the last message.

'Tell him there is a military presence on the island and it will be defended if he tries to land.'

Slowly, Steve delivered Keith's message so that it was clearly understood. He hoped that the radio operator on *Endurance* could hear what was happening. He then asked to change frequency and repeated the message, trying to attract as much attention as he could.

Tombetta's reply came briskly back. 'I am sending troops ashore by helicopter. You must come out into the open.'

Steve cut straight back. 'Your landing is illegal and will be resisted.' He repeated the message.

These messages were all being monitored by *Endurance*, and by the Signy and Faraday Islands; even a thousand miles away the BAS flagship RRS *Bransfield*, with the managing director Dr Laws on board, was listening in. All over the island the fid scientists in their tents and huts listened in horror to the exchange. Within seconds everybody broke radio silence and there was a clamour to contact Steve.

On board *Endurance*, Captain Barker made a last ditch attempt to contact Keith. 'Grytviken, this is *Endurance* ... I assume you can hear me. Rules of engagement are as stated earlier this morning. *Defend if you are provoked.* Over.'

All to no avail. Through the radio shack window, steaming slowly round Hope Point and into the narrow cove they watched the frigate *Guerrico*, its heavy 100mm gun pointing directly at the base. Every man looking out from his position felt that he was looking directly down its barrel.

28

Frigate *Guerrico*, Cumberland East Bay, South Georgia, Saturday 3 April 1982

The frigate *Guerrico* was the pride of the Argentinian navy. Only four years old, she was built at the Lorient naval dockyard in France for the South African navy and named the *Transvaal* but due to a UN embargo of weapons to South Africa she was never delivered and was finally sold to Argentina at a knockdown price and armed as a general-purpose warship. She was light and fast and fitted with a large 100mm gun on her foredeck and a rapid-fire 40mm cannon on her stern. Amidships she carried a French surface-to-surface Exocet missile system. Two hundred and sixty-two feet in length, she was slender and manoeuvrable and in an open sea battle would be a formidable opponent.

Hugo had transferred to her from the *Bahia Paraiso* that morning while the two ships were refuelling at Leith Harbour and had been shown around by Captain Raul Parades. He liked what he saw; it was an efficient, well-run ship. Preparations on board were going ahead for the arrest of the British scientists at Grytviken.

It had been a surprise to all of them when HMS *Endurance* was not in the cove. Looking from the sea the base looked almost deserted and it seemed a good idea to take over as quickly as possible before she turned up again.

Nobody was expecting serious trouble. The change in the weather was dramatic – none of the crew of *Guerrico* had seen the island properly, as the great storm of the last few days had made it almost invisible. Now, as they sailed up the coast, the peaks of the Allardyce Range were gleaming in the morning sunshine – Mount Paget, the highest on the island with its glittering array of glaciers, and Mount Sugartop shimmering at the back of Cumberland Bay. They sailed in on calm waters with the odd iceberg floating gently by. The crew relaxed and enjoyed the view.

Looking across at the *Bahia Paraiso*, Hugo could see that the Puma helicopter had been pulled clear of the hangar and Alfredo Astiz was briefing his men ready to go ashore. He was as immaculate as ever and within the next hour or so expected to become the new military commander of the island. At the morning's conference he had looked flushed and excited and Hugo had the uneasy feeling that if problems arose he would instruct his men to shoot first and ask questions afterwards. The hard line that they intended to take with the British scientists didn't appeal to him. They seemed defenceless and he felt that a deputation ashore would be the easiest and least threatening way to persuade the base commander to surrender.

The shore looked deserted. They could see the old whaling station at the end of the cove quite clearly and there was no sign of life. Lieutenant Remo Busson and his navigator Guillermo Guerra were already airborne in the Alouette and were skimming low into the cove. Hugo knew that Remo would be sensible and would not go in close until he knew there was no threat. There was still a sneaking suspicion that the *Endurance* was lurking somewhere close by but both helicopters had flown along the coast earlier that morning and nothing had been seen.

Remo's voice came over the radio. 'I can't see any activity at the base, and there's nothing in the harbour. I have flown over the whaling station. Everything seems deserted.'

A few minutes later, he flew out of the cove and landed on the *Bahia Paraiso*. Captain Tombetta's voice came over the radio, ordering the base commander to send his men out into the open.

There was consternation on the bridge as the base commander steadfastly refused. It seemed inconceivable; they must be bluffing. Tombetta spoke to Captain Parades on a different frequency. 'Go and try to flush them out, Raul,' he snapped. 'Don't shoot, but make it clear that you mean business. Teniente Astiz, prepare to send your troops ashore.'

The *Guerrico* purred into motion. 'Action stations.' The whole ship was now on full alert; gun crews in position. Everybody was expectantly watching the shore. The great white cross at the entrance was gleaming in the sunshine as she passed into King Edward Cove. The narrows were guarded by the dangerous Hobart Rocks, forcing the ship close in to the shore; in the confines of the cove the *Guerrico* looked enormous. She passed the base; all was quiet with no sign of life. As the ship manoeuvred gingerly around the cove, her guns remained all the time lined up on the buildings. The base commander's voice again came on the air.

'There is a military presence on the island and it will be defended if you try to land.'

Captain Parades had now turned the *Guerrico* around and was heading out of the cove. He turned to Hugo in exasperation. 'They must be bluffing!'

As they slipped out through the narrows they heard Tombetta order the marines ashore. Remo took off and slipped the Alouette in low on the far side of the cove. As the ship headed out round Hope Point, Hugo spotted four men walking down from the base towards the jetty.

'They have sent out a party to meet us,' he exclaimed to Captain Parades. It was too late: Remo's Alouette appeared round the headland and made a rapid landing. Soldiers were jumping out and running for cover.

For the second time, Lieutenant Keith Mills walked out to the jetty expecting a deputation. The *Guerrico* had passed close to the base and was now slowly turning in the bay; on the way down he picked up the explosives party of marines – Church, Daniels and Porter – who had been standing ready to blow the mines; they would act as his escort. He still had no idea what to do other than stall for time. They stood nervously waiting on the jetty, expecting at any moment that a boat would come ashore. To his surprise the *Guerrico* passed them by and headed out of the cove. As if from nowhere the Alouette helicopter appeared round the point and landed about fifty yards from him. Armed men leaped out and sprinted for cover. Keith kept his rifle slung over his shoulder and waved to them, still expecting some kind of deputation. One of them spotted him and shouted a warning to an officer, who instantly dropped down and raised his rifle.

'Christ!' Keith yelled. 'Get out of it.' The four marines sprinted for cover; zigzagging and dodging back up to the base at Olympic speed, at any time expecting a bullet between the shoulders. Steve Martin, the only civilian still at the base, decided that the time had come to leave and, dressed only in his shirt and slacks, sprinted out along the track to the whaling station. He never made it.

There was confusion among the rest of the marines, who hadn't been able to see what was happening. The troops from the beach started to advance towards them and the *Guerrico* came back into the narrows. There came the dull thump of a big helicopter coming in fast to the stony beach. The Puma, filled with armed men, was yawing in to land, its doors open and two machine guns pointing out at them. Men were poised, ready to jump.

Closest to the front, Corporal Andy Larkin yelled to Keith. 'Sir, what are we going to do?'

Mills had seconds to make up his mind. 'If that thing lands we're in the shit! *Hit it!*' he yelled.

The huge helicopter hovering above the beach was a sitting duck: all twenty-two marines opened fire. It was devastating, a hail of bullets from all directions. Sergeant Leach, hidden in the tussock grass with a clear line of sight for his deadly accurate sniper's rifle, scored repeated deadly hits into the hold. Andy Lee let rip with his 66mm rocket launcher. The rocket passed a hair's breadth below the Puma or it would have disintegrated there and then. In their excitement, they targeted the hold and not the cockpit or they would have brought it down immediately. Most of the soldiers in the hold were either dead or wounded. The machine managed to stagger into the sky emitting black smoke and wobbled across the cove before finally crashing and turning over on the far side of the fjord.

Steve Martin, running for his life, dived into a hollow in the tussock grass. Bullets were sailing over his head. He was dressed only in his base clothing and lay in the freezing grass with the ever-present worry of a terrified giant elephant seal crawling over him. He stayed there, hidden and suffering from exposure, for the next few hours.

The marines were screaming war-whoops and yells. The giant marine 'Brasso' Hare, known as the mad axe-man, jumping up and down laughing and shouting: 'Brum, Brum, we've got it, we've got it!'

Steve Holding yelled a warning to Sergeant Leach. 'Pete, look at those daft buggers in the open down there.' The group of seven soldiers from the Alouette were advancing cautiously along the shore.

'Well, don't just look at them, shoot the bastards,' Leach yelled. Holding let rip with his small machine gun and three of the Argentinians fell to the ground. The rest dived into the cover of nearby sheds, tracer bullets flashing around them as they ran.

So far none of the marines was hurt and the battle had been one-sided but the odds were about to change. The *Guerrico* had passed through the narrows and was retracing her previous course towards them. This time, however, her big guns were firing. The marines dived back into their trenches as the 100mm high-explosive shells screamed over their position. At this range she was too close and unable to fire the big gun at a lower trajectory; the shells were whistling just over their heads and exploding behind them in the scree slope. The 40mm quick-fire in the stern was playing havoc, shells exploding all around them. Two of the marines jumped out of their shallow trench and dived into the deeper trench with Holding, Hare and James. From his vantage point Keith Mills watched the *Guerrico* sailing slowly towards them and realised that her captain was putting her into a very dangerous position. She was forced close inshore as she followed the deep-water channel into the cove.

'Stop firing,' Keith yelled. 'Nobody fire till I give the word. We'll wait until she has committed herself.'

The *Guerrico* slid steadily on towards them, oblivious of the danger that she was facing. Confident and all powerful, her guns blazing. Closer, closer, forced in by the deep-water channel. At this range she was the perfect target. Six hundred yards ... five hundred and fifty yards ... five hundred...

'Fire!' Every weapon the marines possessed opened up on the warship. Hundreds of rounds of machinegun and rifle fire smashed into her aluminium superstructure. The marines were screaming their heads off as they blasted away at the ship. Crouched in their trench, Dave Combes and John Stonestreet sighted the Carl Gustav 84mm rocket launcher; its effective range was only about four hundred and fifty yards and *Guerrico* was around five hundred. Hoping and praying, Dave fired. The missile streaked across the water and blasted into the ship just above the waterline. There was a loud booming explosion and as the smoke and spray cleared they could see a surprisingly large hole in her side.

Nigel Peters launched a 66mm rocket, which fell short as the ship was now moving away past the base. Tracer rounds from the automatic weapons were still blasting into the ship amidst a storm of rifle fire. The big 100mm gun appeared not to be able to traverse and ceased firing as she moved further into the cove. The 40mm gun on the stern was still in action and putting accurate fire into their position, its crew protected by an armour-plated screen. As she sailed on past into the bay, the gun crew became visible to the Bren gun position of Parsons and Chubb, covering the cove entrance above Hope Point. The Bren is a surprisingly accurate weapon, even at long range. Parsons waited and then, as *Guerrico* swung away, fired a series of short bursts into the five-man guncrew. Two of the men fell to the deck and the remainder dived for cover.

Peter Leach sprinted into Shackleton House and up the stairs to the first floor, bashing out the windows with the butt of his rifle. Dragging the large dining table into the middle of the room, he lay down on top of it. From here he had a perfect view of King Edward Cove. Adjusting the telescopic sight of his L42 sniper's rifle to five hundred yards, he waited. The only way out of the bay for the *Guerrico* was the way she'd come in. His blood was up...

Guerrico had just cleared the entrance to King Edward Cove and the frigate was in the process of turning back as Remo's helicopter landed the first group of troops on the beach. As the ship put about, Hugo and Captain Parades watched the big Puma troop carrier take off from the *Bahia Paraiso* and fly in towards the base. It was piloted by Lieutenant Juan Villagra and his co-pilot, Lieutenant Eduardo Leguizamon, both very experienced airmen. They fully expected that the base commander would realise that he was totally outnumbered and surrender immediately.

On board the *Bahia Paraiso* the sound of gunfire echoing around the bay came as a total surprise and at first they thought it was their own men firing warning shots but the radio suddenly sprang to life.

'I'm hit, I'm hit!' Juan Villagra's voice came over the intercom with the clear sound of gunfire in the background.

Eduardo Leguizamon came on the air. 'Standing by to ditch, the aircraft is damaged and we have injured on board.' He sounded calm and matter of fact.

The stricken craft now flew into sight, wobbling across the bay, smoke pouring out of her engine. Hugo realised that if she ditched into the freezing waters there would be little chance for the men on board. Juan Villagra was fighting the controls, desperately trying to keep the damaged machine in the air.

'There are soldiers at the base; it seems to be heavily defended.' Eduardo again, speaking calmly over the radio as the Puma staggered across the beach on the far side of the cove. 'We need medics...' His voice cut out as the helicopter crash-landed, bounced into the tussock grass and somersaulted onto its side.

The *Guerrico* was turning quickly back into the cove. Captain Raul Parades angrily called his men back to the alert as they sailed in through the narrows, the Hobart Rocks close to their port side. Remo Busson in the Alouette was already landing alongside the crashed helicopter as they rounded Hope Point and the base again came into view. The group of officers on the bridge scanned the shoreline through their binoculars as the ship eased towards the buildings. It was hard to see where the shooting had been coming from but there were obviously men on the high ground behind the huts and Raul gave the order to open fire. The big explosive shells from the 100mm gun exploded slightly above the tussock on the scree slope.

'That should put the fear of God into them,' Raul muttered to Hugo, as the stern gun came into action with much more accurate fire. They could see the shells exploding around the British positions. Nothing happened as the ship moved slowly in.

And then, suddenly, all hell broke loose. Within seconds, almost every window on the bridge exploded into smithereens. There seemed to be bullets flying everywhere, and tracers coming in from different directions all along the coast. Everybody on the bridge had dived to the deck. By some miracle nobody was hit. The seaman at the wheel was crouched down behind the superstructure trying to keep the ship on course as the hail of bullets continued. There were screams of anguish coming from the deck. Captain Parades shouted into the intercom for the guncrews to keep firing and was ordering full speed ahead as a huge explosion shook the ship. She seemed to groan in anguish. Screaming could be heard along the companionway. The hail of bullets continued but as the ship moved on past the base she began to move out of range.

The 40mm rear gun was mounted above the galley, giving a clear view as they passed and began to get a more accurate fire onto the British positions behind the base. Shells exploded around the buildings. Almost from nowhere, a burst of machine gun fire slammed into the guncrew. It was devastating: two of the gunners were killed outright and the remaining men, some wounded, dived for cover behind the superstructure of the galley.

'Can you go and assess the damage, Hugo? Half the phone lines aren't working and the engine room is reporting a fuel leak,' the captain asked, as they sailed into the heart of the cove.

Hugo dashed down the companionway. Below deck the scene was chaotic; a number of injured men were being carried into the officers' mess, which was being used as an emergency first-aid room. Smoke was coming up the stairwell and a fire crew in respirators were carrying an injured man from below.

'What's the damage down there?' Hugo asked.

'We have a hole in the side, sir, it's above the waterline on deck two, and there is a small fire but it's mainly in the crew cabins and shouldn't affect the ship. There are at least two dead down there. There seems to be a lot of cable damage,' the man said.

There didn't seem much that he could do so Hugo headed back to the bridge. Captain Parades was anxiously assessing damage reports. Small-arms fire was still hitting the ship but at this range was doing little damage. All the windows were shattered and it was bitterly cold on the bridge.

The angry voice of Captain Tombetta came on the radio asking what had happened, and Raul gave him a quick assessment of the situation.

'Some of the ship's communications systems are not working and messages are being sent by runners. We are holed amidships on the starboard side but the engines seem to be working OK. The main gun is working but the control cable on the turret appears to be cut and the gun will only swing one way, so we are unable to fire from our present position.' He went on to explain how it had been impossible for the big gun to lower its trajectory at such close range. 'If we can get outside the cove it may be possible to shell their position more accurately. There seems to be a large garrison of soldiers at the base,' he added.

'You'd better get out of there, Raul,' Captain Tombetta ordered. 'We are putting troops ashore on the other side of the cove and will need some covering fire from you.'

Captain Parades acknowledged him and, turning to the group of officers around him, he smiled weakly. 'You had better keep your heads down, gentlemen; the only way out of here is back through the way we came.' It was a grim and anxious moment. He gazed around at the devastation of broken glass and equipment that, fifteen minutes earlier, had been the wheelhouse of his beautiful ship. 'Take her about,' he said, turning to the crewman at the wheel.

At the far side of the cove, the Alouette was flying back and forward between the beach and the *Bahia Paraiso*, ferrying men to the shore. The *Guerrico* swung gently round the bay, passing the rusty old buildings of Grytviken whaling station and the wreck of the whaler *Louise*. The whale catcher *Petrel*, parked at the jetty, looked as if she could sail off at any moment. There was no sign of life. As she completed her turn they were now facing back, directly up the deep-water channel, towards King Edward Point base.

Five hundred yards away Sergeant Peter Leach lay on the dining table in Shackleton House squinting through his telescopic sight. The ship swung slowly round the cove in front of him. He had a clear view straight into the window of the bridge. A group of men, whom he took to be officers, were clearly visible, staring directly towards him. The *Guerrico* puffed black smoke, dipped her stern and began rapidly to increase her speed towards him. He took a deep breath, blinked a couple of times and calmed himself, then gently squeezed the trigger.

Hugo felt a massive blow in his side, crashing him to the deck as a series of shots exploded all around him. Raul Parades fell with him. As Hugo crawled to his knees he saw that the captain was dead. A bullet had entered his left temple and blood was oozing onto the deck. His second officer was also hit and lying groaning beside him. He felt surprisingly calm. He knew he was hit but it didn't feel serious and there wasn't much pain. He crawled out of the wheelhouse and stood up in the shelter of the superstructure. The seaman at the wheel was kneeling, trying to control the ship by bobbing up and down behind the bridge housing. The hail of fire was once again raining down from King Edward Point as the *Guerrico* sailed flat out through the deadly channel.

From his vantage point, Hugo shouted instructions to the wheelman. Everybody was lying flat behind anything solid they could find as bullets rattled like a riveting gun into the ship's side. Almost in slow motion, he watched a missile snake up from the beach and streak towards him. His warning shout was too late as the thing slammed into the Exocet launching gear behind the wheelhouse and exploded.

Hugo screamed instructions. 'Get a fire crew up there fast! If one of the Exocets explodes it will wreck the ship.'

The thousand-yard run through the narrows seemed an eternity. The ship was at full speed and the run out past the base could only have taken three or four minutes but the devastating fire from the shore caused terrible damage. Once round Hope Point they were out of the fire and Hugo went back onto the bridge and took control. He was surprised how well the crew were reacting to the situation. All over the vessel teams were working to sort the damage; a first-aid crew had come into the wheelhouse and was attending to the wounded. His own injury was minor, the bullet having passed through his armpit and grazing his ribs. A seaman had put a shell dressing on for him but he had been too occupied to take much notice.

He had taken control of the ship immediately after the death of Captain Parades. He was now the highest-ranking officer on board but was surprised that nobody had questioned him. The situation was appalling. The seemingly simple task of taking over the British base was turning into a fiasco. The wound in his armpit was throbbing and sore but he was able to hold the padded dressing in with his arm and compress it against his ribs, and he gritted his teeth and got on with the job. A deep anger gripped him. He could hear a fire crew hosing down the Exocet missile system behind the bridge and tried not to think of the horrific consequences if one of the damaged missiles were to explode.

Captain Tombetta came on the radio and Hugo told him of the death of Raul Parades and the serious damage on board. Tombetta had problems of his own. Troops were being ferried ashore by the Alouette helicopter onto the far side of the cove but were under constant small-arms fire from the base. Remo had radioed that the aircraft had been hit a number of times and his flotation gear was damaged.

'I must have some covering fire,' Tombetta demanded urgently. 'It's imperative that we get the men ashore; can you get into a position to use your guns?'

Hugo contacted the gunnery officer, Lieutenant Roberto Mattasa, over the ship's intercom. The young officer sounded shocked and shaken; two of his crew were dead and one injured, but he had already made a careful assessment of the situation.

'The gun is undamaged, Capitan, but it can't traverse; the control cables are only pulling one way. If you can get into position facing the base I think I can get the distance all right. Can you direct the ship for me? The ideal range would be about two miles. I can lob shells down onto them from there – any closer and it will be hard to get the trajectory correct.'

In the open, windowless bridge the cold was intense as they brought the *Guerrico* out into the open of Cumberland East Bay and swung her round to face King Edward Point. At this range the buildings looked tiny. Hugo could see Remo Busson flying backwards and forwards to the stricken Puma helicopter, dropping off troops and flying back the injured. The men were moving carefully around the cove and into Grytviken whaling station.

As the ship's bow lined up on the point, Lieutenant Mattasa's voice came onto the intercom. 'Two degrees to port.'

The big gun fired its first salvo. The deadly shells screamed across the bay and hit the scree about a hundred yards to the right of the base. To Hugo's surprise he heard the ship's crew cheering. Everyone was watching the coast.

'Can you take her back about two hundred yards, Capitan, and aim the bow about five degrees to port?' Mattasa asked.

'Slow astern,' Hugo commanded. The next salvo slammed into the hillside, much closer to the base. Slowly and painstakingly, the ship manoeuvred back and forth. Steadily, the rain of heavy shells began to fall on the positions around the base as the *Guerrico* systematically began to wreak her vengeance...

Peter Leach smiled with grim satisfaction as the *Guerrico* sailed past the base. She's going out a lot quicker than she came in, he thought.

Jumping from the table, he dashed into the next room overlooking the narrows and smashed out the windows with his rifle butt. There was a muffled yell from below as the shattered glass crashed onto the big marine Brasso Hare, who was collecting ammo from the cache below him.

'Sorry, pal,' he yelled, sticking his head out of the window for a second. Instantly, a burst of machinegun fire splattered the woodwork besides him. He dived back and hit the floor, shocked and shaken at the near miss. Promising himself he would be more cautious, he found a safer position and began to fire carefully at the ship.

In the trenches, Dave Combs and John Stonestreet were having trouble with the Carl Gustav rocket launcher. The ship coming past the base was a sitting duck from their position but the rockets were refusing to ignite. They realised that during the storm the damp conditions must have affected the ignition system. According to the manual you shouldn't remove an unexploded round for about a minute after a misfire but at great risk to themselves they were feverishly changing rounds one-by-one as they failed to ignite. Bullets were whizzing all about them from across the bay as the ship raced by. Finally, just as *Guerrico* passed the point, one of the rockets fired. It streaked high across the water and exploded just behind the bridge. There was a lot of smoke and it had clearly done some damage. The two friends grinned and Stonestreet slapped Combs on the back. They continued trying to get more rockets off but with no more luck.

Further down the trenches, Corporal Nigel Peters, Spike Poole and Paddy McCalion were preparing the 66mm rocket launcher. Nigel scrambled to his feet in the trench and took careful aim as the ship sailed past him. There was a rattle of machinegun fire from the buildings by the jetty. Peters was flung backwards, the rocket launcher spinning out of his grasp. Two bullets hit him in the arm, breaking it badly, and he fell into the trench in a pool of blood.

'Sir, sir, Corporal Peters has been shot in the arm,' Spike Poole called across to Keith Mills, who was over in the adjacent trench trying to figure out his next move.

'Yes, OK. Stick a field dressing on it,' Mills yelled back across. He had little time for niceties.

While Poole wound a bandage around Nigel's arm, Paddy McCalion angrily opened up on the building where he thought the sniper had fired from with his GPMG, raking the building with devastating fire. Mills was looking anxiously across the bay as the helicopter plied back and forward from the *Bahia Paraiso* to the shore. He could see soldiers moving steadily along the far beach past the cemetery where Shackleton lay and round into the whaling station. He ordered his men to concentrate their fire at the helicopter, which was almost out of range at fifteen hundred yards, but he hoped that they would be able to deter it. Every available rifle opened up at the Alouette and it swerved in the air and moved rapidly away.

The *Guerrico* had now reappeared and was about two miles off, out in the main fjord. She turned towards them and began determinedly to open up with her big gun. At first the shots were wildly away from them but Mills, crouched in his trench with Nocker White, could see that whoever was controlling the ship was carefully manoeuvring her into a more accurate position and at each salvo the big explosive shells were getting closer. He ruefully admired the determination of whomever it was conning the ship; he knew she had taken a terrible beating and was seriously damaged from their point-blank fire. It must be hell on that bridge, he thought. Shells were coming in as bursts of four or five rounds every twenty seconds, followed by a short pause while the *Guerrico* changed her position. Each time, she got more accurate and there was nothing they could do about it.

Mills knew that his escape route was cut off. Their rucksacks and equipment were hidden behind the church at the whaling station and he could already see Argentinian troops moving around the buildings. It was difficult to shoot in that direction without endangering the fids, who he suspected were now in enemy hands. The small-arms fire had calmed down and there was little to shoot at. He realised that a single hit from the 100mm shells now screaming in across the bay might well wipe out half of his men. As each salvo came in the noise was deafening. So far he had only one wounded man and his marines had behaved superbly. He had done his best but, as the Argentinian troops began to close in from the whaling station, he realised that, short of a suicidal defence of the base, his options had just about run out.

He waited for a lull in the firing and for the next salvo from the ship to finish and then stuck his head over the top of the trench. 'Well guys, that's it. We've made our point, that's enough. I've decided to surrender. Does anybody have any violent objections?'

His shout was greeted with stony silence. 'Good, because that's what I've decided.'

Upstairs in Shackleton house, Peter Leach had the message passed on to him. Shouting for covering fire, he dashed down and across the open ground and threw himself alongside Mills in the trench. 'What's the problem, sir? What the hell for? We're winning hands down!'

Keith briefly told him the situation as he saw it. Somewhat angrily, the sergeant muttered, 'OK, whatever you say. Personally I'd like to carry on, but you're the boss.' Leach was disappointed and angry but dashed back to the building screaming for his men to cease fire.

Mills nervously raised Nocker's rifle, covered with the white inside lining of his Arctic warfare jacket, above the trench. It was met by a burst of gunfire from the sheds at the jetty. He lowered and raised it a second time. After a moment the shooting ceased. This was it. He slapped Nocker on the back and stood slowly up, still holding the white jacket in the air. He stood in the open for a few moments and then, casually shouldering his SMG, he walked once more the never-ending track to the jetty. As he arrived at the sheds, a uniformed Argentinian officer stood waiting. Mills paused a moment and then lay his gun on the ground and walked over.

'Hello, do you speak English?' he asked.

'Yes, I do.'

'Look, you are in a difficult position,' Mills said. 'We are well dug in and can go on fighting for a long time. We shall all get killed, but we don't care. You will lose more and more of your own men. To avoid needless casualties on both sides, I am prepared to surrender now if you will guarantee good treatment for my men.'

The officer grabbed him by the hand and shook it vigorously; he clearly thought he was in a fight to the death. He spoke rapidly into a radio. Keith shouted to his men to come forward very slowly with no weapons, and one by one they emerged from the buildings and trenches around the base. They were lined up and counted. Suddenly, the Argentinians became very tense and moved to cover with their weapons cocked.

'Where are the rest of your men?' the officer asked.

The motley crew of twenty-two marine prisoners seemed too small and the soldiers feared that they had been drawn into a trap. For over two hours they had fought off and played havoc with two large warships, helicopters and over eighty of their Special Forces. It seemed incredible that this small unit was all that they had been fighting.

Up at the church Bob Headland, the only fid to speak Spanish, had surrendered. Until then they had been putting out radio signals, reporting what they could see to the rest of the personnel on the island and, hopefully, to *Endurance*. Transmission ceased as the Argentinians arrived at the whaling station.

A few minutes later, the Alouette flew into the base with Lieutenant Astiz and his retinue. He was as immaculate as ever, as were his aides. He formally congratulated Keith and his men on their defence of the base. Keith showed him the hidden mines and the booby-trapped jetty and Les Daniels, who had set them up, agreed to make them safe, which he did, watched by a very nervous bunch of Argentinian soldiers.

Astiz then walked along to the church at Grytviken where the fids were brought out one by one and searched. They were grouped together and marched back to the beach below Shackleton House, where they met up with the marines. It was only then that they realised that Steve Martin was missing. Very concerned, Keith spoke to Astiz and was allowed to walk along the coast track with some of his captors. After some shouting, a very cold and shaken base commander emerged from the tussock grass. He recovered quickly when he learned that everybody was alive.

Some of their belongings were returned but much of the base was looted. The fids were allowed to collect some of their most valuable possessions from the base and these were bagged and returned to them safely some time later. Their cameras were opened but they found later that some of the photographs survived. Sergeant Peter Leach managed to leave a note on the dining-room table, apologising for breaking the windows and promising to be back to fix them. He meant it! They were taken out to the *Bahia*

Paraiso on the landing craft. As they passed the *Guerrico* they suffered the indignity of having to lay face down in the bilges, as their captors didn't want them to see the damage they had done to her. The Argentinian garrison was moving into the wrecked Shackleton House.

Corporal Nigel Peters and Captain Hugo Corti were treated together in the sickbay on board the *Bahia Paraiso*. Nigel's wound was very painful and he would take some time to mend. Luckily, Hugo's was minor. It had been decided that he would stay at King Edward Point in command of the garrison there. Astiz would be in overall command of the main garrison at Leith Harbour. Hugo was somewhat relieved at this: there was certainly going to be an inquiry into the terrible mistake that the *Guerrico* had made in going blindly into King Edward Cove and he would be spared any retribution over that debacle. He did not relish the idea of spending a lot of time on the island with Alfredo Astiz but as he would be mainly at the other whaling station it might not be so bad. He had already gone over the whole operation with Captain Tombetta, who was a worried man and in a rush to get his ships away.

A very tired-looking Remo Bussan came into Hugo's cabin as he was packing. The pilot helped him sort out his kit and the two men sat quietly smoking. There was not much to say. It was only mid-afternoon on what seemed to have been the longest day of their lives. Remo said that both pilots of the Puma had survived the crash but he was still shocked at the horrific carnage that had taken place in the aircraft's hold. Most of the soldiers were dead. Hugo watched the prisoners of war being taken on board. They looked tired and disoriented but held their heads up proudly. The young officer looked confused and was obviously suffering from battle fatigue. For a moment their eyes met but there was no response and he was ushered on down the companionway. What possibly could be going through his mind? Hugo wondered. And which one was the marksman who had almost ended his life and had shot Captain Raul Parades?

Hugo's kit was loaded onto the landing craft and he stiffly climbed down the ladder himself. His side ached and he felt weak and incredibly tired. Captain Tombetta saluted him smartly as the landing craft pulled away from the *Bahia Paraiso*. It was still a glorious windless day and the mountains were reflected in the calm waters of King Edward Cove. Hard to believe that only a few hours ago this beautiful place had been desecrated by men trying to kill each other. Argentina had her victory but the price had been too high. The seamen and pilots had behaved marvellously but he knew it had been badly managed and unnecessary: it was not the men but the leadership that had blundered. He was certain that a bloodless surrender could have been negotiated. He wondered what would happen to the British prisoners.

News was already going out on Argentinian television and tomorrow the papers would no doubt be full of the glorious victory. The world's media would soon be hearing that Argentina now controlled another island in the South Atlantic. Is it worth it? he wondered.

29

Antarctic Bay, South Georgia, Saturday 3 April 1982

The voice of Governor Rex Hunt came onto the air: '*Dear friends, I am afraid I have not been given as much time to say farewell to you as I would have wished, by speaking to you all personally, but the new Argentinian governor has kindly given me permission to send you this last message of good wishes and thanks for all your support in the two years I have served you. I shall never forget you and hope we shall meet again someday. In particular, Mavis and I would like to say goodbye to all the Government House staff who we were not able to see today. Goodbye and God bless you all.*'

Alison and Anna sat speechless in the tiny hut, listening to the radio. Both girls found themselves blinking away tears and trying to control their emotions as Rex Hunt made his final farewell address from Port Stanley. The Falkland Island radio service had come back on air soon after the invasion and had been broadcasting music and messages from the islanders to friends and relatives that they were OK and not to worry. There had also been a short service in Spanish, which they took to be a memorial to soldiers killed during the siege of Government House.

The whole thing was a bizarre nightmare. The women had stopped for a week in the Islands on their way to South Georgia and had visited Rex and his wife, as all the fids did, on their way to the bases. The islanders were a friendly and cheerful community of sheep farmers living in a fairly harsh part of the world and it seemed the last place on earth that anyone would want to invade. What possible purpose would it serve? It was hard to imagine thousands of Argentinian troops on the island and in the tiny town of Port Stanley.

The hut in Antarctic Bay had become a warm haven in the three weeks that the two women had been there. The weather had been mostly fine, but was getting colder as the Antarctic winter approached, and the great storm that hit the South Atlantic at the beginning of April, holding up the invasion, had shown what incredible forces nature could throw at them in this part of the world. They had made the place as comfortable as possible. There was a pot-bellied stove and plenty of coal, delivered earlier in the summer by the Survey ship *John Biscoe*. BAS food boxes were stacked outside the hut. It was monotonous eating but there was food aplenty for at least two months; a little more if they were careful. Inside the hut, the Tilly lamp hissed cheerfully, giving warmth and light. They had books and a chess set. Anna had rigged the solar battery charger for the cameras on the roof. The filming was going well and they were getting along famously.

Each evening they chatted to Grytviken and the other fids scattered around the island and on occasions to Signy Island, the nearest Antarctic base, some eight hundred miles south-east of them.

It had been hard to take seriously the initial problems with the scrap-metal workers at Leith Harbour when the troubles began to occur. When Bob Headland and Peter Stark started the surveillance of the Argentinians from Jason Peak, they began to take much more interest. And when David Asquith made his sortie behind the whaling station Alison had found herself becoming very concerned. It seemed totally inconceivable that the island would be invaded; after all this was 1982 – weren't we all supposed to be civilised? Surely the British Government would sort out the problem! As the situation worsened, their time spent listening to the radio increased and as the great storm hit the island there was little else to do but listen in.

All over South Georgia the fids were beginning to realise the enormity of the situation. In stunned incomprehension they had listened to Rex Hunt's declaration of the emergency and then, a day later, the surrender of the Falkland Islands.

Steve Martin's reaction had been decisive and quick and he had dispersed as many of his people to St Andrews Bay and the Lyell Glacier huts as he could. Over the radio, Steve had sounded calm and confident and was still hoping to find a diplomatic solution. There was no mention of the marines on the air and he said he had no idea of the whereabouts of *Endurance*. The women had a good idea that a lot was going on at King Edward Point that was not being said.

David spoke to Alison immediately after his conversation with Steve.

'I think it's a good idea for us to come over to Antarctic Bay, Alison, this place is too close to the Argies for comfort. The problem is that although it's only six miles as the crow flies it's impossible to get along the coast and over the mountains the direct way. The only reasonable route seemed to be to retrace Shackleton's journey up the Fortuna Glacier and descend the Crean Glacier into the back of Antarctic Bay and that's twice the distance.'

'It looks OK from this side, David. When the weather fines up Anna and I'll walk up the Crean Glacier and find out what the route's like from this side. The bottom end of the Crean looks crevassed but I'm sure there is an easy way.'

'Sebastian's no mountaineer and it will mean climbing the steep slope that Shackleton and his men slid down on their crossing in 1916. We'll hang on for a day or two to see what happens,' David decided. 'I've only got the tent and about two weeks' food. We've moved as far as we can along the beach from Leith but I'm sure if we stay here for long we'll have visitors.'

'There's plenty of food and fuel here, it will be great to have you.' They signed off. Alison felt elated; it looked as if her prayers had been answered; it was hard to imagine that the crisis would last for long and it would be a good chance to get to know David better. Telling herself not to be foolish, she found it hard not to stop smiling.

The two women slept badly that night, with the storm blasting and shaking the hut but in the small hours the wind suddenly abated and they slept fitfully until dawn. Fresh snow had fallen and they awoke to a cloudless sky. Listening to the radio, they heard Steve talking casually to Signy Island. Anna began to clean up the hut and Alison wandered outside, enjoying the spectacular view.

'Alison, Alison!' Anna's anxious voice called from the hut. 'The *Bahia Paraiso* is on the radio; they're asking Grytviken to surrender!'

Alison ran back into the hut in time to hear Captain Tombetta's ultimatum to Steve, ordering him to bring his men out into the open. Suddenly *Endurance* broke radio silence and Nick Barker's voice came on air.

'Rules of engagement are as stated earlier. *Defend if provoked.*'

The air became alive with radio traffic, all trying to contact Steve Martin at Grytviken, but no reply came, just the hiss and buzz of radio static. The field parties all began calling each other, and Signy Island and various other Antarctic bases were all trying to make contact but to no avail. A few minutes later the BAS ship RRS *Bransfield* came on air, calling, 'Red Plum, Red Plum.' She was one thousand miles to the north, off the coast of Chile and the director of BAS, Richard Laws, was trying to contact *Endurance* and make some sense of the situation. He was greatly concerned and trying to make sure that his personnel remain calm and neutral but was getting no reply. He finally read out a message, which was meant for all sides to hear.

The Foreign and Commonwealth Office do not consider you in danger. Stop. You should cooperate fully with the military governor, including evacuation if this instruction. Stop. We are considering whether voluntary evacuation is desirable but you should use your own judgement on the various options and we will support you. Stop. In either case you should if practical take with you what low bulk valuable equipment you can. Stop. Next of kin being kept informed as and when they enquire.

Stop. Best wishes and good luck from all here. Stop. Please confirm message passed and received at South Georgia. Message ends.

Stunned, they looked at each other. Alison found herself once again near to tears. What on earth were they supposed to do? It seemed pretty clear that their lifeline to King Edward Point had been severed and the Argentinians had taken over the base. It also seemed likely that they and the other fids on the island were likely to be visited and arrested during the next few days. A flood of emotions gripped Alison: fear, anger, resentment and confusion. She took a firm grip of herself. She had always been adventurous but had never been in a situation like this.

'Well, I haven't surrendered yet,' she said turning to Anna. 'As far as I'm concerned this island is still British. There's not much we can do if they turn up but I'm damned if I'm going to surrender!'

Anna agreed. In fact, her first concern was not for herself but for her film. During the time they had been in Antarctic Bay she had shot some wonderful footage of wildlife and the thought of losing it seemed more important to her than anything else.

'I wonder if we should hide the film?' she asked. They considered burying it somewhere clear of the hut to be picked up at a later date but in the end packed it up in a food box and hoped that they would be able to take it with them. They began to pack up the rest of their equipment.

The sun had set to a beautiful, cold, cloudless evening when they heard the faint thumping drone of a helicopter echoing around the bay. Uneasily, they pulled on their parkas and gloves and went outside. Slipping in at low level down the Crean Glacier a small, darkly painted Wasp came skimming towards them. With relief they recognised one of *Endurance*'s once bright red helicopters, now repainted in military camouflage. It circled them and they saw the smiling face of Tony Ellerbeck waving from the cockpit. It did not land but the navigator tossed out a cigarette tin, which landed in front of them. The pilot saw they had the box, waved cheerily and spun the machine back across the bay and vanished once again up the glacier.

The note inside read:

Hi girls, sorry we can't stop for tea, greetings from everybody. Apologies from Nick, we could get you aboard but feel that you are safer where you are at present. Arrangements are being made to get you out. If you have visitors, don't tell them we are around, it might spoil the fun! Unsure as yet what has happened at Grytviken but nobody hurt in Port Stanley, military or civilian. Rex and Mavis Hunt should be in London by now. We can't visit David and Seb, too close to Leith, try to let them know what's happening. Keep contact via Signy. Love Tony.

What a relief! Somewhere, hidden among the icebergs, the gallant little ship, showing not the slightest signs of surrender, was watching over the island. The lifeline was still there.

In much higher spirits, they contacted David Asquith on the radio. Unable to tell him what had happened for fear of compromising the ship, Alison hoped that she could at least pass on her optimism. As ever, David sounded totally unconcerned.

'We'll hang on here for a couple of days and see what happens,' he said. 'Seb's up for the walk so we'll come over and join you, weather permitting. If you can find a way over from your side it will save us a bit of time.'

'That's great, David. It looks easy enough from here, so we'll come over and meet you.'

'How much food have you got, Alison?' he asked.

'Two months if we're careful.' As the words spilled out she realised that once the men arrived there would be four of them. 'Only one month when you arrive!'

'There is no way we can carry all the food and equipment, we plan to leave most of the kit hidden on the beach. Sebastian's insisting that we take the gravity meter and theodolite with us.

He feels there's little point of being here if he can't work and I guess he's right.'

'I wonder how long it will take them to sort this out?' Alison asked.

'These things tend to take time and time we don't seem to have. I'll bring what food I can of ours but we may have to go on a diet – Seb could do with slimming a bit anyway. We'll see you in a couple of days.' He signed off.

He's right, she thought despondently. This could take months to sort out. What can the government do eight thousand miles away? A feeling of isolation swept over her. What happens now?

Part 2

South Georgia Falls

30

London, Tuesday 6 April 1982

The first forty-eight hours following the invasion had been the worst days of Margaret Thatcher's political career. She was exhausted and felt alone, friendless and isolated. Nobody in government had seriously expected that the Argentinians would invade at such short notice and now, with all links to the Islands severed, the only information they had was coming jubilantly over the airwaves from Argentina.

The evening's Cabinet meeting on Friday 2 April had been a dismal gathering of badly informed ministers. The only bright spot was Admiral Leach's report on the activity of the navy and the Royal Marines. Some of the ships were already on their way to Ascension Island and the carrier *Invincible* would be under way by Monday followed by the larger carrier *Hermes*, which was being rushed out of maintenance and would be close behind.

Somebody whispered cheerfully in her ear, 'Every one of Leach's commanders knows they'll be shot if those ships are not ready to sail by the weekend,' and she laughed for the first time in days.

Things had gone from bad to worse: the attack on the government in Parliament on Monday had been brutal from all sides of the house. Screams of 'Resign!' came thick and fast from the Labour front bench. Michael Foot, leader of the opposition, who only a few days earlier, during the Trident debate, had claimed to be a 'Peacemonger', was now yelling at the top of his voice for action, not words. The whole episode was akin to the change of heart by the Argentinian people from violent opposition to the junta to glorious approval of the invasion.

The British Parliament gave little thought to the practicalities of fighting a war six thousand miles away. Their blood was up. Why had the government's response been so slow? The previous Labour prime minister James Callaghan stood up and stated that his government had sent a nuclear submarine and two frigates to ward off just such a threat in 1977.

Margaret braced her back and defended her Cabinet as best she could. 'It would have been absurd to dispatch the fleet every time there was bellicose talk in Buenos Aires,' she retorted.

In the Lords, Peter Carrington was defending the government, and in his absence in the Commons, John Nott made a poor job of the government's defence.

'Resign! Resign!' Opposition MPs, excluded from the joys of government, revelling in indignation, took their revenge.

By Tuesday, it was all over. Lord Carrington and two of his Foreign Office aides, Richard Luce and Humphrey Atkins, resigned; the first British causalities of the Falkland Islands War! There had never been any great love between Margaret and her foreign secretary but there was a high degree of mutual respect. She tried everything to dissuade him, even wheeling in two ex-prime ministers, Lord Home and Harold Macmillan, but the opposition and press were having none of it and were baying for his blood. *The Times*' headline ruthlessly demanded that 'He should do his duty.'

Very isolated, the prime minister took advice from Harold Macmillan and a leaf out of Harold Wilson's book. She hated the large and mostly unsupportive Cabinet and had managed to make major decisions through sub-committees from which she had excluded opposition. She decided that the scale of war, should it come, would not require a full-scale War Cabinet and formed instead a sub-committee, which she called ODSA and manned it mainly with political allies that she could trust. Francis Pym, a political enemy who she distrusted, became her new foreign secretary, divine retribution for the present situation, she thought, knowing full well that in the event of her failure Pym would be her likely successor. Later that morning she sent for Sir Henry Leach, Colin Figures (the head of MI6) and Cecil Parkinson, a young and loyal supporter – she needed someone she could trust to watch her back.

Peter Bacon-Smith dashed out of his office in Century House, the ugly multi-storey office block in Lambeth that is the head-quarters of MI6, hailed a cab and within minutes was entering No. 10 Downing Street. He was ushered through the police cordon and a crowd of tourists at the street entrance and entered the famous door, where an aide was expecting him. He was taken immediately upstairs to the prime minister's office with little time to take in his famous surroundings. He was quietly introduced by his chief, Colin Figures, a portly, bespectacled man who had recently taken over MI6. Like all his predecessors, he was known to the public only as 'C', the real life version of 'M' in the James Bond novels. Mrs Thatcher smiled at Peter, acknowledged his existence and paid him a searching look. He had expected the meeting to be similar to that at the Houses of Parliament, four days earlier, but this time a more comfortable and smaller group of people surrounded the prime minister and a positive atmosphere prevailed. Admiral Leach, sitting comfortably, now in civilian clothes, nodded to him and smiled. The fourth person at the table was only slightly older than himself and turned out to be Cecil Parkinson, an up-and-coming MP. Around the table was an almost conspiratorial atmosphere.

Colin Figures was filling them in with as much information as MI6 had been able to glean of the situation in the Islands and Argentina and of the weaponry and present state of the Argentinian services. 'I'm not sure about American policy, Prime Minister,' he said. 'Usually the CIA keep us informed with or without Congress permission. We could do with their satellite information and any other covert knowledge they have. We think they may be able to monitor their telephones.'

Mrs Thatcher smiled. 'The Americans will support us,' she stated confidently, 'I have a good relationship with Ronald, who understands our position. General Haig is more difficult – he's been sent by the White House to try to keep our two sides apart and find a diplomatic solution.' She banged the table angrily. 'The Falkland Islanders are our people: the Argentinians must back down!'

Admiral Leach broke in, 'We only have a short window of opportunity. By the end of June the southern winter will be on us, which means from this moment we have only just over two months, twelve weeks at best. If we haven't taken the Islands by then we will almost certainly have to withdraw. The Argentinians will do everything to stall for time.'

'The Americans will insist on some mediation and it will be against world opinion if we don't look for some kind of diplomatic solution. We will be forced to slow down,' Cecil Parkinson said.

'If only we had a quick win,' the prime minister mused. 'As yet the Argentinians are not well established and world opinion is mainly on our side. Whatever we do is going to take weeks; goodness knows how things will have moved on by June. We need to show them we mean business right now!'

Leach smiled. 'The navy planners have an idea that might work,' he said, reaching into his briefcase and spreading out a map of the South Atlantic on the table. 'The Argentinians will expect a determined attack on the Falkland Islands, which will take us some weeks to prepare and must in the end be our prime objective. But just suppose that we quickly sent a small squadron of ships ahead of the main Task Force to retake the island of South Georgia... Here!' he said, pointing to the tiny dot eight hundred miles to the south-east. 'They'd never expect a serious attack here and there's only a small garrison. It's isolated and if we act decisively could be retaken with minimum loss of life and would show the Argentinians we mean business. Not only that, but in the event of serious escalation of hostilities in the Falklands it will give the navy a safe and sheltered deep water harbour in reasonable range of the Islands.'

The prime minister smiled, quickly grasping the implications of what was being suggested. Here was an idea that might save British face and show that she was resolute and determined to fight back and at the same time give the diplomats time to find a solution. 'How can you keep this quiet?' she asked. 'The whole world will be looking on.'

'The whole operation would have to be done under maximum security,' the admiral replied. 'I've already earmarked the ships. I intend to have a separate planning group away from the navy's main control HQ at Northwood. The whole thing should be on a need to know basis, top secret. The fewer people who know, the better. That's why I asked for the MI6 representative to be here,' he said, turning to Peter. 'We need to know as much as we can about what is happening on South Georgia without attracting attention; I'd like the two services to work together on this.'

'Peter has been running the South Atlantic area and knows the situation as well as anyone,' 'C' murmured. 'You can work with him and we'll put every resource we have at your disposal.'

The prime minister nodded. 'The ODSA Committee will have to know and some of the Cabinet but I suggest that we play the whole thing very quietly, and keep the politicians out of this as much as we can. There will be plenty to do as the main Task Force is heading south. How can we avoid our ships being spotted, Admiral?'

Leach smiled again. 'There's a lot of ocean down there, ma'am, all eyes should be on the fleet. Our main concern will be Russian satellites and surveillance aircraft. It depends on how much they pass on to the Argentinians. If we can get them away from the main force as quickly as possible they will be just three or four ships in a vast ocean. Once we get within range of South Georgia we may have enemy submarines to contend with but it's my guess that they will be more concerned with protecting the Falklands.'

'Is everybody in agreement, then?' Margaret Thatcher glanced around the table and they all nodded affirmative. 'Then I suggest you get on with it, First Sea Lord. I trust you will keep me informed.'

As they left Downing Street, Peter couldn't hide his amazement at the speed with which Mrs Thatcher had made her decision and how rapidly events were unfurling.

'Can you come and see me at Northwood tomorrow?' the admiral asked as they parted. 'Morning prayers is at 9 a.m. Can you be there?'

Peter agreed, wondering what possible reason Leach could have for inviting him to a prayer meeting. He hadn't taken him for a religious man. He shrugged as he joined Colin Figures in the taxi back to Century House.

31

Fortuna Bay, South Georgia, Tuesday 6 April

David Asquith stood quietly on the beach of Fortuna Bay anxiously assessing the weather. The whole waterfront was crowded with thousands of king penguins and the racket was terrific, like the braying of huge herds of sheep. A colony of fur seals gambolled playfully in the water in front of him and, on the grassy hillside behind, a small herd of reindeer grazed quietly, ignoring his existence. There had been no sign of the Argentinians.

It had remained reasonably fine for the four days since the occupation of the island but he could sense a change coming. There were streaky clouds above the mountain tops and an icy chill in the breeze. In their small way the remaining fids scattered on the island were beginning to get their act together and fight back. It was possible to talk on the radio to the closest British Antarctic Survey base at Signy Island. They were uncertain whether or not their transmissions were being monitored by the Argentinians but, by keeping their messages short and sharp, considered it would be difficult for prying ears to understand them.

David knew that two of the Lyell Glacier fids, Damian Saunders and Ian Barker had decided to climb Mount Hodges, a mountain behind the whaling station at Grytviken, in an attempt to spy out what the Argentinians were up to. Further down the coast at St Andrews Bay the other party were taking a look at the Barff Peninsula to see whether there was any enemy activity, and all this information was being passed on to the base commander at Signy.

Earlier that morning David had discussed the situation with

Alison on the radio. 'The weather's on the turn, Alison, it's today or Seb and I might well be bogged down for weeks before there's another chance to come over to Antarctic Bay. It can't be that difficult – as the crow flies it's only about six miles but the only reasonable route seems to be the one that Shackleton took almost seventy years ago and that's almost twice the distance.'

'It looks OK from here, David,' Alison said, trying not to sound too enthusiastic. 'The lower end of the Crean Glacier looks impractical. Anna and I walked up yesterday; there's an easy way up onto the Murray Snowfield. We found the place where Shackleton must have come over. It's steep but crevasse-free. We'll come up and meet you there. It will be great to see you, David.'

'OK, we'll be away within the hour.' He went off the air.

It seemed amazing to David that in all the ensuing years Shackleton's route across the island had never been repeated. 'It can't be that difficult,' he thought. Like all the fids he had read and re-read the account of Shackleton's crossing of the island.

Shackleton and his two companions, badly equipped and half starved with absolutely no knowledge of the terrain, had taken only thirty-six hours to traverse South Georgia. Surely he and Seb, with their excellent modern equipment, could easily cover half that distance in a day. They were fit and healthy and although Seb was no mountaineer David felt confident in himself and his ability to look after him. The weather was his adversary: he knew that Shackleton had been extraordinarily lucky having fine weather for the whole crossing. On the face of it the weather looked OK for today and if Alison could meet them on the way and navigate back to the hut that would be a real bonus.

The previous evening he had once again read over Frank Worsley's extraordinary account of Shackleton's crossing. Stranded in the Weddell Sea when his ship, the original HMS *Endurance*, sank crushed in the ice, he and his crew floated north for almost fourteen hundred miles on the floes. They lived through a polar winter until, finally, after fifteen months, it was possible to escape the pack ice in the ship's three lifeboats. They sailed north to

Elephant Island, a scarcely visited, mountainous and glaciated island at the northernmost tip of the Antarctic Peninsula. Realising that being found was out of the question, Shackleton and five companions left the ship's crew on the beach, living on penguins and seabirds, and in the tiny ship's lifeboat, the *James Caird*, made one of the most gruelling sea journeys ever undertaken in an open boat, crossing eight hundred miles of the Antarctic Ocean to South Georgia.

With incredibly accurate navigation by Frank Worsley, the New Zealander captain of the *Endurance*, they made the crossing in sixteen days only to founder in King Haakon Bay on the western and wrong side of the island. The *James Caird* was de-masted and damaged. For the next ten days the half-starved and exhausted men rested under the upturned boat, living on baby albatross and seal meat, waiting for the weather to improve.

At the time little was known about the hinterland of the island but, with no choice, Shackleton, Frank Worsley and Tom Crean set out to cross it on foot. Harry McNeish, the ship's carpenter, fixed wood screws into the soles of their boots to give them some purchase on the ice, a sort of primitive crampon. McNeish, Tim Macarty and the bosun Vincent remained with the damaged boat.

The thirty-six-hour crossing of the unmapped range of mountains, to reach the whaling station at Stromness, was a feat of superhuman courage and endurance. At one point in falling darkness the three men sat on their rope as a makeshift sledge and slid down a mountainside in a do-or-die attempt to reach the glaciers on the east side of the island.

In Frank Worsley's words:

In the darkness it was impossible to see whether the slope steepened to a precipice or eased out onto the level so dim and so far below. It looked like the latter, so again Shackleton said: 'We'll try it.' Each coiling our share of the rope beneath us for chaffing gear, I straddled behind Sir Ernest, holding his shoulder. Crean did the same to me, and so, locked together, we let go. I was never more scared in my life than for the first few seconds. The speed was terrific. I think we all gasped at that hair-raising shoot into darkness. Crean had hard work to prevent the short-handled adze coming round and cutting us. Then to our joy, the slope curved out, and we shot into a bank of soft snow. We estimated that we had shot down a mile in two or three minutes, and had lowered our altitude by two or three thousand feet. We stood up and shook hands – very pleased with ourselves – until we inspected our trousers! Bad enough before, they were in rags now. No more glissades! We really couldn't afford it.

It must have been a terrifying experience, David thought, remembering that they had still had hours of toil ahead of them to reach Stromness whaling station. How sad that although through Shackleton's relentless determination not a single man from the expedition was lost, some, including Tim Macarty, were to die very soon in the horrors and carnage of the First World War, which had broken out on the first day of their expedition more than two years previously. David guessed that he and Seb should make it to Antarctic Bay easily in a day. Unlike Shackleton and his men they were well equipped and reasonably fit.

The previous day, Alison and Anna had reconnoitred the route from their side. They had found the lower end of the Crean Glassier very crevassed and virtually impassable but discovered an easy way inland up onto the Murray Snowfield. This was a longer way round but relatively crevasse free and easy going. From here it seemed pretty obvious that the way that Shackleton had found passed a small group of peaks called the Tridents. The two women climbed to a col and looked down a steep slope onto the Crean Glacier. This, Alison was certain, was where Shackleton and his men, in desperation, had sat on their rope and sledged off into the night. It looked amazingly steep for about five hundred feet and very icy. Not difficult for an experienced mountaineer but Anna had been horrified at the thought of climbing down. 'Imagine sliding down that!' she muttered.

'Don't worry,' Alison had said, smiling. 'David will come up that without much bother. We can fix a rope for them down the steepest part at the top and we can haul Seb up the hard bit if he needs help.'

David and Seb left Fortuna Bay by going up the Konig Glacier and then up a steep scramble over a low ridge onto the Fortuna Glacier. The scenery was spectacular, the huge glacier, flanked by snow-capped peaks, flowing into the open sea and discharging icebergs as far as the eye could see. They stopped and took gravity and magnetic readings every half hour. It only took a few minutes and the short stops were a welcome rest. Progress on the Fortuna Glacier was much slower than they expected, and their feet kept breaking through a thin crust on the snow's surface. There were a lot of crevasses to skirt and David realised that when Shackleton had come through it had been later in the season and the crevasses would have been iced over. By lunchtime they reached the high point of the Fortuna and could see the long thousand foot descent to the Crean Glacier. Sebastian was beginning to tire; they were about half-way but still had the long slog up the Crean to where they hoped to meet up with Alison and Anna.

Lenticular clouds were forming over the mountains, huge, beautiful flying saucer shapes, the herald of wind. Already, great plumes of spindrift were streaming off the mountain tops and there was a noticeable change in the temperature.

'We'd better get a move on, Seb. The weather's on the change. It's fairly sheltered down here but it's going to be windy when we get up on the Tridents. The women will be very exposed up there.'

Sebastian groaned inside; he was feeling the strain badly and weighed down by his pack, but he managed a cheerful grin and tramped off behind David. In this kind of terrain distance on the map seemed to bear no relationship to the ground they were covering. It was no more than a couple of miles to the foot of the Tridents but David knew it was going to take at least two hours in this soft snow. They were now looking down into Antarctic Bay and could see the broken icefall and massive crevasses at its lower end – so near and yet so far. Alison had been spot on; there was no way down the Crean. After crossing the glacier and a low ridge, the head of a large snow basin and the Tridents came into view with a steep snow slope up to a little col, which must be where Shackleton and his companions had slid down. It was much steeper than David had expected.

'My God! They must have been tanking when they slid down there!' Seb said, shaking his head. 'I wonder how far they shot down the glacier?'

'Worsley said miles; it must have been utterly terrifying. I think we should dump the instruments here, Seb. Alison and I can come over and get them when the weather improves.'

Sebastian didn't argue, so they cached the equipment and with lighter loads began the long plod up to the headwall of the glacier, David breaking trail and Sebastian struggling behind him. Spindrift was now streaming through the saddle at the top of the slope and there was no sign of the two women. I hope they headed back, David thought. It must be wild up there. If this gets any worse it's going to be the devil's own job to find our way down to Antarctic Bay.

That wasn't the worst of his concern. Seb was visibly tiring and their pace was slowing dramatically. They stopped as the slope steepened and put on their crampons, the first real gusts of wind now beginning to hit them. Seb sank into the snow exhausted.

'Not so far now, Seb. Once we're up this it's downhill all the way,' he lied.

They were out of the soft snow now and the steep slope curved up above them into the spindrift and cloud. The sky had turned ice grey, the mountains vanished into mist and it was hard to tell if it was snowing or just drift in the wind. David kicked steps steadily up the slope running a rope length at a time, anchoring to his ice axe at the top of each pitch and cutting a small stance. He brought up Seb on a tight rope, getting more anxious about his companion the higher they got. By now the wind was shrieking over the top of the saddle and a constant pile of drifting snow was pouring on to them. In the blasting wind it was hard to breathe.

'Sorry, Dave, I'm absolutely knackered.' Sebastian collapsed onto the stance alongside him, clearly in some distress, his face and beard plastered in snow and ice. It was obvious that he was showing signs of exposure, the dangerous consequence of cold and exhaustion.

'Not far, Seb, we should be able to dig in somewhere once we get over the saddle but we can't stop here.' Huge gusts of wind were now buffeting them. David was feeling less than confident himself; in this wind there was no way they could get the tent up even if they found a possible site. It was pointless going back – the only way seemed to be up and over and then look for shelter. Leaving his friend on the stance, he crawled up the steep upper part of the slope, his crampons scraping on the now icy surface, spindrift pouring down and almost suffocating him. How on earth was he going to get Seb up this?

In the gloom, he almost missed the rope. It was hanging down from the col, almost invisible in the snow. With great relief he tied himself onto it and cut a large stance, anchored himself and then began hauling Sebastian up to join him. He seemed to take an age to struggle up and seemed not to comprehend that they now had some kind of lifeline to the top. The rope suddenly went tight and David felt a firm pull. Incredibly, somebody was up there in the shrieking storm. With a mixture of relief, anger and disbelief he began the final pitch. What on earth were the women doing out in these conditions? As he reached the last fifty feet, the angle steepened. In the blasting wind he was totally blind and the drifting snow stung his face. Mostly he climbed with his eyes closed, and then there was a slight lip and he was over the top onto almost level ground.

Alison was sitting in a shallow trench just behind the rim; she had built a wall of snow blocks around the edge and was tucked well in, sheltered from the wind, the rope firmly around her waist. David had never been more relieved to see anybody in his life.

'Hi, David, what kept you?' she asked brightly, grinning at him.

He fell into the rough shelter and hugged her. 'Seb's all in, we've got to get him up quickly. Where's Anna?'

'We've dug a snow hole on the other side, it's only a couple of hundred yards away, and she's over there now. Come on, let's get Seb up.'

Painstakingly slowly, they hauled in the rope. After some minutes Sebastian crawled over the edge. The light was beginning to fade as they left the small shelter and forced their way into the gale over the saddle, supporting the tired man as best they could.

The snow hole was dug into a bank behind some rocks. Anna was inside, still enlarging it, a grin on her face. 'Welcome to the Trident hotel!' she said, as the snow-covered trio crawled into the shelter. They stripped Seb of his snow-covered wind-proofs and had him in his sleeping bag within minutes. He was all in, but smiled with relief at the unexpected shelter. A pot of hot tea was boiling on the Primus stove and a warm fug filled the snow cave. It was difficult to believe that outside the gale was shrieking with hurricane force. The two women were like mother hens fussing, and David sat comfortably in the corner relaxing and letting the fatigue take its course.

Alison told her story. 'We set off after we spoke on the radio this morning and easily followed yesterday's tracks and reached the Tridents by lunchtime with ages to spare. I had the idea of coming down the big slope to meet you but it was windier than we expected so we started building the snowhole to fill in the time and give ourselves some shelter. Anna spotted you crossing the Crean Glacier ages ago and realised that you were moving very slowly. It was getting windy, blowing up dreadfully, so we dug out the trench at the top of the slope and built a wall of snowblocks. We've been taking turns waiting at the top for the last couple of hours. It was getting obvious that we weren't going to get back to Antarctic Bay tonight so we got to work on improving the snowhole. We began to get anxious about an hour ago when the wind really began to blast and there was no sign of you. I thought we might have missed you in the storm.'

'I'm glad you were there. It was much harder going across the Fortuna Glacier than I expected and there were far more crevasses than Worsley mentioned in his book. The glacier may have changed quite a lot in the last seventy years. Seb did really well but the last slope up the Crean Glacier was a real slog!'

'It's an easy walk back down the Murray Snowfield,' Anna said. 'About three miles, downhill all the way and there don't seem to be many crevasses in the snowfield. Once off the ice it's an easy walk down to the hut. We should be able to make it in almost any weather.'

Sebastian was fast asleep, tucked up in his bag. The other three sat in their sleeping bags drinking tea and talking over the strange situation that they were in. Outside, the storm raged. It seemed unlikely that there would be immediate rescue. Alison reckoned that there was enough food at Antarctic Bay for about five weeks, more if they were careful, and if necessary there were seal and penguins in huge supply. It was little more than a couple of hours' walk down to the hut in Antarctic Bay. The *Endurance* was somewhere close by, hidden among the icebergs, and she knew where they were, and there seemed to be no immediate threat from the Argentinians.

Tired and relieved after the exhausting day, they dozed into a fitful sleep. David woke during the night to find Alison's face against his. He could feel her body in the sleeping bag alongside him and her gentle breathing. Her eyes flickered open and they found themselves staring at each other. Almost without thinking, he leaned over and kissed her. She smiled and moved towards him and they lay quietly, lips touching, oblivious of their surroundings until they finally drifted into deep sleep.

32

April Fools, Thursday 1 April 1982

On the evening of 1 April, as the Argentinian fleet massed off East Falkland at the entrance to Port Stanley Harbour, Major Guy Sheridan, second in command of 42 Commando Royal Marines, returned with his wife and daughter to a quiet farmhouse in the Pyrenees where they were taking a well-earned holiday. He had just got back from three months' intensive Arctic warfare training with his unit in Norway. Pinned to the farmhouse door was a telegram asking him to phone the British Embassy in Paris. Suspecting an April Fools' joke, he nevertheless made the call and received the unwelcome and curt message: '*You must return to your unit immediately.*' Within the hour the family was motoring furiously across France, sleeping for a short time in a field alongside the car and listening in consternation to the BBC News as the Falkland invasion unfurled.

Lieutenant Mike Hanna RN was getting married in New Hampshire, USA to the most beautiful girl he had ever seen. His family had flown out the previous day and had just met their prospective in-laws. His best man and fellow officer, Lieutenant Robert Norman, had already received the telegram and had booked their flights home without telling Mike the news. The wedding took place on time but the reception came to a sudden and unexpected end as the best man gave a quick speech, read out the telegrams and finished off by saying, 'Right, Mike, the flight's booked for twenty-one hundred hours, you've got two hours to consummate!'

From near and far the call was going out ordering servicemen back to their units. The British military machine was awakening from its lethargy and doing what it does best, improvising and preparing for the worst. Within the week some form of organisation was taking shape. Admiral Sir John Fieldhouse had become the commander with overall responsibility for the operation, and the relatively junior Admiral Sandy Woodward took command of the Task Force and was now on-board his flagship, HMS *Glamorgan*, and, in tandem with the aircraft carrier HMS *Hermes*, was heading south. Across the North Atlantic ships were spread in a huge muddle; RAF VC10s and the giant Belfast G-BEPS freight aircraft were flying helicopters, armaments and men. Two giant passenger ships, *QE2* and *Canberra*, had been requisitioned as troop ships and were preparing at Southampton to take on their unexpected cargo. Everything was heading towards Ascension Island, a tiny atoll in mid-Atlantic, just south of the equator. The small American garrison who leased the island from Britain had their quiet life turned upside down as the number of flights they would normally receive in a year started to arrive on a daily basis.

As the battle fleet headed south the seriousness of the situation began to sink in. Admiral Sandy Woodward spoke to his sailors. 'Up till now you have seen fit to take the queen's shilling. Now you must stand by to front up and earn it the hard way. There is no possibility for anyone to opt out now – this is what you joined the navy for.'

There's a saying among sailors at times like this that adequately sums up their feelings: 'You shouldn't have joined up if you can't take a joke.'

33

Bickleigh Barracks, Plymouth, Tuesday 6 April 1982

At Bickleigh Barracks just outside Plymouth, on the morning of Tuesday 6 April, Major-General Sir Jeremy Moore watched, with some satisfaction, as the long line of heavily armed men trooped past him taking the salute. In an earlier incarnation he had been the commander of this same troop himself. Outside the gates lines of buses waited to transport the entire brigade to the awaiting *Canberra* at Southampton.

In a moment of high drama the unit's commander, Lieutenant-Colonel Nick Vaux, requested the general's permission to leave the parade ground. There was a curt nod from the general.

'Forty-two Commando, to the South Atlantic, quick march!'

With a crash of boots the grinning troop of men marched smartly out through the barrack gates. To their surprise the one hundred and thirty-two men of 'M' Company at the rear of the column were ordered, 'Right turn,' as they left the square and were marched away from the main force to the station gymnasium where Colonel Vaux addressed them.

'You are not sailing on *Canberra*,' he told the surprised men. 'You will be operating independently of 42 Commando under the command of Major Guy Sheridan. You are to be flown ahead of the main force to Ascension Island. This is a high security operation; there must be no telephone calls. You are confined to barracks awaiting your flight. I'm sorry but there will be no questions.'

The disappointed troops had been looking forward to a pleasant sail through the tropics on the luxury liner. Nobody as

170

yet seriously imagined that Britain would go to war with Argentina; most thought it was more likely to be a navy skirmish of some kind.

34

Northwood, London, Wednesday 7 April 1982

Morning prayers

Peter Bacon-Smith took the tube and then a short taxi ride through the northern suburbs of London to HMS *Warrior* at Northwood, the Command Centre of the British navy. It was also the HQ of the NATO fleet and he noticed a conglomeration of American and European uniforms as he approached the modern-looking brick building. It didn't look much like a ship to him.

Nothing had prepared him for the surprise awaiting as he was ushered through the security screen and taken in the lift down into the huge underground bunker known as the 'Hole'. He entered what looked like a large theatre, the floor of which was filled with lines of desks littered with computers. It was three stories high. The top level was a large balcony surrounding the whole auditorium; this was more palatial than the lower level and filled with comfortable seats, looking down onto a huge electronic screen twenty-feet high and almost twice the width. At mid-height at one end was a large stage-like platform that looked as if it should house an orchestra. Here sat Admirals Leach and Woodhouse with their various aides. There was a general hubbub from what Peter estimated to be a couple of hundred senior uniformed officers; they were mostly navy but there was a scattering of air-force blue and army khaki among them.

All eyes were on the big screen where a moving map of the world's oceans was the centre of attention; there were flashing indicators that presumably marked the position of ships. The place was like an underground version of the Kennedy Space Centre at a moon launch and much the same atmosphere prevailed. Here was the nerve centre of the British navy as the admirals checked the readiness, serviceability and fuel situation of the fleet, as well as the known positions of thousands of ships around the world. So this is morning prayers, he thought as he watched, intrigued, as the admirals orchestrated the movements of the flotilla of ships down the North Atlantic towards Ascension Island.

Peter was shown into a room at the far end of the 'Hole' with a 'No Entry' sign on the door. Two smartly dressed Wrens were sitting at computers and one of the women offered him a coffee and said that he was expected. He could hear the noise from the Hole faintly in the background. After a few minutes Admiral Leach arrived and introduced Admiral Sir John Fieldhouse and a younger man, Commander Denis Davies.

'Denis is an instructor from the Maritime Tactical School, Peter,' Leach said. 'He's a torpedo and anti-submarine expert but for this operation we have a new job for him. We'd like you to liaise with him directly with all the information you can get us about South Georgia.'

Admiral Fieldhouse smiled. 'We're taking everything to do with South Georgia off the screens: the fewer people who know about this, the better. Denis will brief you fully about what is happening, this room is to be the operations cell and nobody gets in here without his sanction. It's his job to put together a plan to retake South Georgia. We've codenamed this *Operation Paraquat*; it was *Parakeet* but somehow a weed killer seems more apt don't you think?'

'How many ships are involved?' Peter asked.

'We're dreadfully short; I need most of the fleet to deal with the Argentinian navy,' Admiral Fieldhouse said. 'I've put the operation under the command of Captain Brian Young, HMS *Antrim*; he's a personal friend of mine and very reliable. *Antrim*'s a county-class guided-missile destroyer and very fast. Captain Young is still in the dark about this operation but has been sent ahead of the main fleet to Ascension Island. The only other warship I have available is HMS *Plymouth*; she's an elderly Type 12 frigate but her captain, David Redmond, is very sound. Then of course there's *Endurance*; she's not really a warship at all but has better communications than the others and a satellite navigation system. Captain Barker's a bit of a firebrand and he knows South Georgia like the back of his hand.'

Peter nodded uncertainly: three ships didn't sound much of a war fleet to him.

'I'm sending RFA *Tidespring*, one of the big fleet tankers down with them; they'll be a long way out on a limb and fuel will be one of their biggest problems. The tankers are vulnerable, particularly to submarines, and we're banking on the Argies being more concerned with the Falkland Islands and not having a welcoming committee waiting for us.

'For the moment we've sent one of our supply ships, RFA *Fort Austin* ahead of the fleet to restock *Endurance*,' Admiral Leach said. 'The poor buggers are just about starving and very short of fuel. They'll meet up in the next two or three days. We have a unit of SAS on-board *Fort Austin* and I had thought they might be able to mount a swift counterattack on Grytviken but the risk seems too high. If we lose *Endurance* we lose our communications. I'm also hoping that the nuclear submarine HMS *Conqueror* can be spared to go down and have a look to see what we will be facing.'

'As yet we have no proper plan,' Commander Davies said. 'So far a company from 42 Commando have been sent ahead to Ascension to be taken on-board *Antrim* and *Tidespring* and we can get the SAS from *Fort Austin*. We'll just have to make it up as we go along. The scary part is going to be getting these ships away from Ascension Island with nobody knowing.'

'I'll find out what I can,' Peter said thoughtfully. 'I think my first port of call should be at the British Antarctic Survey HQ at Cambridge. There are still some scientists on South Georgia and we may be able to get in touch with them and find out what's happening on the island.'

As the meeting broke up Admiral Leach drew Peter aside. 'We have a big problem: the Argentinian services are equipped with French Aerospatiale Exocet missiles. They are the same type that we use but our defence systems are not good against them. Can you find out how many they have and if there's any way of stopping them getting more?'

Peter said he would do what he could. Now they tell me, he thought anxiously as he took the lift up from the Hole. It sounds as if the Argies have a way to blow us out of the water and we have no way of stopping them.

He took the train to Cambridge that afternoon and walked past the beautiful old university buildings up Madingly Road to the Antarctic Survey HQ, a modern building in attractive grounds. He was ushered into an office with Director Dick Laws and his deputy Dr Ray Adie. Both men were scientists and very concerned about the whereabouts of their staff.

'This is a non-political scientific organisation,' Dick Laws told him flatly. 'We're already being accused of moving troops on our ship, the *John Biscoe*, and information gathering could well be construed as spying. At the moment we're trying to negotiate with the Argentinians through the Red Cross to rescue our staff from the island and we may have to ask them to surrender themselves. We have no idea what has happened to our people at King Edward Point.'

'I assure you that the Foreign Office is doing everything it can to get your people home and of course we don't want them to spy for us but we do need to know about the island. I can't tell you what's being planned but we must gather whatever information we can in case we have to mount some kind of rescue operation.'

'We'll tell you what we can as long as it doesn't compromise our staff,' Doctor Laws said. 'Communications are very difficult now that we've lost our radio station at Port Stanley. You must remember that we're still operating our bases in Antarctica and there is a worry that the northern bases at Signy and Faraday might be attacked. Our main ship, the *Bransfield*, is down there at the moment. We have her at the edge of the pack ice, south of the sixty-degree parallel. That's inside the Antarctic Treaty area and we don't think that the Argentinians will touch her there. She has quite powerful transmitters on-board and is managing to relay messages back via the BT ship-to-shore network at Portishead and they pass them down to us on the phone lines. The field personnel on South Georgia all have good radios and are sending their messages to Signy Island base, about six hundred miles south of them. David Roots, the base commander, is passing them on to *Bransfield*, at the moment every three hours.'

Peter began to warm to the two scientists as he realised the enormity of the distances across which the BAS directors had to operate and the concern they must be feeling for their missing staff.

Ray Adie smiled bleakly. 'A large number of the *Bransfield* crew are Falkland Islanders and Captain Stewart Lawrence thinks they have been near to mutiny because we haven't allowed the ship to go to the Islands' rescue. We did manage to blank out Stanley Radio when the Argies were issuing orders that no civilian could use a transmitter. The *Bransfield* played the theme music to the film *Born Free* and every time they play the Argentinian national anthem we give them a good blast of "Land of Hope and Glory". It lets the islanders know that we're still with them. So you can see BAS is not popular with the Argentinians.'

'You'll be visited by a lot of military people in the next few weeks,' Peter warned. 'They won't be able to tell you what's going on but I assure you your people won't be put at risk. If you can persuade them not to surrender it will be a big help. We don't want them to be used as a human shield or be in the way if we make an attack.'

'One of our parties is at the Lyell Glacier, only five miles from Grytviken, and very short of food. The hut is only seven-feet square, it's very cold and one of them has a kidney complaint. They've been discussing their situation with us and considering their options. I'll try to persuade them to hold out but ultimately the decision has to be their own.'

Peter agreed. He left Cambridge feeling much happier that he would get the information he needed. There were people at BAS who knew the island intimately and a way of contacting the people their. His staff would get to work correlating everything that they could find out. He would now turn his attention to Exocet.

35

Grytviken, South Georgia, Friday 9 April

Captain Tombetta's hasty departure from South Georgia had left Grytviken woefully lacking in men and of equipment, most of which was twenty miles round the coast at Leith Harbour, with the main garrison under the command of Alfredo Astiz. Almost every window in the base was broken. The men patched them up as best they could but materials to fix them were just not available. Worse still, the base generator wouldn't work. Hugo suspected ruefully that one of the British marines had sabotaged it when they were allowed to collect their belongings. The place was freezing cold and draughty.

Hugo had been slightly feverish for the first few days but his wound was healing well. He relied heavily on Lieutenant Tono Cassin, the young officer commanding the Special Forces group. The first few days had been spent setting up defences. They had booby-trapped the landing stage in much the same way that Keith Mills' marines had done, and they'd mined the most likely landing beaches and the tracks leading to Hope Point and the whaling station. They set up rocket launching and machine gun sites overlooking the cove. It seemed woefully inadequate. Hugo asked for reinforcements but the only means of transport they had was the landingcraft at Leith Harbour and Astiz refused to risk it across the open sea. The BAS cutter *Albatross* failed all attempts to start her. The general feeling among the men was that the British would be highly unlikely to return.

A week after they had occupied the base, Lieutenant Cassin came to see Hugo. Like himself and most of the men, he had the beginnings of a beard. He looked tired and uncomfortable.

'Sir, I'm having trouble with the men; they aren't used to this kind of cold. If we don't do something to make things more comfortable we will be courting trouble. My commandos are fine, they're used to roughing it, but the ordinary ratings are inexperienced and not used to this.'

'What have you got in mind, Tono?' Hugo asked.

'I think we should chop up the big table in the common room; there's a load of wood in it. We should have a fire and a party of some kind. There's plenty of food and drink. It will cheer them up.'

It seemed sacrilege; the table was a work of art and must weigh almost a ton. Shackleton House had obviously been a pleasant home before the invasion but was now a miserable wreck. They had expected to occupy a fully operational Antarctic base and live in reasonable comfort until the diplomatic situation was sorted out. Instead they were camped in a draughty, freezing shed, the triple-glazed windows broken and roughly boarded up, and already the floorboards had been removed from some of the rooms for firewood.

Reluctantly, he nodded. 'Yes, it's a good idea; see what you can find to make it a pleasant evening.' He offered Tono a cigarette.

'How long do you think we are going to be here?' Tono asked. All of them had been listening to the news that the British navy was putting together a large fleet that was already heading south across the Atlantic.

'I don't know. We didn't expect the British to retaliate. I had a signal from Admiral Anaya yesterday saying that he thinks they are bluffing. The Americans have sent General Alexander Haig to mediate and he's in Buenos Aires at the moment. I expect it will all be over in a few days. The Malvinas garrison is being reinforced by thousands of our troops; I can't imagine that they will be able to dislodge such a large number of our men.'

'What about us being attacked here, sir? We have sentries

watching round the clock but they are freezing to death and we have to rotate them so often that I haven't got enough men.'

Hugo thought for a moment. 'There's no sign of enemy ships in the area, Teniente. I think the British have plenty on their plate without worrying about us. Any attack is likely to come from the sea. You can cut out some of the sentries at night. Make sure that there is a lookout at Hope Point all the time, though, just in case.'

Tono smiled with relief. 'Shouldn't we be doing something about the British scientists on the island?' he asked.

'There isn't much we can do at the moment,' Hugo said. 'We planned to arrest them when we arrived but the ships had to take off in a hurry. So we have no means of getting to them. The helicopter is away and all we have is the Survey cutter and nobody can get the engine to start. The British have been trying to negotiate for one of their ships to pick them up but Teniente Astiz won't allow them near. I'm sure we'll pick them up when one of our ships arrive. He thinks they might make useful hostages if we are attacked.'

Lieutenant Cassin nodded with a look of distaste. 'I wonder how much food they have? They are probably better off where they are than in the hands of "El Rubio". Are the stories about him true, sir?'

Hugo winced. 'I'm sure they're exaggerated. He's a highly efficient officer specially chosen for this operation.' He cut the conversation short, not wishing to be drawn in. He guessed that Astiz had been very involved in the general's activities during the dirty war. His past career must be protecting him – he knew too much. Hugo shuddered to think of what had happened in the Naval Mechanics College during the last few years. If Astiz was indicted for the war crimes he was accused of his would not be the only head to roll.

That evening they built a huge fire in the bar and the entire garrison held a party. It was a strange situation. King Edward Point base was a wreck. Almost everything that could be burned was used, and the beautiful table was no more, but heat had returned. For the first time since his arrival Hugo was warm. He and Lieutenant Cassin sat watching the antics of the troops as they enjoyed their first real break since the landing.

During the evening they received a signal from Buenos Aires. The submarine *Santa Fe* had left Mar del Plata that afternoon and would be arriving with reinforcements, more weapons and mail. A spontaneous cheer went up from the men. Hugo realised that at last the junta had acknowledged that Foreign Minister Costa Mendez was wrong in his assumption that the British would not retaliate.

There was a curt message for Hugo from Admiral Anaya. '*You will return to Argentina on-board* Santa Fe *and report to me in Buenos Aires as soon as possible.*'

Hugo sighed with relief. The situation he found himself in was not what he had anticipated and it would never have happened but for the unexpected strong defence of the base by the Royal Marines. He was a naval strategist, and wasn't comfortable running a garrison. Operating under the command of Alfredo Astiz, who he outranked, was particularly galling. He wanted to be back and involved with the Malvinas defence. With luck he would be home to see his wife Maria within the next few weeks. There was little he could do in this godforsaken place. He wondered how his son, Raul, was managing on his first posting to the battle cruiser *General Belgrano*. The navy must be preparing to take on the British fleet. With luck he would be home in time to play his part.

He opened a bottle of Scotch whisky, liberated from the British, and poured Tono and himself a liberal glass.

'I think we'll have this without ice, Tono,' he said, grinning cheerfully.

36

Antarctic Bay, South Georgia, Monday 19 April 1982

Long before dawn that morning four fully tanked-up RAF 'Victors' lumbered into the sky above the airstrip on Ascension Island and struggled up to their ideal altitude of fifty thousand feet. These were old remnants of the 'V' force, from a time in the sixties when Britain kept an atomic bomb permanently in the air as its nuclear deterrent. Old and subsonic, these giant four-engine monsters were converted to long range in-flight refuelling tankers and were the only aircraft available with sufficient range to give Captain Brian Young on HMS *Antrim* and the *Paraquat* cell at Northwood the information they required about Argentinian warships guarding the waters around South Georgia.

Two hours later, as the sun rose out of a cloud-covered sea, two of the planes transferred all their spare fuel to the lead pair and peeled off for home. Another two hours and the third aircraft transferred its precious cargo and turned back to Ascension Island. Squadron Leader John Elliot and his crew were now on their own, still flying south-east into the sunrise on what was to be the longest reconnaissance flight in history.

At 9.20 a.m. Elliot's vapour trail was spotted through a gap in the clouds by officers watching on-board HMS *Antrim* as the *Paraquat* fleet approached South Georgia. Over the island Elliot dropped to eighteen thousand feet and switched on his cameras and radar surveillance equipment. Flying in a huge triangle, he was able to record a vast area of almost two hundred thousand square miles of ocean. Apart from the *Paraquat* fleet there was not another ship or iceberg anywhere within the north surrounds of the island. Turning north and urgently watching the fuel gauge, he started the long flight home. Long after sunset and after almost fifteen hours' flying, Victor XL193 landed safely back at Ascension Island.

David Asquith and Sebastian Holmes spotted the aircraft that morning as they surveyed the beach at Cape Constance, the northern tip of Antarctic Bay. David swung up the theodolite sight and watched the aircraft fly down the island. Other than the two women it was the first sign of life they had seen since the occupation. Looking out to sea had become a habit, ship watching, but there was never anything to see. They kept constant radio contact with Paul Goodall-Copestake at Bird Island, the small field hut on the north-west tip of South Georgia where messages were relayed to David Roots, the Antarctic base commander at Signy Island. Other than that there was the radio, and they listened avidly to any news they could gather, mostly from the BBC World Service.

The epic night in the snowhole at the Tridents had been uneventful. The wind had dropped during the night and they made it down to the hut in Antarctic Bay the following morning without difficulty. There just wasn't enough space in the hut for four, and it was cramped and uncomfortable. To ease matters, at night the men moved outside into a tent, not an ideal situation. Two days later David and Alison climbed back over the Murray Snowfield and descended the steep slope onto the Crean Glacier to retrieve Sebastian's instruments. In perfect conditions it had been an easy day and the two climbers were alone together for the first time.

'This is one hell of a way to begin a relationship,' David muttered in exasperation. 'A freezing tent at night and expecting to be arrested at any moment by a bunch of crazy Argies!'

They looked at each other and then burst into laughter and hugged each other. The situation seemed ludicrous.

It was now a fortnight since the invasion. In the early days they had been expecting to be arrested at any time but to their surprise nothing had happened. They knew that the BAS flagship, the RRS *Bransfield*, was cruising around the edge of the Antarctic ice, negotiating to pick them up, and they assumed that repatriation might happen at any time.

So with little else to do they continued with their fieldwork. Seb began a detailed gravity and magnetic survey of Antarctic Bay, David lugging the theodolite around after him, working the delicate readings onto the map. Anna and Alison unpacked their equipment and got on with the filming. The weather was growing colder by the day and it was difficult to work outside for long periods. The amount of wildlife was extraordinary and made wonderful film but with freezing fingers trying to work delicate cameras it was painstakingly slow. But they had all expected to be picked up at any time and there was a general air of optimism.

All this changed when, two days earlier, on 17 April, negotiations with the Argentinians had reached an all-time low and that morning the BAS informed Captain Stewart Lawrence that he should quit the Antarctic and take the *Bransfield* to Ascension Island. It had become clear that if she approached South Georgia she risked being sunk or captured. Unaware of the approaching *Paraquat* force, the captain and crew believed they were leaving the people on South Georgia to their fate. Horrified, Stewart spoke with them over the radio and indicated that he and his Falkland Islander crew were very reluctant to leave.

'Everything possible will be done in the UK to arrange evacuation and repatriation. We will be back next summer or earlier. My personal best wishes to you all. May God be with you.'

There was a stunned silence around the radio in the tiny hut and then Seb muttered in consternation: 'Next summer, my God. I was expecting them next week!'

David laughed. 'Well, this is going to be interesting. We have three weeks' food left and that leaves five months until the penguins start laying their eggs again.'

The radio sprang to life again as each of the field parties came on air. Alison was amazed at everyone's resilience. Not one of them believed that they would be left stranded. They knew that a British fleet was building up at Ascension Island but had no idea if or when it would engage the Argentinians. The Americans, they knew, were trying to negotiate a peaceful settlement. Alison listened to Cindy Buxton at St Andrews Bay calmly saying that they would get on with their work. The building party at Bird Island said they had plenty to do. Only at the Lyell Glacier was there a serious problem.

Trefor Edwards spoke to David. 'We're only five miles from Grytviken and are very short of food,' he said. 'This hut's in a terrible state and we are unequipped to last for long. One of us is sick and we have no means of heating the hut. The practical thing seems to be to hand ourselves over to the Argies.'

'Aw, Trev!' David broke in with his broad New Zealand drawl. 'How long can you hang out? We've no idea what's happened to Steve and the rest of the boys. The Argies sound a trigger-happy lot to me, you'll be better off where you are.'

David Roots, the Signy base commander, came on air. 'Trefor, the decision is yours but I keep getting signals from BAS in Cambridge asking us to hang on. They seem very keen for us not to surrender. I'm sure that something's going on.'

There was a long pause while the men discussed the situation. Earlier in the occupation Trefor and Damian Saunders had climbed Mount Hodges and spied down on the Argentinian positions and nobody knew the situation better than them.

'OK, we'll hang on for a few more days but I'm not kidding you, we're shitting ourselves here. If the weather gets much colder we can't hang on and an Argentinian patrol is bound to find us sooner or later.'

'Wait as long as you can,' David Roots said, as emphatically as he could, unable to say on air what he knew. 'The decision is ultimately yours but I'm sure help will come.'

Alison guessed that somewhere the *Endurance* was lurking in the vicinity and the men at Lyell Glacier could not possibly know. She felt helpless, and unable to tell them for fear that they were being monitored. She too had her doubts as she looked at their diminishing food stocks.

'We have only about three weeks' food left in the hut,' she said, voicing everyone's concern. 'We can probably spin that out to five weeks if we're careful. There's the small dump that you left on the beach at Fortuna Bay, David, and a food dump at King Haakon Bay that we could probably get to if things get really serious.'

'We can live here almost indefinitely,' David said. 'Look how Shackleton and his men survived for nearly two years. There's seal and penguin in abundance. We'll just have to take it as it comes.' Seb and Anna exchanged concerned glances.

Spirits reached an all-time low, though surprisingly Sebastian seemed more cheerful the worse things got. Scruffier than ever, he worked on furiously with the gravity survey of Antarctic Bay, keeping David fully occupied. Two days later they were working along the coast when an urgent call from Alison set them dashing back along the beach.

'Seb, David. On the radio. They're OK!' The BBC World Service news was announcing that the Argentinians had freed the scientists and marines captured at Grytviken. They were in Uruguay. The men burst into the hut in time to hear the voice of Lieutenant Keith Mills saying that they had been well treated. Keith sounded tired and guarded. He said that everybody was well, Corporal Nigel Peters was slightly wounded but was recovering, and none of the fids were the worse for their ordeal.

The relief was tremendous; it had been the unasked question on everyone's mind. With soaring spirits they determined to hang on.

Unknown to them not twenty miles away another predator had reached the island. The nuclear submarine HMS *Conqueror* had left her base at Faslane on the river Clyde and dived immediately to deep water. In addition to her crew was a detachment of SBS

(Special Boat Squadron) marine commandos. Travelling at a speed of over thirty miles per hour, she had not surfaced since leaving Scottish waters. It had been an uneventful journey halfway around the world with a slight warming of temperature as they crossed the equator and now noticeably colder in the Antarctic sea. Two days earlier as the RRS *Bransfield* was ordered north she had overtaken the *Paraquat* fleet and was now patrolling the waters of Cumberland Bay.

As David and Seb watched the vapour trail of the RAF Victor, this five-thousand-ton sea monster had slid silently to periscope depth and checked out Grytviken and Leith Harbour. There was little to see, no ships and only slight activity on land. Much relieved, her commander, Christopher Wexford-Brown, ordered her away; fifteen miles off shore she slipped her antenna above the surface. A quick satellite call to Northwood and within minutes Commander Denis Davies in the *Paraquat* cell knew that the coast was clear. All looked well and was running according to plan. As the small group of ships prepared for action they were a hundred and fifty miles north of the island.

As usual in this part of the world all was not as it seemed. Fifteen hundred miles to the south-west in the Bellingshausen Sea the second great Antarctic storm of the season was beginning to accelerate towards the Drake Strait. As the small fleet of ships approached South Georgia the South Atlantic was once again about to demonstrate the forces that nature could unleash.

37

Paraquat flotilla, South Atlantic, Monday 19 April

The main British Task Force made its way slowly south towards Ascension Island, held back politically as General Alexander Haig shuttled around the world between London, Buenos Aires and New York in the American attempt to find a diplomatic solution to the crisis.

The Naval Auxiliary RFA *Fort Austin* had reached Ascension Island ahead of the fleet on 9 April, refuelled and took on-board a combined team of SAS and SBS Special Troops. She had then raced immediately south in a dash to reach HMS *Endurance*, which was heading up the South Atlantic to meet her. There were no plans in the *Paraquat* cell at Northwood as yet but Commander Denis Davies considered it sensible to get the Special Forces forward as quickly as possible.

During the last week the Red Plum, or Red Iceberg as her crew had now christened her, had remained hidden among the bergs in the South Georgia fjords. She was desperately short of food and fuel. The last egg had been ceremoniously eaten a fortnight earlier and Captain Nick Barker had instigated a harsh rationing regime. There was no breakfast, lunch was soup and one roll and there was a small one-course evening meal. The crew had a mean and hungry look about them.

On board the *Fort Austin* Corporal Christian M... SAS climbed up onto the upper deck to get some wind in his face. For good reason surnames of regiment members are kept under strict security. He was medium height with sandy hair cut short. A quiet man in his early thirties he moved with the cat-like grace of a born athlete. He found the slow twisting roll of the ship hard to stomach. The cramped and overloaded sleeping quarters below deck were airless and claustrophobic. There was a lot of sea sickness among the troops.

'Don't worry, mate,' a friendly seaman called. 'You'll be fine when you get on-board *Endurance*; she's as steady as a rock.'

Christian's relief was short lived. They met *Endurance* three days later; and the Red Plum was pitching all over the ocean like a cork in a washing machine. Refuelling was a nightmare, the pump-over taking every bit of the two captains' skill. The salivating crew of *Endurance* watched in horror as the first net full of fresh food was dumped in the sea by a nervous helicopter pilot caught in a down-draught. However, the restocking mission was finally accomplished and the *Fort Austin* turned back to Ascension to service the rest of the *Paraquat* force. The *Endurance* turned back for South Georgia fully laden and carrying the contingent of SAS.

The sailors watched with interest as the Special Forces trained to keep fit on board ship. Some of their feats of strength were incredible but they settled in with the ship's crew and seemed a very ordinary and unassuming bunch of soldiers. But, as one seaman said, 'They seem OK but there's something about the eyes you know, they're different from the rest of us!'

Just after midnight that same morning, under the cover of darkness, the remaining ships of the *Paraquat* force slipped away from Ascension Island. It had been a hectic two days. Major Guy Sheridan and the men of 'M' Company flew in to Ascension and split themselves between the three ships. There had been a frantic rush, what with the loading of men and equipment, cold-weather clothing, weapons and ammunition. The big auxiliary tanker *Tidespring* drained her swimming pool and turned it into a reserve magazine and took on-board a detachment of SBS. A satellite navigation system was removed from HMS *Sheffield* and fitted to

Antrim and the frigate *Plymouth*, not much bigger than *Endurance*, was loaded to the gunnels with men, food, weapons and ammunition.

Soon after they left, a giant Soviet Tupolev TU–95 reconnaissance aircraft crossed their wake but apparently failed to detect them. They caught up with *Endurance* the following day, six hundred miles south. Now well clear in mid-South Atlantic, they were under way, running free and undetected. Back at Northwood in the *Paraquat* cell Commander Davies breathed a sigh of relief.

The first great wandering albatross joined the wakes, gliding effortlessly through the waves only inches above the surface as the four ships ploughed steadily south, slowed by *Endurance*'s maximum speed of only thirteen and a half knots. They still had two thousand miles, a week's steaming, to go and Captain Young was determined to use the time to its best advantage. As their plans formulated almost all the troops and equipment were in the wrong ships for their task in the final attack. The helicopters were constantly in the air cross-decking personnel and stores. They were kitted out with machine guns and painted in dark colours, and the larger Wessex were fitted with strap-on launchers for two-inch rockets, each pod containing fourteen missiles. When not shifting loads they began live aerial target practice. On board the ships the soldiers began weapons drill and a rigorous keep-fit campaign. *Antrim* and *Plymouth* began gunnery exercise. Both ships were fitted with the same twin-turreted 4.5-inch guns. This meant that with both barrels firing each ship could lob three-quarters of a ton of high explosives at a target ten miles away with devastating accuracy, every minute.

On board the ships were three different types of troops. The main assault force of Royal Marines was the 'M' Company of 48 Commandos and with them were two groups of Special Forces from the SAS and SBS. Although they are used to working together, there is a fundamental difference between these two special services: the Special Air Service (SAS) is an army-based regiment with all its traditions while the Special Boat Squadron (SBS) is a naval organisation. It is said that 'the SAS look to the sea from landward while the SBS look to the land from seaward.' It takes bitter determination to join the ranks of either of these elite branches of the armed forces. Unlike normal servicemen they act independently, using their own judgement. Their officers will indicate what must be done, give them an objective and then each man will state his own ideas on the best way to tackle the problem. Their commander was Major Cedric Delves and although junior to both Captain Young and Guy Sheridan, who was in overall command of all land forces, his opinion was constantly sought as the operational plans took shape. In many ways the Special Troops were acting on their own initiative.

The SBS practised launching their Gemini assault boats. Christian watched with professional interest as the men climbed down the ship's side on nets and jumped nimbly into the tiny inflatable craft and admired the skill with which they eased away from the ship. The small boats were vanishing into huge troughs between the waves and almost immediately the outboard motors began to cut out. He could see the men struggling to restart them but water was pouring over the engines as one by one they lost power.

'Those bloody outboards are ancient,' Christian muttered. 'It's no wonder they keep cutting out; they're museum pieces.'

'We've been complaining for years,' said one of the SBS officers who was standing watching with him. 'The government's cut our budget so tight that half our equipment is obsolete.'

Christian nodded in agreement. His personal mountain equipment wasn't much better; time and again they had applied for more modern equipment with absolutely no response. Many of the men bought their own specialised kit. From what he had gathered about South Georgia weather his mountain troop was woefully ill equipped. If the Special Troops were poorly supplied God knows what state the ordinary services were in.

One of the helicopters took off and hovered above the four inflatable boats but the men seemed to be managing and were paddling franticly back towards *Antrim* as she rolled alarmingly in the heavy swell. They all managed to get back and somewhat sheepishly climbed the nets while the Geminis were hoisted back on-board. Christian noticed Captain Young and his officers watching from the bridge with looks of consternation on their faces.

On the morning of 19 April, Christian and the rest of the SAS mountain team were transferred from *Endurance* to *Antrim*. He was sorry to leave the red ship; after the initial shock of her ungainly roll in heavy seas he had enjoyed his time on-board. She was a happy ship and, as one of the crew said to him as they watched the grey-clad destroyers sailing alongside, 'They're in the navy, we're in the Plum.'

It's funny, I feel the same way about the SAS, he thought.

Later that morning a briefing was held on-board *Antrim*. All the senior officers and NCOs were present along with the SAS, SBS and helicopter pilots. The SAS mountain team sat quietly at the back of the wardroom listening to what was being said. There had been a lot of discussion during the last week on where the landings should be and everyone wondered what had been decided.

Captain Young spoke first. A normally quiet man, he commanded the respect of everybody. With the responsibility of the entire operation on his shoulders he found it difficult holding together a mixed team from different services who had never worked together before. He let the various commanders get on and formulate their plans without interference, realising that in this project the navy's role was to get the men into the right position at the right time. He was a cool customer, having trained as a pilot with the Americans on 'Sea Hawks', taken part in attacks over Egypt during the Suez crisis and commanded a 'Sea Vixen' squadron during the 1960s confrontation with Indonesia.

'This is the first British operation to regain our rightful possessions from the Argentinians,' he said, opening the briefing formally. 'Our orders are quite clear. We are to recapture South Georgia with minimum force and loss of life and with as little damage to buildings as is possible to allow a garrison to take over the island in time for the oncoming winter. I need hardly say that failure or a serious bloodbath will seriously jeopardise the diplomatic initiative at present taking place by us and the Americans at the United Nations. A great deal depends on us in the major objective to retake the Falkland Islands.' He indicated to Major Guy Sheridan to take over.

'Our first task is a reconnaissance of the whaling stations,' Sheridan said. 'We have a small amount of intelligence from the scientists still on the island but it is sketchy and unsubstantiated. We think that the garrison between Grytviken and Leith is in the order of one hundred men of the Buzo Tactico Special Forces. If that is the case we have a two to one advantage. From a military point of view we would prefer three to one but with our Special Forces I think the odds don't seem too bad. The only way we can avoid casualties will be to achieve total surprise.'

He walked over to a large-scale map of South Georgia. 'We arrive on the twenty-first, the day after tomorrow, and intend to insert an SAS mountain team by helicopter from *Antrim* onto the Fortuna Glacier. It's the nearest we think we can get without being observed from Leith Harbour. It will be their job to reconnoitre the three whaling stations in Stromness Fjord, particularly Leith. At the same time a team of SBS using Gemini inflatable boats will land, here, at Hound Bay, from HMS *Endurance*.' He indicated on the map. There was an anxious stir among the Boat Squadron, everyone remembering the trouble with the faulty outboards. 'They will have to go on foot through the Sorlings Valley and slip into Cumberland Bay under the Nordenskjold Glacier and see what is happening at King Edward Point. As yet we have no complete plan for the main assault by "M" Company. They remain on board the ship until we have the intelligence but teams must be prepared to go to the assistance of the Specials Troops if they get into trouble.

'We intend to refuel the ships from RFA *Tidespring* before we move in – she will remain one hundred miles to the north; we'll keep her out of the way just in case. These big tankers are very susceptible to submarine attack. Are there any questions?'

Christian knew what was coming. There was a clamour from the SBS. 'What about the Gemini outboards, sir?'

'We have them in the aircraft hangar at the moment and the mechanics are giving them a thorough overhaul. It's not ideal but the best we can do under the circumstances. Let's hope the government will give us new ones in the future.'

'Fat lot that's going to do us right now!' a burly SAS sergeant sitting next to Christian muttered.

'What about crevasses on the Fortuna Glacier, sir?' one of the SAS men asked.

'We know that two of the scientists crossed the glacier recently,' Guy Sheridan answered. 'We don't think the part you have to cross is badly crevassed and it's only for a couple of miles. We think that if Shackleton and his half-starved men could cross the whole island by that route a fit SAS team should do that short section without trouble. Once off the ice it's easy going.'

Christian raised an arm. 'Sir, some of our mountaineering kit isn't up to scratch. Most of us only have standard issue army boots, which won't be much good on the glacier.'

Sheridan nodded. 'We've thought about that. Captain Barker still has the boxes of climbing equipment they were returning from Bob Veal's joint service expedition to South Georgia onboard *Endurance*. You can break into them and see what you can find.'

So the plan was made. The ships began their careful approach to South Georgia. Out to the west the pressure was dropping as a colossal storm gathered in strength to hurl itself out through Drakes Passage, the narrow gap between Cape Horn and the Antarctic Peninsula. South Georgia was directly in line.

38

Paris, Monday 19 April 1982

Two men sat quietly drinking coffee at a street café overlooking OFEMA, the offices of the French Government's bureau for armament sales. It was a spring morning in Paris, the street busy with commuters hurrying to their offices. The older man was Alexis Forter, the senior British SIS agent in France. His career in the Service was legendary. Of white Russian descent, he had graduated with a first at Oxford and served in the RAF during the Second World War. He joined the Secret Service in 1950 and worked in Basra, Baghdad and Tehran and had lived in the hills with the Kurds in northern Iraq. This was followed by Saigon and a tour in Nairobi. A brilliant linguist and great raconteur, his final placement was Paris, an easy posting to end a brilliant career.

What was intended to be a cushy number was turning into something very different. The advent of the Falkland crisis had changed all that. Since the Carter administration's ban on all US arms sales to Argentina, France had become the main supplier. Alexis' report to Colin Figures, his boss at Century House, had made uneasy reading and 'C' had immediately sent Peter Bacon-Smith to see for himself what was happening.

Alexis met Peter at the British Consulate and took him down to the main business district to see for himself. They sat waiting in the spring sunshine watching the crowded street.

'There they go now, Peter.' He indicated with his cup. 'The tall man is Captain Carlos Cortez; he's the main buyer of armaments for the junta. The man with him is his deputy, Julio Lavezzo.

195

They're based in the Argentinian Military Commission in Avenue de Merceau but have an office in this building.'

Peter watched two smartly dressed men in dark sunglasses walk out of the OFEMA and climb into a waiting taxi.

'Don't worry, we have them under constant surveillance, GCHQ at Cheltenham are tapping their international calls and the French Secret Service is watching them like a hawk. Carlos is a nasty piece of work. He's married to the sister of Licio Gelli, a Mafia boss now living in Argentina. He's wanted all over Europe for money laundering through the Italian Bank Ambrosiano. We think that the Argentinian funding for the arms is coming from the South American Blanco Andino, one of Ambrosiano's subsidiaries, run by the Italian financier, Roberto Calvi. Both Cortez and Lavezzo have diplomatic status and are considered as honoured customers by Aerospatiale, the state-owned aircraft manufacturer.'

'I saw your report to "C"; how on earth did you find out what has already been supplied?' Peter asked.

'It's not been that difficult; we knew that Aerospatiale had a very lucrative contract to equip fourteen Super Etendard aircraft with Exocet. The Argentinians paid a hundred and sixty million dollars up front and half the stuff has already been shipped. The whole consignment was insured through Lloyd's of London and I got the manifest lists from them. Most of the Argentinian navy has been fitted with Exocet surface-to-surface missiles but as yet only a few of the aircraft are fitted out. The air-to-surface equipment has not been shipped yet. A technical team from Aerospatiale is scheduled to go out to Argentina anytime now to help them fit the equipment.'

'We should be able to put a stop to that,' Peter said. 'The French have supported us in the Security Council and signed up for Resolution 502 ordering Argentina to withdraw from the Falklands, and the European Community has an arms embargo on them. They even fixed it so RAF aircraft can land at Dakar, en route to Ascension Island.'

'I wouldn't be so sure about that; arms supply is a funny

business. If they can't get them one way they may go another. A contingent of Exocet is due to be delivered to Peru any time now and their government has been asking for early delivery. You can be damn sure where they will end up if they get delivered.'

The two men paid the bill and headed back through the crowded streets towards the Metro.

'We'll organise some dummy arms dealers to contact Carlos Cortez and see if we can sell him some duds,' Peter grinned. 'We already managed to do that in the States when they tried to buy long-range tanks for their aircraft. Argentina is having difficulties finding friends in this conflict, not too many South American governments trust them, they're too right wing, but there are still arms getting through. We know that Brazil has offered to supply reconnaissance aircraft and our old friends the Libyans have sent a boatload of weapons.'

'Relations between France and Argentina are not good at the moment,' Alexis said. 'There are a lot of dissidents living here who escaped during the dirty war, mostly *Montanero* and the like. An Argentinian hit team abducted a number of exiles living in Paris a year ago. They were under the leadership of an officer called Alfredo Astiz. He's already wanted here for the disappearance of two French nuns, Alice Domon and Leonie Duquet, in Buenos Aires. It's been a national scandal, and the French public aren't keen on arms supply to Argentina.'

'I've heard that name before – I'm sure Astiz is the name the Argies are using as the Military Governor of South Georgia,' Peter said.

'We need to put pressure on the French to make sure those missiles don't get delivered, Peter. The head of Aerospatiale is General Jacques Mitterrand, President Mitterrand's brother. It would be highly embarrassing for the President of France to sign up to the arms embargo and at the same time turn a blind eye to his brother supplying arms to Argentina.'

'I follow your drift. I wonder if the prime minister will have a private word with the president? "C" might be able to arrange it.'

Peter caught the next flight back to London and that evening gave his report to Colin Figures, who immediately called the prime minister. An hour later Margaret Thatcher called President Mitterrand on the clear line to the Elysée Palace and the two leaders spoke for some time. She got her assurance that no further weapons would reach Argentina from France and that the Peruvian aircraft delivery would be stalled. Much to her relief Anglo-French cooperation remained high throughout the conflict.

Peter still did not get home; there was a note on his desk that there had been a call from Arnie Schwartz at the US Embassy in Buenos Aires. He checked the time: it was 10 p.m., early evening in Argentina, so he phoned immediately, patching through the CIA offices at Langley. The affable American came directly onto the line.

'Howdy, Peter, thanks for calling back. I cleared it with Langley to have a chat with you. Things are not going well with General Haig's mission. The president says we should help you as much as we can but try to keep a working relationship with the Argentinians. Harry Shlaudeman, our ambassador here, has been negotiating with General Galtieri, who we think is wavering with a heavy dose of cold feet, but every suggestion and compromise we make falls victim to the junta's system of veto. Admiral Anaya's the principal hawk and totally intransigent. The Argie navy is spoiling for a fight.'

'The prime minister's been holding the Task Force back while your people negotiate, Arnie, but time is against us. If the navy is to stand any chance to oust the Argentinians it has to be done before the winter storms set in. She can't hold them back much longer.'

Arnie sighed. 'There isn't much more that we can do. General Haig is just about worn out and very frustrated. Harry Shlaudeman thinks it's a waste of time.'

Peter felt the muscles in his neck tighten with the realisation that this was it, the peace negotiations were falling apart. It looked almost certain that Britain and Argentina were going to war. Just about the only thing he could think of that might bring the generals to the negotiation table would be the early recapture of South Georgia.

'I have a few pieces of information that might keep your analysts thinking,' Arnie continued. 'Three Argentinian submarines are at sea. The *Santiago del Estero* and her twin sister *Santa Fe* both left Mar del Plata on the ninth of April. They're both US ex-wartime diesel boats and you can hear them coming a mile away. We think the *Estero* is in poor shape and not likely to go far from port. The *Santa Fe* is the one they used to drop off the commandos in the Falklands and we think she has another group of Special Forces on-board right now. The third boat, the *San Luis*, is a type 209. She will almost certainly be trying to stalk your Task Force; she has quite a heavy punch with eight twenty-one-inch bow torpedo tubes.'

'Thanks, Arnie, I'll see that goes to the right place.'

'Good luck, Peter. I'm glad I'm not in your prime minister's position right now.' Arnie replaced the telephone.

Peter's next call was to Commander Denis Davies in the *Paraquat* cell in the Hole at Northwood. Denis sounded tired and on edge.

'The *Paraquat* ships are just about in position to attack,' he told Peter. 'So far we don't think they've been spotted and we don't think there are any enemy ships in the area. With the element of surprise we are hopeful of a successful outcome.'

'There's an Argentinian sub at large, Denis.' Peter filled in the details.

There was a long silence and then Denis's anxious voice. 'There would be no reason to take commandos on a submarine to the Falklands; it's a reasonable assumption that the *Santa Fe* is taking reinforcements to South Georgia. It's a bit rough but I've calculated that if she left Mar del Plata on the ninth she will reach South Georgia sometime between the twenty-third and twenty-fourth, right in the middle of our operation. Our ships will be sitting ducks if they are caught close inshore. We had the nuclear submarine HMS *Conqueror* patrolling down there; the *Santa Fe* would never have got past her, but she went north to protect the Task Force two days ago.'

'Well, I think you should try to turn her round again. I hope these nuclear boats can go as fast underwater as we think they can. The *Santa Fe* could scupper this whole operation.' Peter rang off leaving a dispirited and exhausted Commander Davies with a long night ahead of him.

39

South Georgia, Wednesday 21 April 1982

Three Wessex helicopters flew in line, low over the sea, towards South Georgia. Sitting on a pile of kit and ammunition in the back of the second aircraft, *Yankee Foxtrot*, Christian just managed to look out through the side window. There was not much to see, just the white-capped waves below and clouds of billowing snow. The chopper was bucking about in the turbulence and he could sense the tension of the aircrew as the pilot, Mike Tidd, fought to keep her steady.

'Look at that!' exclaimed his companion, Lofty, the big SAS corporal sitting alongside him, with his face to the window. Out of the murk an enormous cliff loomed vertically from the crashing sea and rose for at least a thousand feet, its top vanishing into the cloud.

'That must be Cape Constance,' Christian shouted over the aircraft noise. This was the first time he had seen the island and it was an awe-inspiring sight. 'We must be flying into Possession Bay, that's where Captain Cook first landed; it must have been a hell of a place for a sailing ship.'

The aircraft crossed the inlet and began to climb steeply above a narrow glacier. All around squalls of snow were falling and the helicopters swerved away attempting to keep out of the clouds. Another fjord came into view below them with glaciers pouring into it on all sides and dozens of icebergs carving into the water. Visibility was appalling and the men could see great plumes of drifting snow swirling down the mountainsides.

'We're over Antarctic Bay,' Lofty said. 'That must be the Fortuna

Glacier.' He was pointing uneasily down at the large open crevasses plainly visible crossing the frozen river of ice.

The lead helicopter, *Humphrey* as she was affectionately called by her pilot, Lieutenant-Commander Ian Stanley, was manoeuvring cautiously down to land. She was an old Mark 3 Wessex, a 'Pinger', equipped for anti-submarine warfare with a computerised flight-control system that could be set to hover automatically over a fixed position, in effect a highly complex auto-pilot. The other two helicopters were not so fortunate: although newer version Wessex 5s they were utility aircraft, with unsophisticated instruments, used mainly for carrying men and equipment. Both pilots were 'Jungleys', trained in commando helicopter flying in Ulster and Norway, but on this occasion they were tagging behind Ian Stanley like chickens following a mother hen, as he used his instruments to guide them in the appalling visibility.

Christian watched *Humphrey* inch its way down onto the ice, great billowing clouds of snow thrown up and spraying around the machine. It was impossible to see the surface, which blended perfectly into the horizon. Mike Tidd inched *Yankee Foxtrot* down behind him but overshot his landing and spun away to make a second attempt. This time he landed OK but the airspeed indicator was still reading sixty knots and the seven-ton machine was sliding sideways in the wind. Behind him the RAF pilot, Flight-Lieutenant Andy Pulford, had managed to land *Yankee Alpha*, the third helicopter, and he too was struggling to keep his machine on the ground. They were on the level area of the Fortuna Glacier where three weeks earlier David Asquith and Sebastian Holmes had crossed on their difficult journey to Antarctic Bay.

Christian jumped out onto the glacier. Snow was blasting all over the place from the downdraught of the helicopter as the weapons and equipment were bundled out, and they crouched over their packs as the big Wessex lifted away into the air. It was only then that he realised how strongly the wind was blowing. It was difficult to stand and the spindrift lashed his face. For the moment the sky cleared and he watched the three helicopters flying back down the glacier into the comparative shelter of Antarctic Bay. The wind was blasting between sixty and eighty knots as the sixteen SAS men sorted their equipment. Another squall had hidden the view, and visibility was down to only a few yards; the only thing they could see was a large crevasse gaping ominously alongside them.

The three helicopters flew carefully back to the ships. Once clear of the glacier the pilots began to breathe more easily and all landed safely, *Humphrey* onto the bucking deck of *Antrim* and the two Wessex 5s on the tanker *Tidespring*.

A somewhat shaken Ian Stanley reported to Captain Young. 'All's well, sir, everybody's in place with no casualties. It's murderous flying, I'm glad we'll never have to go up there again!' How wrong can you be! The barometer was dropping like a stone, and the current storm was minor compared to the approaching hurricane.

Back on the Fortuna Glacier the sixteen SAS men checked their weapons to find that condensation had frozen most of the mechanisms but there was little point in sorting things out in these conditions. They roped up into groups of three and four and set out hauling their small sledges of equipment, led by their team leader, Captain John Hamilton. Conditions were bad but this was what they had trained for and they moved slowly across the flat surface of the glacier. The snow lay unevenly: windswept clear glacier ice and then deep powdery drifts. The first man broke through a crevasse within fifty yards of starting out. One minute he was walking on solid ground and a second later he was up to his armpits in a hole, feet flaying above a bottomless abyss. He was quickly pulled clear but everyone began to take the glacier very seriously.

Christian was the second to fall through: it was sudden and unexpected; Lofty had walked unaffected over the same spot a couple of seconds earlier. Suddenly there was a dull crump and about twenty feet of snow bridge dropped on either side of Christian, and in a moment he found himself dangling over what felt like the Albert Hall. He was on a tight rope between Lofty and Sergeant Phil Curass who pulled him out, grinning, but they realised that there were far more crevasses than had been anticipated.

The pace was frustratingly slow: on average somebody broke into a crevasse every thirty or forty yards. As night approached they had travelled less than half a mile and the increasing wind made pitching the tents impossible. They called it a day and searched around for any form of shelter they could find. Mostly they dug shallow trenches and lay down wrapping the tents around themselves.

Christian and Lofty chose a poor spot and in a bad moment lost their tent as a gust of wind tore it from their grasp. They spent the next hour scrambling around the glacier trying to find shelter before climbing in beside two of their companions. By now it was snowing heavily and one hundred-mile-an-hour gusts of wind were screaming between the mountains. Snow was filling into the trenches and burying the frozen occupants. John Hamilton realised that some of the men would suffer hypothermia if conditions did not remarkably improve. The SAS reconnaissance was becoming a fiasco; they were fighting for their lives and not a shot had been fired.

Christian lay between Sergeant Phil Curass and Lofty, his thin sleeping bag giving little protection, the blasting wind overhead blowing the powdery snow everywhere. His teeth rattled uncontrollably, the only consolation being that he could hear Lofty making the same sound alongside him; the big marine corporal was in the same boat. No one complained. Christian looked at his watch:10.35 p.m. To his horror he realised that it was less than five minutes since he had last checked the time. Determined not to look again for at least an hour, he shivered on, calculating in his head how long it would take them to get off the glacier. It was little more than two miles but at this rate it would take at least a full day to leave the ice and it was impossible to move in these conditions. It would take another two days to do the recce; without adequate shelter an appalling thought. He looked at his watch. Damn, less than five minutes had passed!

On-board *Antrim* an anxious Captain Brian Young and his officers watched spellbound as monstrous green waves crashed along the superstructure. Everything moveable was re-lashed, the ship's stabilisers virtually ineffective in a storm such as this. The six-thousand-ton destroyer was rolling and pitching mercilessly. No one had been in seas like this before. There was no point in trying to sleep and the off-watch officers joined the rest on the bridge. The line on the barograph plummeted to an alarming nine hundred and sixty-five millibars.

'One day you'll tell your grandchildren about this!' the captain muttered to his second officer as another huge wave crashed down the entire length of the deck. 'I don't know how much more of this the ship can take without suffering serious damage.'

At the stern another epic was taking place. It had been impossible in these conditions to get the helicopter into the hangar and *Humphrey* was sitting on the open flight deck. The service crew, attached to safety lines, were frantically trying to tie the big helicopter down. The canvas socks, designed to tie the tips of the rotors, were tearing apart and as one hundred mile-an-hour winds hit the ship the blades were causing lift. Ian Stanley watched in horror as the men fought in the wind and driving snow to get lines around the flapping rotors of his beloved machine.

They had the same problem on *Tidespring*. One of the Wessex 5s was in the hangar but Mike Tidd's *Yankee Foxtrot* had been left on deck in case of an emergency and now the crew were fighting to save her. The big tanker had already suffered damage to her superstructure and was pitching and rolling from side to side dangerously as Captain Redmond attempted to keep her bow into the wind.

*   *   *

Twenty miles down the coast the two smaller frigates, *Endurance* and *Plymouth*, were taking a similar battering. At the same time that the SAS were flown onto the Fortuna Glacier, their job was to insert a twelve-man team of SBS into Hound Bay. The plan was that they should cross the Barff Peninsula to East Cumberland Bay and, using three of their Gemini inflatable craft, slip across the fjord and climb Brown Mountain where they would have a good view of King Edward Point and Grytviken. The team were led by three SBS sergeants known as Kiwi, Flip and Willy.

As evening approached *Endurance* left *Plymouth* covering her from the sea and slipped quietly into Hound Bay. In fading light Lieutenant-Commander Tony Ellerbeck prepared to fly the first of the three patrols ashore. The tiny Wasp helicopter was only able to carry two men at a time. With few or no instruments and unable to use the radar for fear of alerting the Argentinians, it was a daunting exercise. Everything moveable had been stripped from the helicopter to save weight and the first two SBS men sat on their equipment behind the pilot. The observer, Lieutenant Dave Wells, lay on the floor with his head out in the open air holding a night vision aid, to guide the pilot in to the chosen landing site.

The weather was deteriorating rapidly but it was still possible to fly in the lee of the Barff Peninsula and the first flight was uneventful. Kiwi and his partner, Scobes, unloaded their weapons and kit and the Wasp returned to *Endurance* and collected the second pair of his patrol. This time the wind had increased dramatically and the second flight was much more exciting but the men were safely delivered and the helicopter made it back to the ship. Unfortunately there was no chance of inserting the remaining eight commandos, who remained stuck and frustrated on *Endurance* as she was hit by the raging storm.

On the beach Kiwi soon realised that there was little chance of the rest of the team arriving so he left two of his men and he and Scobes set off to reconnoitre. Neither of them had been in this kind of country before and they soon found themselves walking through an alarmed penguin colony. Worse, there was a sudden commotion and a huge animal reared up grunting: Kiwi had stepped on the tail of a sleeping elephant seal. A noisy and nerve-racking start to a clandestine operation.

Moving cautiously up the hillside, Scobes stopped suddenly in his tracks. 'Watch it, Kiwi, there's a light!'

They approached what turned out to be a small hut with draped windows.

'Cover me, I'll knock on the door and try to draw them out.' Kiwi slipped quietly up to the door and tapped gently. There was a sound inside and the door was opened by a bearded and very startled man.

'Good evening,' said a very English voice.

The two men in the hut were Miles Plant and Tony North, two of the fids staying with Cindy Buxton and Annie Price at St Andrews Bay; they had walked over the previous day to spy out the Barff Peninsula for enemy activity. The two SBS men now found themselves sitting cheerfully down to a cup of tea and exchanging news with the two scientists.

'We've been along most of the Peninsula and through the Sorlings Valley,' Miles said. 'As far as we can tell there is no sign of the Argies. In fact we have seen no one since we have been on the island.'

'Stay here for the night, lads, but I think you should get the hell out of here first thing tomorrow. This place could become very dangerous in the next few days,' Kiwi advised.

Much relieved, the two troopers slipped out into the night and rejoined the others on the beach.

Back on *Endurance* Tony Ellerbeck made several tries to fly the remaining two patrols ashore. By now the storm was increasing in intensity and after two attempts he gave it up.

'We nearly hit the surface twice, Nick,' he told Captain Barker. 'It was awful, there's a classic katabatic wind blowing and it's bouncing off the mountains and changing direction all the time. It's gusting seventy knots and we were taking a real hammering. David and the two marines weren't strapped in because we had no seats and I thought they might be thrown out. At one stage we were hit by a downdraught, which pushed me very close to the sea, not that I could see it. Snow was building up on the windscreen and my fundamental orifice was biting a hole in the seat.'

The only solution seemed to be to land the commandos using the Gemini inflatables. Captain Barker eased *Endurance* in as close to shore as he dared. Two of the SBS officers acted as ferrymen and in overloaded boats managed to convey the remaining troops to the shore. They were easily located by Kiwi's group who heard them crashing through the penguin rookery like a herd of elephants.

In the early hours of the following morning the twelve commandos made their way through the Sorlings Valley. It was tough going through soft, newly fallen snow; they were laden down with weapons and heavy equipment but they reached the snout of the Nordenskjold by midday. Ahead of them Tony Ellerbeck had taken advantage of a short break in the weather and flown two Gemini inflatables, slung in nets below the helicopter, to the beach of Cumberland Bay. It was impossible for him to fly through the Sorlings Valley, which was in line of sight from the Argentinians at King Edward Point, so at first light he managed to slip the Wasp round the foot of Mount Paget and down a narrow gorge running along the side of the Nordenskjold Glacier. He returned quickly to *Endurance*, which immediately headed off out of harm's way.

The commandos reached their boats two hours later and began to assemble them. To their dismay one of the inflatables had a bad cut in the rubber and was unserviceable and they were one boat short. Only one party would be able to make the crossing and Willy's team, the more experienced boatmen, drew the short straw. Worse still, the wind had increased again from the north and the fjord was filling up with small bergs and brash ice. As night fell they prepared to make the crossing.

They set out in a rising gale through a gap in the ice, making for open water. The men were wearing drysuits and their equipment was well protected but heavy seas began to crash over the bow of the small rubber boat. To make matters worse the ice was closing in on either side and the outboard motor began to play up. They were about eight hundred yards from shore and couldn't see a thing when the Gemini began to fill with water. Reluctantly Willy decided to pack it in and try to get back to shore. One of the men lay in the bow fending off the ice and flashing his subdued torch in an attempt to warn Kiwi of their plight. They were navigating back on a rough compass bearing as the ice closed around them with every possibility of the boat being punctured. The boat finally crashed onto the beach on a roller, almost before the men knew they had made it, discharging a much shaken patrol who had survived disaster by the skin of their teeth.

'We'll wait till morning and see if the sea subsides; we may be able to get across then,' Willy said. 'We could try it in daylight if visibility is poor and we can't be spotted.'

A cold night was spent sleeping among the rocks in heavily falling snow. By dawn there was little change: the bay was now filled with jagged lumps of floating ice driven in by a stiff onshore wind. They discussed attempting to push the Gemini through to open water but realised that it was futile. They had given it their best shot. Reluctantly Willy hung out an aerial for the radio and called *Antrim* requesting evacuation. The hiss of static echoed in his headset. He tried a number of frequencies without success. The men looked at each other in consternation – where the hell was the ship? It was going to be a long wait!

Antrim had her own troubles and had moved away from the island. The SBS were on their own.

40

Fortuna Glacier, South Georgia, Thursday 22 April 1982

The call for help was not unexpected. The almost endless night had turned into a steel-grey morning, snow showers continued to settle on the ships and, although somewhat abated, the wind was still gusting between sixty and seventy knots. Everyone was concerned for the SAS on the Fortuna Glacier and it came as no surprise when the radio operator on *Antrim* received a weak signal from John Hamilton asking for evacuation.

Major Cedric Delves, the SAS commander, who had pushed very hard for the incursion, discussed the situation with Guy Sheridan. Himself an experienced Himalayan mountaineer, Sheridan had been unhappy about the choice of the Fortuna from the start. He and Nick Barker had both argued that the weather on South Georgia was far too unpredictable. Nick, who probably knew more about the island and its weather than anyone else on the *Paraquat* force, thought that Shackleton had been extraordinarily lucky in having two days of fine weather for his crossing. The odds of picking the perfect day for the 'SAS drop-in' were very low but such is the reputation of the SAS that they had bowed to Delves' wishes and let the mountain troops get on with it. It was essential to have some idea of the Argentinian strength and how the SAS carried out the recce was their affair. It had all seemed rather gung-ho and it was difficult not to say: 'I told you so.'

'John Hamilton wouldn't pack it in unless things were very serious,' Delves said, his frustration and anxiety clearly visible. 'The signal said that some of his men were hypothermic and showing signs of frostbite.'

'We'd better try and get them out as soon as possible,' Sheridan agreed.

An equally frustrated Captain Young gave orders for the helicopters to stand by to fly at the earliest opportunity and for the ship's hospital to prepare to take casualties.

'Our timetable is very short, I can't keep the ships hanging around here in this exposed position much longer, we need another plan. The Argies are bound to realise we are here pretty soon,' he said.

The exhausted service crews had done a remarkable job protecting the helicopters through the night on the open decks and surprisingly all three were ready to fly. Normally a day like this would not have been considered 'flyable'. The flight decks were rolling in heavy seas and the wind was gusting unpredictably, but within minutes the machines lifted off and headed for the island. Conditions were far worse than the previous day, great plumes of cloud spewing off the mountains. The two Wessex 5s landed on the narrow neck of land behind Cape Constance while Ian Stanley in *Humphrey* attempted to fly up the glacier using his specialised instruments, but after half an hour of frustration he admitted defeat and packed it in. The three aircraft returned to the ships and refuelled. The second attempt was more successful: a clearance in the weather allowed them back into Possession Bay and, flying in line, they crossed Antarctic Bay and made their way carefully up the Fortuna Glacier.

On the glacier it had been a horrendous night, and long before dawn the shivering men had emerged from their trenches. They had been buried in light powder snow that had penetrated their clothing and melted, and they were soaking wet. It was impossible to brew up in these conditions, so they reloaded their haul sledges and miserably continued across the glacier. But in the blasting wind and driving snow it was hopeless. There was no shelter on the flat surface. For three hours they struggled on but made absolutely no progress. By mid-morning John Hamilton realised that the game was over. Bitterly disappointed, he instructed the signaller to radio the ship for help. Even this proved a problem. In these conditions the radio operator's hands froze when he removed his gloves to work the set and the men had to form a human shield against the wind to protect him while he made the call.

'I can't see the helicopters getting to us in this,' Lofty said. 'This is much worse than when we came in.'

'They'll come; those guys fly in almost anything,' Christian said optimistically. 'This wind could go down any time.' Surprisingly, he had warmed up with the sledge hauling but could see that some of his companions were looking the worse for wear. They had stopped attempting to cross the glacier; the crevasses were all around and nobody wanted to fall through in this chilled state. They prepared for a long, cold wait.

Sometime after 1 p.m. there was a clearance between the snow squalls and the sound of approaching helicopters. Hurriedly somebody ignited a smoke flare and to everyone's relief the three machines flew in and landed almost immediately. They bundled their equipment on board and scrambled into the shelter of the aircraft. Christian and Lofty climbed into *Yankee Foxtrot* where the big aircrew man Tug Wilson grinned at them and handed out flasks of coffee. At the controls Mike Tidd was apprehensively watching a snow squall moving down the glacier towards them.

'Ready to go, Ian. I've good visibility right now; I'd like to get off before that snow arrives,' he called to Ian Stanley, who was still loading troops into *Humphrey*.

'Go ahead, Mike,' Ian agreed and *Yankee Foxtrot* lifted into the air. Within less than a minute the squall hit him. In the blinding snow the pilot lost his horizon and frantically fought the controls.

'Tug, I've got a problem!'

The big crewman sprang to the door looking out desperately for the surface of the glacier. Mike knew that there was a mountain quite close on one side and the rising ice slope on the other; the last thing he wanted to meet was a granite cloud. He peered through the windscreen looking for anything that would give him a reference, at the same time trying to watch the altimeter that was spinning erratically between zero and forty feet. Tug felt the helicopter slew to the left and yelled a warning to the pilot who rammed on full power. It was too late.

They hit the surface flying at thirty miles per hour. Christian had a slow-motion image of the left undercarriage sailing past the open door a second before the main rotors hit the ice. The next moment the big helicopter somersaulted onto its side and hurtled along the glacier for about eighty yards. The left side of the cockpit collapsed instantly, filling the aircraft with flying snow and smashed Perspex. Had there been a second pilot on-board he would have been killed instantly. The hold resembled the inside of a spin dryer: the men were flying about among weapons and ammo boxes. They bounced along a shallow depression in the glacier filled with fresh powder snow, which miraculously acted as a cushion to the wrecked machine and they came to stop in a whirl of spindrift.

'Chris, are you OK?' Buried under a tangled heap of weapons and kit, Christian felt strong hands dragging him up. Lofty and Sergeant Phil Curass struggled to pull him clear.

'Come on; get out, this thing's likely to go up any second now!' The sergeant was bleeding profusely from a deep cut over his eye. He and Tug Wilson were urgently hauling the shocked men out of the tangled wreck into the driving snow.

A horrified Ian Stanley was just taking off as he saw *Yankee Foxtrot* engulfed in a cloud of flaying snow. The helicopter was about half a mile away, flying low across the ice, trying to keep below the cloud. He had no chance to warn him over the intercom before the machine went in. Horrified, he watched the Wessex bouncing across the glacier with pieces flying in all directions. He called Ian Georgeson, the pilot of *Yankee Alpha*, to follow him and, using *Humphrey's* instruments, flew over to the crash site. The men were still clambering out as the two remaining helicopters landed. As Ian touched down his aircrew man, Fitz Fitzgerald, dashed out to help the struggling men. Miraculously, nobody was seriously hurt, although they looked stunned and disoriented.

Mike Tidd had just emerged from the wrecked cockpit. Strangely the windscreen wipers were still thrashing back and forth across the empty space where the screen had once been. He scrambled over to *Humphrey* and plugged in his headset to talk to the pilot.

'You messy bastard, you've left your wipers running,' Ian said.

They split the men into two parties. Christian and three other SAS jumped into *Yankee Alpha* along with Tug Wilson, who had slightly twisted his back. Mike Tidd and two other SAS men joined Ian Stanley in *Humphrey*. They left some weapons and ammunition and dumped fuel to compensate for the additional weight and, greatly relieved, took off ten minutes later with *Humphrey* in the lead flying on instruments and Ian Georgeson following in *Yankee Alpha*. Still somewhat shaken, Christian and Lofty were patching up Phil Curass's eye and discussing the size of whisky they would have when they arrived back on *Antrim*. For the moment visibility improved but within less than a minute they were hit by a second snowstorm. It couldn't have happened at a worse moment.

Ian Stanley, using *Humphrey's* auto-hovering equipment, was flying over the surface at a fixed height with *Yankee Alpha* following, using him as a reference point. What neither pilot could possibly know was that there was a snow ridge running along the glacier. Just as the snowstorm hit, *Humphrey* rose automatically over the ridge and sank down the other side, still maintaining the same height above the surface. The effect of this from Ian Georgeson's viewpoint was to see the lead helicopter sink suddenly out of sight into the invisible surface of the glacier. He was now flying in total whiteout and *Humphrey* had simply vanished. He slowed the machine down and tried to maintain level flight but moments later his wheels touched the top of the ridge. He almost got away with it; the helicopter bumped along the surface, slewing sideways in the strong wind. He careered along trying to lift clear but at the last moment one of the wheels caught in a small crevasse and over she went.

For the second time in twenty minutes Christian felt a huge thump and his world turned upside-down in a whirl of raining ice and steel. There was a blinding flash of light in his head and then everything went black. Somersaulting down the glacier, *Yankee Alpha* ended her days as a tangle of broken Perspex and twisted metal.

Humphrey's co-pilot, Lieutenant Stewart Cooper, was watching *Yankee Alpha* from the side window and calling instructions over the intercom. Listening to the conversation from a seat behind him was Cedric Delves, the SAS commander, who had come on the flight to see that his men were safe.

'Fine, OK, OK.' Stewart's voice rang out over the headsets. 'Following at fifty yards, keep her steady, all OK. Oh God, he's gone in!'

Struggling with *Humphrey's* controls, there wasn't a thing that Ian Stanley could do. He was overloaded as it was and frantically trying to fly in a whiteout. Major Delves turned to the remaining SAS team, none of whom had headsets and were oblivious to what was happening, and with an ashen face he drew a finger across his throat. *Humphrey* flew on alone back to *Antrim*; both the chicks were lost. Stanley dumped his passengers and with a heavy heart took off immediately on yet another mission back up the glacier.

Christian came round with the blast of wind and snow on his face. It was like a bad dream; nobody moved. He heard Jan Lomas's voice yelling, 'For fuck's sake jettison the cabin window, get out, this thing's likely to go up anytime.'

Lofty and Phil Curass began struggling to disentangle themselves. Some of the men kicked out the window and they began to tumble out into the snow. Tug was already attempting to free Ian

Georgeson, the pilot, who was upside down tangled in the harness of his life raft, cursing but unhurt. Once again, by some miracle there were no serious injuries.

Jan Lomas managed to inflate the aircraft's life raft as a makeshift tent and he and Christian scrambled in with Phil Curass and patched up the protesting sergeant's eye. The two commanders, John Hamilton and Ian Georgeson, discussed what to do next.

'There's no chance of help coming in this wind,' Georgeson said. 'We've got to get more shelter.'

'We should be able to get back to the other helicopter and get some food and some of the men's rucksacks,' Hamilton suggested.

He and some of the troopers set out for *Yankee Foxtrot* with Tug Wilson. In the event they managed the short journey twice and brought down the second life raft and recovered a working radio. They all took shelter in the comparative warmth of the rafts and settled down for a long wait. Suddenly the radio sprang to life, with Ian Stanley's voice urgently calling them on the emergency band.

Ian Georgeson answered. 'Hello, Ian, sorry about the fiasco, everybody is OK.'

'Got that, I'm over the glacier but can't see a bloody thing. There's no way I can get to you. It will be tomorrow at the earliest.'

'Got that, Ian, we are OK. Standing by.'

A bitterly dejected Ian Stanley peeled off and twenty minutes later landed back on the heaving deck of *Antrim*. He was utterly shattered, having flown up the glacier five times in the last twenty-four hours with little or no sleep. Worse still, he was playing mind games with himself.

'Should I have allowed Mike Tidd to take-off? Should we have left the SAS until the weather improved?'

Humphrey, the Wessex 3, unlike the newer Mark 5s, only had a single engine and had a reputation for engine failures. Ian had twice in his career suffered catastrophic power loss and once ditched into the sea in a Wessex 3. *Humphrey* had been worked desperately hard during the last month and had battered its way overloaded in frightful winds up the glacier. The service crew had done a magnificent job of maintenance but somewhere his luck was bound to run out. There were sixteen men stranded on the glacier; two flights of eight should get them out, but the thought of two more flights up the Fortuna was dreadful. He lay sleepless in his bunk trying to relax.

Less than an hour passed before a gentle knock on his cabin door. The destroyer was still pitching in the heavy swell.

'Sorry to wake you, sir. There's a bit of a clearance over the land.' His aircrew man, Petty Officer Fitz Fitzgerald, handed him a cup of tea. 'It's only four o'clock and it's still light enough for another try.' Fitz had spent the last hour writing a letter to his wife; he was suffering the same mind games as Ian. He had sealed the letter and left it lying on his bunk.

Fifteen minutes later they were airborne and once again crossing Cape Constance. Predictably, the wind had risen again and the cloud was down. Ian took a chance and instead of flying up the glacier he climbed to three thousand feet above the cloud level. Around him the peaks of the Allardyce Mountains floated in a sea of cloud. At any other time this would have been a fantastic experience, towering above him the Admiralty Peaks with the snow-laden Mount Spaaman and huge mass of Mount Sugartop in the background, but he had little time to enjoy the view. The aircraft was buffeting about in the strong wind, and ice was forming on the fuselage. He flew above the glacier for a while when suddenly, through a gap in the clouds, he spotted directly below him the crashed helicopter and the two brightly coloured life rafts. Risking all, he dived down through the clouds and made a hasty landing alongside the wreck.

The wind was still blasting spindrift down the glacier and constantly changing direction. They urgently loaded the first eight men into the hold but as the cloud swirled around them he realised that there was no way he could make a second flight that day.

'Right, Fitz, let's pack the lot in. Dump the weapons and kit.'
Frantically, they bundled everyone into the hold. There were
literally arms and legs sticking out of doors and windows. It was
amazing how Fitz crammed sixteen men into the tiny fuselage
filled with complex radar and communications equipment. Christian
found himself lying on the front seat with Chris Parry, the second
pilot, sitting on his chest. Fitz himself was left hanging half out
of the cabin door.

Humphrey eased into the air carrying a fifteen hundred pound
payload, way in excess of its safety margin. Ian knew that in this
wind there would be plenty of lift but was not at all sure about
the amount of torque he was putting on the rotor gearbox.

Twenty minutes later they were over *Antrim*. The big warship
was bucking about the ocean and the pilot knew that there was
no way that he could come in with a careful, controlled landing.
With his heart in his mouth he flew directly in over the port
side and bounced onto the flight deck. Somehow *Humphrey* held
itself together.

The batman signalling him in walked over to the aircraft as
he was shutting down. 'That was bloody marvellous, sir. The best
controlled crash landing I've ever seen!'

41

Antarctic Bay, South Georgia, Thursday 22 April 1982

The four residents of the hut on the beach of Antarctic Bay were preparing for a late breakfast. There was no rush. For the last few days the weather had been miserable and work had more or less ceased. Earlier in the week Anna had excitedly filmed a school of killer whales that had entered the bay. These beautiful and highly intelligent creatures had swum right up to their position on some rocks above the water and watched them curiously for some minutes and then fooled around as if they were purposely acting for the camera. Anna had been ecstatic. The bay had been filled with a profusion of wildlife but now as the weather deteriorated almost everything had vanished. The glorious weather was on the change and it was clear that a storm was on the way. The same thing had happened to Sebastian Holmes' gravity and magnetic survey. It was impossible for David to keep the theodolite steady in the constant wind and Seb found it too cold to handle the instruments.

When it hit, the storm was the worst they had encountered since the night before the invasion. The two men were still sleeping outside in the tent and it was clearly time for a rethink but God only knew how they would find space in the tiny hut. They had spent a miserable night expecting to lose the tent at any moment. It was getting much colder and the autumn snow was now settling right down to the beach. They had just come in from the tent, kicking the snow off their boots.

Alison gave David a welcome hug; their relationship was out in the open now but it was an impossible situation. There was little or no possibility of privacy. Alison was certain that Anna and Seb wouldn't mind if there was any practical way to move in together but they both knew that it would cause enormous logistical problems, so they would have to wait. Whenever possible they went for long walks together along the coast and occasionally up to the shoulder overlooking Possession Bay. David talked about New Zealand and his home by Lake Taupo on North Island, skiing on Mount Ruapehu and climbing in the Cook Range. They planned to go there when this was all over.

Alison missed her family. She had received a number of messages of encouragement from her parents and had done her best to let them know that she was safe and well, but as the days passed they had all begun to wonder how long this was going to last.

The eight-foot-square hut that they lived in was packed with equipment and there was barely enough room for them to sit round the table. It was, however, a warm oasis in a frozen land. David had sealed every gap in the woodwork and once a Tilly lamp was lit and a Primus running a warm fug would fill the tiny room. They had become avid radio listeners, mostly to the BBC World Service and to the Falkland Islands, which were still broadcasting in English.

Port Stanley was now being called Puerto Argentino; Pat Watts was still running his radio programme, and at one stage he had made an impassioned speech asking the islanders to bear with him as he was under pressure to read out proclamations by the new governor, General Garcia.

'I have a difficult choice to make: I have to obey what they tell me, or I have to disobey what they tell me. To obey is an easy way out. To disobey is not so easy because if I do then I have a gun pointed at my back,' Pat said.

It was fairly obvious that the Falkland Islanders were having a difficult time. As the occupation continued the general's edicts were becoming more threatening. Alison and the others had all made friends in the Falklands and wondered how they were faring.

The daily conversations with Paul Goodall-Copestake and Julian

Hector at Bird Island kept them in touch and they relayed messages to Signy Island base. Everybody seemed to be doing reasonably well with the exception of the four men at the Lyell Glacier hut whose position was becoming more and more precarious. The base commander at Signy kept urging them to hold on. It seemed clear that something was afoot, but what? The Task Force seemed to be dawdling down the Atlantic. The only sign of life they had seen since the invasion was a high-flying aircraft about a week ago.

David had automatically taken charge. He made an inventory of all the food they had and was running a strict rationing system. He had killed a number of penguins and the fresh meat was a pleasant change to the basic rations in the BAS food boxes. Each bird was about the size of a turkey and had two large breasts and two big drumsticks; each part was quite sufficient to feed the four of them. The rest was skin and gristle but the meat was red and rich and tasted surprisingly like venison.

Anna was cooking the breakfast when Sebastian sprang to his feet. 'I can hear an aircraft,' he said.

'It can't be; nobody would fly in these conditions,' Alison said as they opened the door. It was snowing and blowing heavily. There was nothing to be seen.

An hour later they all heard it, the clear sound of a helicopter but still nothing to see. They were now all standing in the doorway peering out into the snow when, after a few minutes, through a clearance they saw a lone helicopter flying down the snout of the Fortuna Glacier and crossing into Possession Bay. Seb, watching through his field glasses, tried to read its markings but at this distance it was impossible to make anything out.

'I think it's a Wessex but can't make out if it's British or Argentinian,' he said.

David put his arms around Alison. 'I'm sure it's one of ours. What on earth are they doing up there?' he said.

42

HMS *Antrim*, South Georgia, Friday 23 April 1982

*'This is the BBC World Service, the news at 0600 Greenwich
Mean Time read by Maggie Clews.*

*'Mr Costa Mendez has said in Argentina that he would not
be making his trip to Washington unless he had some hope of
a settlement. In an interview with the BBC correspondent in
Buenos Aires, Mr Costa Mendez said that he put the chances
of war between Britain and Argentina at half and half. Some
of the British warships in the main naval Task Force heading
for the Falkland Islands are reported to be within striking
distance of South Georgia, which is eight hundred miles from
the Falklands. South Georgia is said to be defended by less than
two hundred Argentinian troops. The Ministry of Defence in
London has denied that British troops have already landed on
South Georgia.'*

'Bloody hell, the BBC is giving our position to the Argies!' Major
Cedric Delves exclaimed. 'If that doesn't alert their reconnaissance
aircraft nothing will.'

'Somebody must have leaked something to the press in
Northwood. This whole operation is supposed to be top secret
and now they're reading it out to the whole blooming world,'
Captain Young growled. This was a common complaint amongst
the military but in this exposed place far from home it was bound
to have serious implications.

Since his unnerving flight back to *Antrim* in *Humphrey*, a very tired Cedric Delves had been brainstorming with Guy Sheridan and Captain Young, planning what to do next. All three officers had received urgent satellite telephone calls from their respective commanders concerned about the lack of progress. Everyone was losing their patience. Brian Young asked the chief of staff at Northwood, Admiral Sir David Halifax, for permission to shoot down any patrolling Argentinian aircraft. This was refused and Halifax insisted that at this stage they were to avoid shipping losses at all costs. It was an impossible situation; they felt like sitting ducks.

'M' Company was on the auxiliary tanker *Tidespring*, waiting a hundred miles to the north, and a second tanker, the RFA *Brambleleaf*, had now arrived. Reinforcements under the command of Captain John Coward on HMS *Brilliant* were on their way. Young decided to instruct a pump-over between the two tankers as a prelude for the insertion of the commando group for a frontal attack on Leith Harbour as soon as possible. He ordered HMS *Plymouth* north to protect the vulnerable tankers as they attempted to transfer thousands of gallons of fuel in heavy seas. He urgently needed to know what the marines would be facing when they made their assault.

It was 6 a.m. in London, 3 a.m. on South Georgia, the darkest time of the night, as *Antrim* slid quietly into the mouth of Stromness Bay. Conditions had improved dramatically during the night and it was relatively calm and moonless with a stiff offshore breeze, ideal for a clandestine operation. Five SAS Gemini inflatable craft were slipped over the side with three Special Troops in each boat. They circled the ship and set off into the blackness heading for Grass Island, the same viewpoint from which a month earlier Keith Mills' marines had observed the *Bahia Buen Suceso* discharging its equipment. The five Geminis were named *Alpha, Bravo, Charlie, Delta* and *Echo*. Each team was dressed in drysuits and armed to the teeth. The plan was to observe the enemy and if possible make landfall and reconnoitre defences.

There was the usual concern about the outboard motors but all seemed well and as the five tiny boats vanished into the night the nervous officers on the bridge breathed a sigh of relief and the destroyer rapidly left the close confines of Stromness Bay for the open sea, glad to be clearing this dangerous place.

Once again the unpredictable weather of South Georgia played an ugly trick. *Antrim* was less than two miles out to sea when the first buffeting of wind hit her. Major Delves was about to turn in for a well-earned rest after his long day of torment on *Humphrey* as the ship again began to roll in heavy sea.

'Here we go again, another bag of worms,' he muttered. 'The Geminis will swamp if it gets any worse than this.'

He wasn't wrong. The outboards of *Alpha*, *Bravo* and *Charlie* had all failed within ten minutes of the team starting out. *Echo* took *Alpha* and *Bravo* in tow while *Delta* towed *Charlie*. This was the situation as gale force winds funnelling down the fjord hit them. Within minutes six-foot waves were crashing over the sides and filling the boats faster than the men could bail. *Delta* managed to crash her way through to Grass Island with *Charlie* still in tow. Tom, her commander, dropped the first Gemini and turned back immediately to help the others.

By now *Echo*'s outboard had also failed. Tethered together, the men were paddling the three boats frantically against the waves but the ropes were causing them to heave together and tangle. Tim X, the operation commander in *Alpha*, shouted instructions.

'OK, cast off the lines, I guess it's everyone for themselves. Try to keep together.'

It was less than half a mile to Grass Island but in these seas the small boats soon separated and the strong offshore wind blew them steadily back. For a while they shouted to each other but it was hopeless. They began to drift out to sea.

'Keep trying, Tony.' Tim instructed his coxswain to keep working on the faulty outboard while he and the gunner alternately paddled and bailed. Tony kept spraying the carburettor with petrol. He was screaming with frustration as he repeatedly yanked the starter cord. They had drifted for about three miles when the motor spluttered to life. Half an hour later they struggled ashore on the lee side of Grass Island just as the first light of dawn tinged the horizon.

It was a similar story for Geordie, *Echo*'s commander, who was now drifting along the coast of the Busen Peninsula. The boat was continually being swamped and although he passed within two hundred yards of the point he couldn't make it to land. He could see the outline of Justa Peak fading into the distance and realised that there wasn't much land between him and Australia. He broke radio silence with a short burst on the VHF distress frequency.

'*Echo* for *Antrim*, Mayday, Mayday. Drifting south-east one mile past Busen Point.'

'Roger, Geordie, got that, will pass on message.' Tim on Grass Island had picked up the weak signal and passed the message on to *Antrim* on his more secure radio equipment. At this precise moment there was little Captain Young could do as he attempted to get his ship clear of the fjord as fast as he could before dawn.

The six men on Grass Island deflated their Geminis and hid them in the long tussock grass. Although very concerned for the nine of their friends who were missing, they still had a job to do and with the arrival of daylight they got their first view of the whaling stations of Leith and Stromness. A few minutes later they heard the subdued sound of an outboard motor and *Echo* arrived on the beach.

'Where the hell have you been?' Tim grinned as they dashed down to help drag the tiny boat into cover.

'Why, just a wee paddle around the bay! Thought we'd look at the scenery,' Geordie replied in his broad Newcastle accent. 'Any sign of the others?'

'*Bravo* and *Delta* are missing, there's nothing we can do about it at the moment. *Antrim* knows we have boats adrift.'

It had turned into a dull grey day with low clouds over the sea and occasional snow squalls. They lay in the tussock grass about three hundred yards from the shore, one group watching, the others trying to fix the dodgy outboards. During the morning a lone workman walked out onto the pier at Leith and lit a cigarette. He stood for a few minutes watching the sea and then drifted back into the buildings. Other than that the day passed uneventfully.

'We'll go ashore tonight,' Tim said. 'We'll go in at Stromness and check there's no one there and then find a site overlooking Leith.' There was a general nod of agreement.

By first light Captain Neil Young had a better picture of the situation. Nine of the SAS team were safely established on Grass Island; two of the Geminis, *Delta* and *Bravo*, were lost, presumably drifting out to sea or drowned. *Brambleleaf* and *Tidespring* were starting the pump-over of fuel in preparation for 'M' Company's attack on Leith. *Endurance* was lurking thirty miles down the coast in her favourite hideout among the bergs awaiting news of the SBS who by this time ought to be sending information about the defences of King Edward Point. As far as he could tell the Argentinians still did not know he was there.

With the men installed on Grass Island it ought to be safe now to try and rescue the Geminis. *Antrim* put about and headed back towards the coast. At 8.10 a.m. *Humphrey* took off in the usual appalling conditions, cloud base of less than a hundred feet over heavy sea with white-capped waves. Ian Stanley and his crew didn't reckon much for their chances. They couldn't use radar for fear of alerting the Argentinians, so everything was by eyesight and guesswork as they estimated the drift of the small boats in this wind. They searched fruitlessly for over an hour and just as they were about to return to the ship they picked up the faint signal of *Bravo*'s homing beacon.

For the men on-board the Gemini it had been a frightful night; constantly swamped and bailing, they were frightened and exhausted. The drysuits had kept them reasonably warm but the realisation that they were drifting out to sea was terrifying. They were sitting quietly preparing for the worst. They had drifted for over six miles and were well beyond the area where *Humphrey* was searching.

'I can hear a chopper,' Chippy said, staring into the murk. They were uncertain whether it was British or Argentinian and waited until they finally made out the outline of a Wessex.

'OK, that's it, switch on the beacon.' His crewman was already firing off an orange flare. A few moments later much to his relief the helicopter changed course and hovered over them and moments later they were being lifted up by the grinning winch-man Fitz Fitzgerald. Chippy slashed the Gemini with his knife as he was raised out of the water and it sank immediately. *Humphrey* searched on for a few more minutes, looking for *Delta*, before an urgent call ordered them back to the ship.

A signal had been received from the Antarctic Survey Base at Signy Island that two of the fids at Schlieper Bay, Bill Doidge and Paul Martin, had reported a Hercules C–1 reconnaissance aircraft flying over the island. The BBC broadcast had done its worst. Within minutes it had flown over the two tankers pumping fuel. Once again Captain Young was refused permission to shoot it down.

A few minutes later *Endurance* broke radio silence. Her operators had picked up high-frequency transmissions that could only be a diesel submarine. Commander Denis Davies in the *Paraquat* cell at Northwood had been absolutely correct in his calculation after the warning by Arnie Schwartz that the *Santa Fe* had left the port of Mar del Plata on 9 April. The submarine had arrived off the coast of South Georgia right on time.

Later that morning the Argentinian press began to report that British ships were surrounding South Georgia, and General Galtieri made an impassioned television broadcast. '*Our troops on South Georgia will fight to the last drop of their blood,*' he said. '*If the legitimate garrison of the island is attacked we will ask the Organisation of American States to invoke the Rio de Janeiro mutual defence treaty. . .*'

The loneliness of command was beginning to show strain even on the cool demeanour of Captain Young. He'd had little sleep during the last forty-eight hours. Within a few minutes the situation had totally changed. It was quite clear that the Argentinians must know that the British ships were now off South Georgia. The two tankers were in imminent danger of attack from the submarine and ships close to land were equally vulnerable. With only one Wessex helicopter remaining there was no means of rapidly lifting 'M' Company ashore to attack Leith, and to take his ship close inshore with an enemy submarine prowling was an unacceptable risk. As the day progressed two more Hercules flew down the coast and he had good reason to believe that his ship had been spotted.

He cancelled the attack on Leith, ordered *Antrim* away from the island and at the same time ordered the tankers to make an emergency breakaway from the pump-over and make best speed out of the two hundred-mile exclusion zone. HMS *Plymouth* was escorting the tankers and repeatedly coaxing them to go faster as the huge ships struggled to build up momentum.

Brambleleaf's Captain Mike Fairly signalled: 'I am making best speed!'

'In that case make better than best speed!'

Crashing through the night at full speed in an unstoppable tanker surrounded by icebergs was hair-raising and after passing a couple of small growlers the ship's officers decided that the risk of hitting a berg was greater than that of being torpedoed and they switched on their sonar and radar for the first time in weeks.

An angry Captain Nick Barker on *Endurance* once again found himself alone and vulnerable hiding among the icebergs, the rest of the British navy having cleared off out of the way to the north. Worse still, they picked up a weak signal from the SBS team stranded behind the ice below the Nordenskjold Glacier. He was bitterly disappointed the men had been unable to cross the ice-filled fjord and reach their target. The operation had been a total failure and a waste of time. Angrily, he dispatched Tony Ellerbeck in Wasp 434 to ferry the Special Forces back from the end of the Sorlings Valley. At the same time Tim Findings flew Wasp 435 to St Andrews Bay to warn Cindy Buxton, Annie Price and the rest of the fids what was going on and to keep their heads down.

Nick, who liked and admired Captain Young, was somewhat aggrieved that *Endurance*'s special knowledge of the area was being undervalued. He had disagreed with both the Fortuna and Grass Island operations and thought them time-wasting. He was pretty sure that one of the Hercules surveillance aircraft had spotted him during the afternoon and was very conscious that his booming old Burmeister diesel engines would make him easy prey for the *Santa Fe*.

The second sighting of an aircraft sent him dashing to the satellite communications system to speak to Admiral Sir David Halifax. Exasperatingly, he was told that the admiral was at lunch. Nick insisted on speaking to him and after a few minutes the admiral came on the air.

'Are you having a bit of a problem, Nick?' he asked.

'Yes, sir, we're in a bit of a pickle.' Nick stuck the microphone out of the bridge side door. 'Hear that, sir? That racket is my ship going to action stations. We're trying to bring our pea-shooters to bear on an over-flying 737 ... Perhaps you'd like to hear the 737's intercepted message in Spanish to the *Santa Fe*. They're giving our position and saying we are landing Special Forces.'

'Oh I don't think the submarine is that close, old chap, there really is very little to worry about.'

Nick muttered a curse to himself. How the hell could somebody in the bunker at Northwood have the slightest idea of the whereabouts of the *Santa Fe*?

'Very well, sir,' he said lamely.

The SAS were all lying along the deck with their rifles trained on the aircraft that was now passing low over the ship. The Oerlikon gunners lined up, ready to fire.

'Stand down, boys, don't shoot,' the captain ordered. 'Nobody back home can make a decision!'

Part 3

Battle, Loss, Victory – 'Rejoice!'

43

Grytviken, South Georgia, Sunday 25 April 1982

The submarine USS *Catfish* was launched in New London, Connecticut, on 19 November 1944 and arrived ready for action in the Sea of Japan two days before hostilities ceased. She was one of many hundreds of American submarines that patrolled the Atlantic and Pacific Oceans at the end of World War Two. In the first eighteen months of her strange career she covered over fifty thousand miles. In August 1948 she proceeded to Mare Island for conversion to Guppy II class. This took nine months and completely altered her external appearance, as well as much improving her interior. Three hundred and twelve feet long, she was well armed with ten torpedo tubes, six forward and four back; she could reach twenty knots on the surface and nine submerged.

Submarines are clandestine creatures and little is known of her travels, but a story from one of her crewmen in the 1950s tells of her striking the bottom somewhere in the Bering Sea and tearing off some of her sonar gear. An even more terrifying event is described by one of the crewmen, Joe Galaske:

'We were laying a minefield where we had to fire a mine every minute and a half from the torpedo tubes in a very specific sequence. The gunnery officer got the sequence confused and fired the wrong tube. This opened up a sixteen-inch poppet valve which caused the forward torpedo room to flood, sending the boat to the bottom, which fortunately was only two hundred and fifty feet or so at the time. Of course, they locked us in the room and we closed all the valves to sea, which actually stopped the flooding, but the boat was taking such a down angle that it looked like we were still taking on water. It was one of the scariest moments in my life.'

A newspaper clipping, undated, announced that USS *Catfish*'s captain, Commander John Varney of Coronado, California, received the Legion of Merit after sailing from the Philippines into the mouth of the Gianh River in Vietnam on mission *Wise Tiger*, where she detected Hanoi's fleet of Chinese-built swallow gunboats.

In October 1966 she was given the dubious opportunity to sink a hulk, and fired two torpedoes at the USS *Suisan* somewhere off the coast of California. It was the only ship she ever sank. By 1971 the age of nuclear submarines had arrived. She was old and unwanted by the Americans and sold as a job lot with her sister Guppy, the USS *Chivo*, to the Argentinian navy where she was renamed *Santa Fe*...

The *Santa Fe* slipped silently into the jetty at King Edward Point just before midnight. She was crowded and uncomfortable with a full crew of seventy-six officers and men and twenty commandos from the Buzo Tactico Special Forces, reinforcements for the garrison. Almost every inch of space was filled with ammunition, provisions and equipment. Men were sleeping in the companionways and moving around, difficult at the best of times, was a matter of crawling over boxes of weapons and sleeping soldiers. Apart from the discomfort it had been an uneventful journey; they had seen nothing in the fourteen days since they left Mar del Plata and had spent most of the time on the surface, only diving below to avoid the storm of the last few days.

The submarine had left Argentina optimistically: the general opinion on board was that by the time they reached South Georgia the British would have come to their senses and reached an agreement with the junta over the sovereignty of the Malvinas Islands. There was no expectation of hostile presence and it came as a nasty shock that afternoon when they received an urgent signal from one of their reconnaissance aircraft that there were enemy ships in the area.

The *Santa Fe* inched her way to the jetty with some difficulty. A dull light on shore that flashed occasionally was her only visual reference. It was snowing lightly as Captain Bicain stepped ashore; his sailors were still in the process of fixing the mooring ropes. Surprisingly, in the pitch darkness there was a large crowd on the jetty – almost the entire garrison had turned out to meet him.

'Hello, Horacio, it's good to see you!'

Captain Bicain didn't recognise the man for a moment. He was gaunt and bearded and dressed in padded winter clothing. 'Hugo, I didn't know you through that beard!'

The two officers shook hands warmly. They had gone through the military training school together and were old friends.

'You're coming back with us, Hugo. I hope you're ready; it looks like being an interesting journey. I'd like to be away before dawn if possible, I'd hate the British to catch us here in broad daylight.'

'Yes, I'm all packed up, come up to the base as soon as you're organised. We have a meal ready but it's not exactly the Ritz.'

'It's okay, Hugo, I'll come now, the men know what they're doing. Can someone show the commandos where they're billeted? We'll stack the equipment on the jetty and your men can sort it out in daylight. There are a couple of sacks of mail that I'm sure they'll want right away.'

The two men walked up the track to the base. Captain Bicain was horrified at the state of the building as they entered. It was cold and draughty and hardly the place to billet large numbers of soldiers in a climate like this. Hugo took him through to a slightly more comfortable room that the officers were using.

'This is Teniente Tono Cassin, Horacio. He's taking over command from me tonight.' Hugo introduced the two men. The younger man poured the two captains a drink.

'We weren't expecting the British quite so soon – we had a feeling that the *Endurance* was not far away but she's hardly a warship and of little concern, and there's been no sign of anything since Capitan Tombetta left a month ago,' Hugo said.

'We must leave before dawn,' Horacio said. 'The whole of Cumberland Bay is full of rocks and badly charted and I need to stay on the surface until we get well clear – we don't want to meet any ships in daylight. We aren't sure what's out there but our plane spotted two tankers and an escort a hundred miles to the north and saw HMS *Endurance* among the icebergs in Hound Bay.'

Hugo nodded. 'I'm handing over to you, Tono,' he said. 'From now on you take orders directly from Teniente Astiz at Leith. You'll have to increase the watch now; it's possible that the British will try to attack you. General Galtieri said on the radio today that we must defend South Georgia to the last drop of blood, but use your common sense. The twenty marines that just arrived with Capitan de Corbeta Lagos are very experienced soldiers but the rest of the conscripts aren't up to much. Use your own judgement if you're facing an unbeatable force – don't waste the men's lives unnecessarily.'

The young lieutenant grinned uneasily. 'It's not going to be easy manning positions in conditions like this, Capitan, but we'll do the best we can. The commandos can rest tonight while you finish unloading the *Santa Fe*. Hopefully the weather will calm down tomorrow so we can improve the defences.'

One of the soldiers came in from the radio shack. 'A coded signal for Capitan Bicain,' he said, handing Horacio a sheet of paper.

The brief signal confirmed the order that Captain Corti was to return to Argentina and continued, '*SAS* Santa Fe *is to return to Mar del Plata at earliest opportunity taking all sensible precautions. If possible sink HMS* Endurance.'

Hugo and Horacio looked at each other in consternation. It was clear that the junta was upping the stakes.

'It looks as if your journey home may be more eventful than you expected, Hugo,' Captain Bicain said quietly.

At the same time that the *Santa Fe* arrived at King Edward Point, fifteen miles up the coast the nine remaining SAS men on Grass Island made their second attempt to reach the old, disused whaling station at Stromness. They had made an attempt the previous night but the usual problems with heavy seas and the failure of the outboard motors had sent them paddling frantically back. They had spent another frustrating day watching the coast that was less than half a mile away but from this vantage point there was little to see. Geordie spent the entire day fiddling with the troublesome outboards. There was the unspoken concern for Tom and his two companions who had drifted off into the night on *Delta*.

In slightly calmer seas they set out at midnight to cross the few hundred yards of open water to Stromness. Less than five minutes out and the outboards of *Alpha* and *Charlie* failed and *Echo* took them in tow. All hands frantically paddling, they finally landed on the beach in front of the whaling station where the river runs out into the bay. It was pitch dark and very eerie as they floundered around on greasy rocks among a large herd of elephant seals grunting and roaring at the intruders. Tim left one of his men deflating and hiding the boats and they entered the old factory. Well trained for just such a situation as they were, it was a scary place in pitch darkness with no moon. The corrugated iron of the old buildings was creaking and making strange whistling noises in the wind, and it took them some time to check out the buildings and streets. Much to their relief there was no sign of the Argentinians and after an hour they regrouped on the beach.

'Right, lads, it's time we took a look at Leith. I'll take my two guys and Geordie up onto Harbour Point, the rest of you set up defences here and cover our backs if anything goes wrong.'

The men melted into the old buildings and the four-man team set silently off, climbing the low hill from where, a month earlier, Keith Mills and Peter Leach had spied on Captain Tombetta and the *Bahia Paraiso*.

They arrived on the summit at around 2.30 a.m. and looked down on the lights of Leith. A generator could be heard running in the distance as they settled down to wait; an hour later it was turned off and silence fell. Sometime during the night a rockfall took place somewhere up the valley behind the whaling station and a nervous sentry fired off a few rounds in its direction, a warning that the Argentinians were watchful, but thereafter all remained silent.

As the first rays of morning sunshine illuminated the surrounding mountains they saw a fantastic panorama – hundreds of snow-clad peaks and glaciers surrounding Cumberland Bay. The SAS men were well hidden among the rocks with a clear view down onto Leith. Less than two hundred yards below them soldiers were manning a slit trench and further down the snout of a mortar position could be seen. Everything was pointing out to sea. At 7 a.m. the generator restarted and they watched an officer leaving one of the buildings and making his rounds, inspecting the defences.

Tim grinned to his companions as he marked the position on his map of each of the defence points the man visited. This was a small garrison, defending the best it could an attack from the sea, but there was nothing protecting the rear. Very satisfied, he switched on his secure radio and contacted Major Delves in the operations room on *Antrim* to make his report.

'The base isn't heavily defended, sir. There's an easy landing beach to the north and a surprise landing attack should be straightforward – we could just about take them out ourselves. A land attack from the rear should be easy.'

'Roger, got that, stand by and keep your heads down,' Delves acknowledged. At that precise moment there wasn't a thing he could do; *Antrim* was on full alert and about to go into action, expecting the attack of an enemy submarine.

44

Buenos Aires, Sunday 25 April 1982

General Alexander Haig sat dismally looking out over the River Plate estuary as the Pan Am Boeing 707 circled to land at Buenos Aires International Airport. The aircraft was fitted with bunks, showers and a full working office but in the weeks he had spent shuttling between the capitals of Argentina, Britain and the USA, crossing innumerable time zones, his body clock was in ruins. His tired secretary had calculated that in the first two weeks of this initiative he had flown over thirty-three thousand miles. God knows what it's up to now, he thought.

What had initially seemed a relatively easy diplomatic squabble to settle was turning into his worst nightmare. The two sides had remained entrenched from the start. On his first visit to London a very angry Margaret Thatcher had left him in no doubt that the United Kingdom would not return to the negotiating table until Argentina honoured UN Resolution 502 and left the Falkland Islands.

Worse was to come. His arrival in Buenos Aires was greeted by mass demonstrations in the Plaza de Mayo, to such an extent that he had to be helicoptered clear of the Casa Rosada, the presidential residence and government headquarters at the eastern end of the Plaza. Huge posters declaring *Death to Margaret's Swine* and *Goodbye Queen, Long live Argentina* adorned the streets, and a large effigy of Margaret Thatcher with a pirate's patch over one eye hung from the trees in front of the palace. Radio and TV stations were pouring out a stream of nationalistic music and propaganda.

They're like two boxers weighing in before a big fight, Haig thought. Neither one will be satisfied until there's some blood on the mat.

Somehow he had to find a formula for an Argentinian withdrawal, which didn't look like a climb-down, and would allow the British to return to the Falklands without it seeming that the Argentinians had profited by the aggression. At the same time the issue of sovereignty must remain on the table for negotiation.

His meeting with General Galtieri and Costa Mendez had been incomprehensible. Galtieri was clearly shaken by the speed of the British military response, and the general's consumption of whisky both awed and alarmed Haig. Costa Mendez was just as irrational and was clearly being orchestrated by Admiral Anaya – he still seemed convinced that the British were bluffing.

From the start the American position had been to try to keep her two allies apart and calm troubled waters. The pro-Argentina faction of the US administration, Mrs Kirkpatrick and Tom Enders, stood little chance against the charm offensive staged by Sir Nicholas Henderson, the British Ambassador to Washington. He appeared daily on US television in his crumpled suit, the embodiment of an English gentleman.

'How can you be even-handed between a democracy and a dictatorship?' he murmured, somehow managing to convey the British stance – down-at-heel yet resolute – in the cause of justice. An opinion poll in mid-April showed that the American people were sixty per cent for Britain and only nineteen per cent for Argentina. President Ronald Reagan finally came down decisively on the British side and told Haig it was time to use the big stick.

Landing in Buenos Aires that morning, Haig went directly to a full meeting of the military junta at the Casa Rosada. The small American team settled themselves awkwardly at the long table of officers who had clearly been drinking. General Galtieri headed the table, looking nervous and indecisive. All eyes were on Admiral Anaya.

'Britain is not bluffing and is determined to go to war if

240

necessary,' General Haig told the junta bluntly, looking Anaya straight in the eyes. 'The president will not tolerate the fall of Mrs Thatcher's government over this. Argentina must enter into realistic negotiations on the basis of Resolution 502 or America will side with Britain.'

There was a silence around the table only broken as Anaya struck a match and lit a cigarette. Leaning forward, he pointed a finger directly at the American. 'You're a liar!' he told the dumbfounded general. 'The British have no stomach for war; their fleet is incapable of surviving the South Atlantic winter and will break to pieces. We know through our own intelligence network that the American administration is divided and requires us as an ally.'

Haig looked over to General Galtieri. 'Is that your last word, Leopoldo?' he asked.

Galtieri would not look him in the eye. 'Argentina's troops will stay on the Malvinas dead or alive!' he said.

Al Haig realised that he was dealing with a regime that was out of control. Their rule was brutal and inflexible, suppressing opposition by disappearance and execution. With such men it was impossible to have rational discussion and argument. He left the meeting feeling subdued and defeated. The junta had not rejected outright any of his proposals. That would have required them to make a decision, he thought.

45

London, Sunday 25 April 1982

Peter Bacon-Smith entered 10 Downing Street for the third time in as many weeks and was ushered upstairs to the large committee room where OSDA, the small War Cabinet, held its meeting at 9.30 a.m. each morning. The prime minister had requested a daily report from him on the *Paraquat* situation. There had been little to tell as the ships headed south. The less said, the better, he thought, but he had been surprised at her interest. Peter adjusted his tie uneasily as he entered the room. As the bringer of bad news he knew that this was going to be an awkward meeting.

The War Cabinet was getting into its stride. There were rumblings in Parliament that the government had taken too much power into its hands but, as Winston Churchill had found, control by a small, powerful group is one of those blissful states that a prime minister can seldom achieve in peace time. Margaret Thatcher was enjoying the freedom of action that it gave her. She sat at the head of the table surrounded mainly by supporters and advisors with a similar mindset to her own. They were all acutely aware that in setting the navy loose they had opened Pandora's Box and embarked on a campaign that, should it fail, would almost certainly bring down the government and have the most devastating repercussions for the country. War had not been declared and the Task Force was heading south from Ascension Island at snail's pace, held back as the politicians awaited the results of General Haig's peace initiative.

Sir Terence Lewin, the chief of staff, read out a note from

242

Admiral Woodward requesting permission to shoot down enemy aircraft.

'The Task Force is constantly being over flown by Argentinian Boeing 707 spotter planes that are monitoring our ships,' he said. 'We now have a nuclear submarine patrolling off Port Stanley and it's requesting permission to sink enemy warships in the area.'

Around the table Mrs Thatcher noticed the look of horror on most of the politicians' faces.

'Such a blatant act of war would jeopardise any of our peace initiatives and will almost certainly turn world opinion against us,' John Nott, the defence secretary said, voicing the opinions of almost all his colleagues.

Exasperated, Sir Terence continued to fight his corner. 'Time is against us, Prime Minister. There are almost certainly Argentinian submarines stalking the fleet and those aircraft are vectoring our positions to them. As yet the navy have no rules of engagement and our ships are at risk. The southern winter is approaching and if we don't take action sooner rather than later we run out of time to retake the Islands.'

'Francis Pym is on the morning Concord flight to Washington with our proposals for Argentinian withdrawal,' the prime minister said. 'We know that it's probably a waste of time but we must be seen to give it our best effort. This has to be handled with kid gloves – it's vitally important that the international community don't see our response as a vengeful act of retaliation. The navy can move into position well down track from Ascension Island and make preparations in case the diplomatic effort fails. Until then do not attack unless provoked.'

Sir Terence bowed his head in resignation. Mrs Thatcher turned to Peter. 'What's the news of the South Georgia operation?' she asked.

'The weather in the South Atlantic has been horrific, Prime Minister,' he said uneasily, 'and the operation is twenty-four hours behind schedule. I regret to inform you that two of our Wessex helicopters have crashed on the Fortuna Glacier and as yet we have no indication of casualties. There's also an SAS Gemini assault craft with three of its crew missing. I'm afraid the details at the moment are very vague.'

There was a silence around the table, all eyes on the prime minister, but she just nodded quietly. 'Keep me informed. I'm sure our people are doing the best they can,' she said, with a strained look on her face.

It was a dull, drizzly spring morning as Peter left Downing Street and took the tube out to Uxbridge in the northern suburbs of London, then a taxi to HMS *Warrior* at Northwood. It was still only 11.30 a.m. In South Georgia it was 7.30 a.m., the same time that Tim was watching the lone Argentinian officer making his rounds of the Leith defences.

Peter went through the usual security checks and took the lift down into the Hole. Each time he visited this bunker he was amazed at the hubbub of action that was taking place. It was hard to believe that few, if any, of the people working here had the slightest idea of the operation taking place in the nearby *Paraquat* cell.

The room had changed somewhat with a much larger staff of officers and there was a palpable air of anxiety about the place. Commander Davies looked terrible. During the last few days he and his staff had been working round the clock with very little sleep.

'Have we any more news, Denis?' Peter asked, shaking his hand.

'Not really, we're having difficulty with the satellite communications. I think the *Santa Fe* put into Grytviken last night; it's my guess that she's taking reinforcements to the garrison and will try to leave before dawn. That means she should be coming out of Cumberland Bay right now. We've alerted Captain Young and they should be trying to find her. If she breaks out into deep water our ships will be in grave danger. We had planned an assault on Leith this morning with 42 Commando but cancelled it. To allow our ships to go close into shore would put them into a desperately exposed position with an enemy submarine in the area.'

Peter could see the exasperation and strain on Denis Davies' face. Until the last few days everything had progressed like clockwork but now it all seemed to have gone pear-shaped. 'I'll hang around for a while if that's OK with you, Denis. If there's more bad news I might as well get it first-hand. If the press get hold of this we'll have a real crisis on our hands.'

'We have reinforcements on the way; HMS *Brilliant* should be in the area sometime today. She's a Type 42 Destroyer with two Lynx helicopters on board specially equipped for anti-submarine operations. There are three other destroyers on the way: *Coventry*, *Glasgow* and *Sheffield*, and the frigate *Arrow*. They should all be in the area during the next few days and the nuclear submarine HMS *Conqueror* has turned back. It's like smashing a walnut with a sledgehammer; this was supposed to be a small low-profile operation with minimum damage and loss of life and now we seem to have turned half the bloody navy loose.'

The two men looked at each other uneasily and prepared for a long wait. Unknown to them, things were beginning to happen very rapidly eight thousand miles away, at the entrance to Cumberland Bay.

46

HMS *Antrim*, 200 miles north of South Georgia, Sunday 25 April 1982

The lack of clear rules of engagement was causing alarm throughout the navy, as the Task Force approached the Falkland Islands and the secret *Paraquat* force hovered around South Georgia. British territory had been openly attacked in both these places. Now, as enemy aircraft began to shadow the fleet and vector their positions to more formidable opponents, there was little doubt that some kind of confrontation was imminent, but still the politicians held them back.

To Captain Brian Young on *Antrim* the arrival of an enemy submarine presented a deadly threat. All his ships, with the exception of *Endurance*, had pulled away over the horizon and were marking time two hundred miles to the north.

Despite the prime minister's instructions not to attack unless threatened, the defence rules against submarines are straightforward: the risk of attack is very serious; she can't be boarded, shadowed or put under arrest. In a situation like this to ignore her would be suicidal, so the only open option was to seek her out and sink her. Once out into deep water and clear of the island she would be free to attack wherever she chose. Her ten torpedo tubes were a formidable weapon against surface-bound adversaries and in an area filled with icebergs and in poorly charted waters she would be a very difficult target to find.

Commander Davies' signal from Northwood, warning of the *Santa Fe*'s likely movement out of King Edward Point, set off an immediate alert. HMS *Brilliant* arrived on the scene during the night and her captain, John Coward, knowing nothing of the secret *Operation Paraquat*, spent much of the night on one of his Lynx helicopters trying to locate *Antrim* to be briefed. In the poor weather, and unable to use his radar for fear of detection, his search proved futile and he returned to his ship with very sketchy information about what was going on.

For HMS *Endurance*, off the Barff Peninsula, it was a nerve-racking situation. She felt very exposed. Her old Burmeister diesel engine clanked out like Big Ben every time she moved. Her crew had been on emergency standby for days, and she felt alone, poorly armed and deserted by the navy — *her* navy, which had vanished over the horizon at the first submarine warning. To say that Captain Nick Barker was an angry man would be an understatement.

Captain Young's orders were straightforward: 'Find the *Santa Fe* and *sink her*, search to destruction.'

Within minutes of Northwood's warning, the ships turned south and headed for the coast at full speed. On *Antrim* the tired crew of Wessex 406 (*Humphrey*) were shaken from their bunks and put on emergency standby. They had been flying for days, far exceeding the allowable peacetime flying hours in conditions that they would not take off in even in their wildest dreams. Most of the helicopter's anti-submarine equipment had been stripped out for the glacier flying and during the night the service crew had worked round the clock replacing the sonar system. By dawn the aircraft was ready to go once more as a submarine hunter.

She was armed with two Mark 11 depth charges. These were old and very basic weapons; as Nick Barker remarked sometime later, 'The modern-day equivalent of a caveman's club, just drop them in, splash, and wait for the big bang!'

At 7.30am, as Tim and his SAS team spied down on Leith Harbour and Peter Bacon-Smith was giving Margaret Thatcher his unwelcome report, the radio operator on HMS *Plymouth* intercepted a transmission in Spanish on the VHF. There was no other shipping in the area; the only possibility was that the *Santa Fe* was on the move. The ships were still a hundred miles from the coast; too late to catch the emerging submarine but there was still the chance that the helicopters might reach her before she vanished into deep water.

Humphrey took off with its usual crew: pilot, Lieutenant-Commander Ian Stanley; second pilot, Stewart Cooper; Chris Parry as observer; and Fitz Fitzgerald now acting as gunner. Flying two hundred feet above the sea, they raced for the coast. This was the first time that any of them had flown into action and there was an air of excitement as they headed inland towards the mountains. At the same time, Lynx 431 took off from HMS *Brilliant* armed with a single Mark 6 aerial torpedo. The Lynx would normally carry two of these smart weapons but with over a hundred miles of flight to a possible target the small helicopter was carrying maximum fuel, so one had to be enough.

On *Endurance* both Wasps were standing by. They were in close range of Cumberland Bay on the east side of the Barff Peninsula. Both tiny machines were armed with French AS12 air-to-surface guided missiles. None of the aircrew had fired a missile from a helicopter before although they had all practised on the ship's primitive flight simulator. Another major problem for *Endurance* was that both her aircraft's radio frequencies were different from those of the rest of the *Paraquat* force; in her role as a liaison ship she used normal civilian channels. This meant that once airborne the pilots, Tony Ellerbeck and Tim Finding, would be unable to converse with the other aircraft.

'We'll just have to do our own thing,' Tony said. 'If we try to relay through the mother ships it will take too long.'

The two pilots grinned at each other excitedly as they waited with their crewmen. It all seemed unreal, standing on the freezing deck in their orange immersion suits, watching the first light of dawn illuminating the icebergs surrounding the red ship.

Humphrey flew south-east into a flaming sunrise out of the snow-clad peaks of the Allardyce Mountains. There was a low mist over the water, making it difficult to see more than a few hundred yards of the sea's surface even though the sky was clear.

They followed the coast around Barff Point and flew down into Cumberland East Bay, keeping well clear of King Edward Cove for fear of detection. Ian Stanley then circled and, putting himself into the track he thought that the submarine might take, began to fly out of the fjord.

Chris Parry switched on the radar for a single, one-second sweep. 'There's something right ahead, Ian, just about five miles out, I don't think that it's an iceberg,' he said.

The crew were all staring into the murk. 'Submarine ahead,' Ian Stanley said quietly.

Chris Parry, peering through the Perspex, recognised her immediately. 'She's a Guppy; it must be the *Santa Fe*.' He switched the radar on for another single sweep. 'She's doing eight knots and looks as if she's about to dive,' he said, flicking the switches arming the two depth charges.

As *Humphrey* closed in Chris made a quick calculation. A submarine at eight knots will travel roughly twenty yards per knot so it was easy arithmetic. If the helicopter dropped the charges directly over the target while flying at one hundred knots it would throw them forward of the boat approximately a hundred and fifty yards and should sink and explode precisely as the submarine sailed over them.

'Fly at one hundred knots, Ian, we need to drop right over the target!'

'Roger, one mile and closing, she looks as if she's about to dive.' Ian began to increase his airspeed and lose height. The submarine was now clearly in view, with its conning tower unmanned and periscope raised. It was a textbook attack; *Humphrey* flew directly up the wake of the *Santa Fe*.

'Five hundred yards, four hundred...' Ian counted out the distance as Chris flicked up the red switch covers of the release buttons. 'One hundred yards ... fifty ... twenty-five...'

Peering through the floor of the helicopter Chris held his fingers over the buttons. Suddenly, directly below him the tail of the *Santa Fe* came into view.

'Now!' Ian Stanley's shout came at the exact second that he pressed the buttons and the two large black canisters arched forward and down from the helicopter as it wheeled away to one side.

The four airmen watched spellbound as the two depth charges splashed into the sea way ahead of the submarine. She sailed on below them for what seemed an eternity and then, as the charges sank to thirty feet, there were two almost-simultaneous massive explosions on her port side. The stern crashed upwards and lifted clear of the water and they clearly saw the propeller spinning above the surface. She slewed sideways, rocking and rolling backwards and forwards, and began to career about erratically in the heavy sea.

Chris switched on his radio; there was no need for silence now. '*Antrim*, this is Wessex 406, we have the submarine under attack,' he shouted excitedly. There was no reply so he changed frequency and tried again. This time Lieutenant-Commander Barry Bryant, the pilot of Lynx 341 from HMS *Brilliant* came on air.

'Roger, Ian, I'm thirty miles up the coast, I'll be with you in a few minutes.'

Fitz Fitzgerald now opened up at the submarine with his machinegun; bullets were ricocheting harmlessly off the hull.

'Aim at the periscope, Fitz,' Ian called, 'and have a go at the sonar housing, it's at the foot of the fin.'

Tracers began to arc up from the stricken vessel; a machine-gunner was firing up from a slot in the conning tower. She had turned now and it looked as if she had decided to head back towards Grytviken. Oil was leaking in her wake but her engines seemed unaffected as her speed increased and it looked as if she might still be able to dive.

Lynx 341 raced in along the coast past Busen Point and Jason Island. Its single Mark 46 torpedo was reckoned to be the best anti-submarine weapon in the navy's arsenal. It was a 'drop and forget' weapon, capable of seeking out a target down to a thousand feet below the surface. Because of its likelihood to attack a surface vessel it was set only to home in on an underwater target. The pilot, Barry Bryant, knew that if the submarine commander knew that a Mark 46 was in the water there was no way that he would risk a dive. The excited voice of Chris Parry was giving him a running commentary. As he flew over Larson Point he spotted *Humphrey* circling the submarine, which appeared to be making rapid headway back towards land.

Bryant's observer, Lieutenant Nick Butler, had already armed the torpedo. 'Put it on the shallow setting, Nick, she won't be able to dive while this is in the water,' Barry shouted.

They watched *Humphrey* dunk a sonar-buoy tracking device into the sea and turn back to the ship to re-arm. Barry flew in along the wake of the *Santa Fe* and released the torpedo. It splashed into the water and instantly dived below the surface and, like a sniffing bloodhound, began to track backwards and forwards. Nick clambered over his seat into the rear, opened the door and began firing long bursts with his machine gun, which jammed after a few moments. Tracer bullets were coming up at them and there was little more they could do until reinforcements arrived. Barry pulled the revolver from his belt but, feeling like a cowboy, put it away again. As the helicopter spun round and flew up the port side of the submarine, Nick grabbed a Sterling sub-machinegun and opened the opposite door. The resulting blast of air through the cockpit split open a plastic container of 'chaff' and the inside of the aircraft instantly filled with a cloud of tiny slivers of aluminium foil, blinding the pilot and gunner and choking them in the swirling silver cloud. Very shaken, Barry lifted away from the submarine and flew around, calming himself and trying to clear the cockpit. Below him the *Santa Fe* was sailing rapidly into the relative safety of Cumberland Bay.

47

Submarine *Santa Fe*, Cumberland East Bay, Sunday 25 April 1982

It had been an anxious night at King Edward Point, taking longer to unload the *Santa Fe* than Captain Bicain had intended. The darkness and lightly falling snow had hampered the work and it wasn't until the early hours of the morning that they were ready to leave. He was confident that his arrival hadn't been spotted by any British ships and was satisfied that he would be well away in deep water long before they had any idea of his presence. He knew that HMS *Endurance* was close by and should make an easy target. It seemed strange that only a few months earlier he had been moored alongside her and enjoyed a number of pleasant evenings with Captain Nick Barker.

She will be a very easy target, a sitting duck without much defence, he thought with some regret.

There had been an angry radio discussion with Lieutenant Astiz during the night. The reinforcements had really been intended for the garrison at Leith but the British warships in the area had forced him to slip into Grytviken.

'There has been no sign of ships here,' Astiz said angrily. 'Bring the commandos round immediately; there is plenty of cover and deep water.'

'It's impossible, Alfredo, the risk is too great. Our aircraft definitely saw warships in the area. I must get out into deep water as soon as I can.'

'You should have come here directly,' Astiz retorted furiously, almost openly implying that Captain Bicain had been negligent.

Hugo and Horacio Bicain exchanged glances. Not for the first time Hugo felt a rush of relief that he was leaving this place. The lack of planning that had gone into the defence of this island seemed extraordinary. Everyone had assumed that the British would have capitulated easily and a small garrison was all that was required. Given adequate resources both Leith and King Edward Point would be easy places to defend but the number of men and the quality of most of them was far from satisfactory. They tried to radio base at Mar del Plata to clarify their orders but reception was poor on high frequency and they made no contact so they stuck to the original plan.

'Take care, Tono, and remember what I told you about risking the men's lives,' Hugo told the young officer as they shook hands on the jetty.

Cassin grinned. 'Don't worry, Capitan; the men will give a good account of themselves.'

Just before 7 a.m. the *Santa Fe* slid away from the jetty. The sky was clearing but a low mist hung over the fjord, the shadow of the mountains black against the first hint of dawn. Captain Bicain conned the submarine through the periscope. Normally he would have been up on the conning tower but in the freezing mist it was more comfortable down in the hold. Hugo watched with interest as the crew made preparations to dive. As the *Santa Fe* passed Hope Point they made another attempt to make radio contact with headquarters but again failed. As they cleared Larson Point at the head of the Busen Peninsula they were out of the shelter of the fjord into the heavier sea.

'Prepare to dive,' Captain Bicain ordered.

Two of the crew were in the process of closing the heavy hatch to the conning tower when there was a sudden roar of motors. Staring through the wide-angle lens of the periscope, the captain watched in horror as the dark shadow of a helicopter whirled away from them and two large falling objects splashed into the water directly ahead.

'Depth charges!' he yelled. 'Hard to starboard.' The submarine began to turn but he knew that it was too late; there was nothing that he could do.

Hugo was standing alongside him looking anxious, like the rest of the crew not fully comprehending what was happening. The two men above were urgently closing the watertight hatch. Captain Bicain counted the seconds, praying for his ship to turn; it seemed an eternity.

The explosion when it came was horrendous. A deafening, echoing roar vibrated through the submarine and she was hurled sideways almost standing on her nose. Men went tumbling down the companionways crashing into the pipe work. The diesel engines screamed as the propeller lifted clear of the water, and she began to roll on her side as if she was about to turn over. Both the men closing the conning tower had fallen to the hold and were lying under a cascade of water crashing down from above. The boat groaned, a sound almost human in anguish. There was an imperceptible pause and then she began to roll upright.

Captain Bicain was still hanging onto the periscope as Hugo staggered to his feet. Most of the lights had gone out and there was a reeking stench of diesel. The engines were still running.

'Give me a damage report,' the captain shouted. 'Get a gun crew into position until we know what's happened.' He handed the periscope over to Petty Officer Felix Artuso.

Reports were coming in from all parts of the submarine as the gunners scrambled up into the conning tower. Unlike the steel hull, the tower, or sail as it's known, isn't watertight and, on a Guppy, is constructed from fibreglass, although the gun port has a steel housing protecting it. Running up through this compartment are the periscope, snorkel, radar and radio antenna, and a host of other equipment. As the men set up the gun bullets began to rattle on the outside of the hull. They were also passing through the fabric of the conning tower and pinging off the periscope housing, and although they weren't causing much damage it was very unnerving for the gunners.

The chief engineer reported that the port ballast tank was

ruptured and that many of the electrical circuits were damaged but the engines appeared to be running well.

'The helicopter's dropping something into the sea, Capitan, I think it's a sonar transducer,' Felix shouted. A few moments later the radio officer reported the sound of sonar in the water close by them.

Horacio was thinking fast. He had two limited choices to save his ship – to dive and hide or cut and run on the surface back to Grytviken. His boat was damaged and leaking oil and would be an easy target for ships equipped for anti-submarine warfare. It wasn't far to the relative safety of King Edward Cove if he could make it before the enemy got to him.

'Take her about; give me the best speed you can!' he ordered.

'There's another helicopter, Capitan, coming up behind us,' Felix yelled.

Horacio sprang to the periscope and took over just in time to see Lynx 341 drop her torpedo. 'Torpedo in the water,' he shouted, cursing under his breath. 'I think it's a homer, we'll be better off on the surface – try to give me some more speed.'

Once again the hammer of machinegun fire rattled harmlessly on the hull and then at last came the sound of their own gun, echoing noisily through the boat as the crew opened fire at the helicopter. There was little else they could do but wait. The radio officer joined them, looking white-faced and tense.

'We can hear the torpedo, sir; it's tracking us somewhere below the surface.'

'Thank you, Ricardo. I don't think it will attack us on the surface,' he said, praying that he was right. 'Can you send an urgent message that we're under attack? Warn them back at King Edward Point.'

'What now?' Hugo asked quietly. He was feeling sick and very afraid and could only admire the cool way that the captain was handling the situation.

'We head back to Grytviken, Hugo. Our chances depend on where the British ships are – they know our position now. It's our only chance to save the crew; if they reach us first we're done for.'

'Is there anything I can do?' Hugo asked.

'I think a prayer might be helpful,' Horacio murmured.

48

HMS *Endurance*, Barff Peninsula, Sunday 25 April 1982

Unaware of the action taking place on the other side of the Barff Peninsula, Tony Ellerbeck and his observer, David Wells, took off from HMS *Endurance*. His small Wasp helicopter was armed with two AS12 air-to-surface missiles. As they flew north-east along the coast, both men peering over the mist-covered sea hoping to spot any signs of the submarine, an urgent radio signal from the mother ship came over the intercom.

'Wasp 434, this is *Endurance*, we've picked up an emergency signal in Spanish from the *Santa Fe*: she's under attack at the entrance to Cumberland Bay.'

'Roger, *Endurance*, we'll go and take a look,' Tony acknowledged.

The Wasp banked east and flew directly up the Merton Channel, flying low between the cliffs of Barff Point and Right Whale Rocks. The last time they had been here was standing on the bridge of *Endurance* on the terrifying night they had slipped away from the *Bahia Paraiso* as Captain Tombetta tried to trap them in King Edward Cove. Seeing the channel from the air, Tony wondered how on earth the red ship had managed to slip through; there seemed to be rocks everywhere. As he emerged from the channel the full sweep of Cumberland Bay became visible, the dawn sunshine striking the mountain tops. Directly ahead of him, about two miles away, he could see the dark shape of the submarine sailing rapidly back into the fjord.

David Wells went through the armament checks and tried to fire off the port missile but nothing happened. He checked and fired again. This time the missile streaked away, guided easily as he controlled it through the cross of his sight with the small joystick. It flashed past a startled Lynx 341, which was still wobbling around the sky as Barry Bryant tried to clear the chaff from his cockpit, and slammed straight through the conning tower and exploded in the water about 30 yards ahead of the boat. The fibreglass hadn't been strong enough to detonate the warhead. Ellerbeck circled, lined up for a second attack and fired off his second AS12 but this time the missile dropped short and exploded in the sea.

'OK, David, we won't hang about, let's go back to mother and get some more fireworks,' the pilot said.

A second helicopter from HMS *Brilliant* now arrived on the scene: a Lynx 342, piloted by Commander John Clark and observer Paul McKay. She was rigged with a magnetic anomaly detector for underwater search and had no missiles on board but immediately joined in with Lynx 341 and the two helicopters opened up on the *Santa Fe* with their machineguns. They buzzed around like angry hornets, doing little damage but forcing the submarine crew to keep their heads down.

In extra-quick time Tony Ellerbeck returned from *Endurance*, having re-armed. The submarine was now entering Cumberland Bay. He dodged through the swarm of helicopters and fired off another AS12 but this proved to be a rogue and it vanished into the sea. His second missile crashed through the conning tower, again without exploding.

'Bullseye!' shouted John Clark over the intercom in a Lynx 342. Their excited banter could now be heard on board the *Paraquat* ships now closing in to within thirty miles of the coast.

Ellerbeck was already on his way back to *Endurance* to re-arm for the second time. By now the submarine was getting very close to the shore and the helicopters were beginning to come under machinegun and rifle fire from Hope Point. Tracers were flashing up towards the angry swarm of aircraft buzzing around the stricken boat. Next in line to attack was the Wasp 445 from HMS *Plymouth*, flown by Commander John Dransfield and his observer

Joe Harper. Very excited, and with tracers and rifle fire flashing around them, they made a textbook attack, firing off their single AS12 missile. This struck the water on the starboard side of the submarine. There was a tremendous explosion and she began to leak more oil and list to one side. The Wasp curved away and headed back to *Plymouth* to re-arm.

Tim Finding, *Endurance's* second helicopter pilot, now fired his first missile, which fell short of target. Keeping calm as tracer bullets arced up at him, Bob Nadin, the observer, launched his second missile. Holding the target in the cross of his rangefinder, he guided the AS12 home, the aircraft following the missile in as it crashed through the conning tower, again failing to explode. Dodging enemy gunfire, the helicopter turned away and, sweeping low over the water, headed back to *Endurance* for more missiles. As he crossed the Barff Peninsula he passed Tony Ellerbeck, re-armed and returning to the fray.

'Careful, Tony, there's heavy gunfire coming up from Hope Point,' he warned as the pilots waved to each other.

'Roger that, Tim, one last shot,' Tony called.

The Wasp flew in towards King Edward Cove as most of the other helicopters had returned to their ships to reload. Tracers were streaking up towards them and an anti-tank missile flashed past, fired from Hope Point. Shackleton's Cross stood out starkly in the sunshine against the snow-clad hillside. There was no sign of the *Santa Fe.*

'What now, Tony?' David Wells asked as they raced in towards the buildings.

'Let's have a go at the radio shack,' Tony suggested. 'There's bound to be somebody controlling things from there.'

The base was now in full view, the buildings standing out clearly on the spit of gravel near the cove's entrance and the old whaling station at the end of the bay, derelict and deserted. There was a light dusting of snow almost down to the sea – it was like a picture postcard. Both men had spent pleasant evenings here with the fids in the warmth and comfort of the base and had socialised with the submarine crew at Mar del Plata; a strange twist of fate!

'Missile away,' David shouted into the intercom as the AS12 sailed off towards the radio shack with the helicopter in hot pursuit. He conned it along using the optical sight but as it flew towards the base he spotted the *Santa Fe* alongside the landing stage with men jumping out and running towards the buildings.

'I see it, I see it – the *Santa Fe*'s at the jetty,' he shouted as he twisted the joystick. The missile rose in the air and changed direction, climbing over the buildings. It swooped along the line of the track where men were running and diving for cover and struck the submarine at the base of the conning tower. There was a massive explosion with debris flying in all directions; the helicopter soared on over the stricken ship and away from the rising tracer fire. This time the aircrew were in no doubt that the *Santa Fe* would take no further part in this war.

49

Submarine *Santa Fe*, Cumberland Bay, Sunday 25 April 1982

For the crew of the *Santa Fe* the race back to King Edward Point was the longest and most terrifying hour of their lives. Having seen one aerial torpedo dropped, Captain Horacio Bicain could only assume that others would be on their way. He knew that it was pointless to try to submerge and that there was nothing that he could do to get onto the offensive. His torpedoes could only be used against shipping. His one aim in life became the desire to save the lives of his crew. If he could reach King Edward Point base there would be some chance of covering fire – after that it would be anyone's guess.

The machinegun fire from the helicopters was rattling noisily on the hull and could be heard peppering holes in the conning tower. Their own returning gunfire echoed through the ship in loud bursts. Most of the gangway lights were back on and they were making good headway. The ship's engineers didn't need any instructions: they were frantically fixing everything they could. Even with the main hatch open the reek of diesel and burnt wire was almost overpowering. Horacio resisted the urge to call for more speed; she was travelling at above her normal maximum speed and he knew that everything possible was being done.

For the next twenty minutes they made good headway back into the mouth of Cumberland East Bay when a sudden shock and a loud bang followed by an explosion in the water rocked the boat erratically. There was an agonised scream as one of the gunners fell through the hatch down into the control room, his leg mangled and spouting blood. A missile – Tony Ellerbeck and

David Wells' first attack in Wasp 434 – had passed through the conning tower without exploding.

'Help that man, Hugo,' the captain asked. He watched the helicopter through the periscope as it launched the second missile. 'Missile coming in! Get the other gunner out of the tower.'

There was a second explosion that rocked the boat but this time it hit well clear of the submarine. Hugo and Felix Artuso were frantically attempting to quell the bleeding, rigging a tourniquet around the terrified young gunner's leg. The anxious crew looked on in shock as they manoeuvred him down the companionway into one of the bunks. A medic arrived and gave him a shot of morphine.

'What're our chances?' the boy asked.

'We'll make it; your Capitan knows what he's doing. It's not far to the base: we'll be safe there and soon get that leg fixed,' Hugo said, just as two more explosions shook the ship. It was torture not knowing what was coming next; he was no submariner and the claustrophobia and inability to see what was happening in this dim, fume-ridden atmosphere was almost overpowering. He left the gunner with the medic and made his way back to the control room.

They were now running along the coast towards King Edward Cove. 'Our men on the coast are in range now and are shooting at the helicopters; we're almost in the bay,' Horacio told Hugo. A moment later he watched another helicopter launch a missile. 'Missile coming in, everybody down!' he shouted. There was a long pause that seemed to go on forever. All eyes were on the captain. Then came a thunderous explosion on the starboard side and the submarine reared sideways. The blast was deafening as the boat rolled onto her side and then, agonisingly slowly, began to right herself. This time she was listing to one side and water was spraying in through a long split in the hull, and most of the lights were out again. There was a lot of shouting as a second missile slammed through the conning tower, this time without exploding.

As they rounded Hope Point and entered the cove the sea became noticeably calmer and the gunfire ceased.

'I'm going up onto the tower,' the captain said, handing over the periscope to Felix. 'I'll try to put her into the jetty but we might have to run her aground up the beach – get ready to abandon ship,' he instructed. They were now round Hope Point and into the calm waters of the cove.

He scrambled up the ladder out into the bright sunshine with Hugo close on his heels. Both captains looked at each other and took a deep breath of the fresh, freezing air. The conning tower was riddled with holes and it seemed astonishing that the periscope had survived the onslaught.

'OK, Felix, let's take her in,' he ordered.

As they pulled alongside the jetty, soldiers were running down the track from the base to help. The two men jumped onto the jetty.

'I need a doctor; one of my men is badly injured,' Horacio shouted to one of the soldiers running towards him just as Hugo slammed into him, shoving him roughly to the ground. He was just in time to see a missile flying over the base and along the track directly towards them. It flashed low over their heads and smashed into the base of the conning tower. The blast shook the whole jetty; there was a brilliant flash and large chunks of metal and fibreglass sprayed in all directions. Hugo lay stunned and deafened over Captain Bicain but found that miraculously he was unhurt. The two men scrambled shakily to their knees.

'My ship, my ship: what a mess!' the captain said, tears coursing down his face as he surveyed the wrecked boat. They clambered back on board and began to climb the damaged conning tower. Men began to scramble up from the control room.

'Is anybody hurt?' Hugo asked Felix as he emerged into the sunshine.

'No, Capitan, we were below trying to get the gunner up the ladder when the explosion happened.'

'Good. Get everybody out and up to the base as quickly as

you can. I don't think they'll attack us immediately but they're bound to follow up their advantage,' Hugo said.

Lieutenant Cassin arrived, running down the jetty. As they shook hands Hugo noticed that much of the equipment they had unloaded from the submarine the previous night was still stacked as they had left it and realised that it was only 9.30 a.m. Less than three hours had passed since they had set sail from here; it seemed an eternity.

'Come on, Tono,' said Hugo, 'we'd better get to work on the defences, the British are bound to follow up this attack.' They left Horacio Bicain organising the submarine's evacuation and hurried together up the track to the base.

'I was in the radio shack most of the time,' Tono said. 'We have orders from the admiral to fight to the last man. There seem to be dozens of helicopters – how do we defend ourselves against the missiles?'

'God knows, Tono; the submarine crew are in no state to defend anybody. Get me Capitan Lagos immediately – we need to prepare for some kind of assault any time now and his twenty marines are the best troops we have; our own garrison are well dug in but not very experienced. We need to arm the submarine crew as best we can.'

The two officers dashed into the base and set about the thankless task of preparing to defend King Edward Point against its second seaborne invasion.

50

Christian and Lofty stood leaning against the rail of *Antrim*, looking out over the island. The sky was clear with a large curving wind cloud arcing over the summit of Mount Sugartop; for once the sea was almost calm. There was an air of excitement. All the helicopters had returned to their respective mother ships by 10.45 a.m. and the troops on board were on standby and bursting to go for the final assault on King Edward Point.

'It's bloody typical. Here we are at the sharp end and the army are two hundred miles away over the horizon,' Lofty grumbled.

It was quite true. The main assault force of 'M' Company were still on-board the tanker *Tidespring*, now returning as fast as she could to the area but still with several hours of steaming to go before she arrived.

'Sheridan can't wait; he'll want to go in while they're still off balance,' Christian said. 'I don't know what's keeping him. Mark my words; we'll be hanging around here for hours while the brass make up their minds what to do.'

He was quite right. On the bridge Captain Young, Major Sheridan and Major Delves were hurriedly putting together their plan of attack. They were joined by Lieutenant-Colonel Keith Eve, a very experienced gunnery expert.

'We still have no idea about the Argentinian defences. I can't take the ships in too close in case they have missiles on shore,' Captain Young said. 'I'm almost certain that they haven't had

265

time to set up an Exocet battery but you know what a mess our boys made of the *Guerrico* with ordinary anti-tank weapons – they're bound to have something set up.'

'We should soften them up with a bombardment,' Keith Eve said.

The captain shook his head. 'No, we stick to our original orders: minimum loss of life and damage to property. We should land our forces as soon as possible and discount "M" Company; by the time they arrive our advantage will be lost. How many men have you got, Guy?'

'We have *Antrim*'s own marine detachment, a couple of sections of 42 Commando and some assault engineers, and then there are Captain Hamilton's SAS mountain troops: they're rested and ready to go. *Plymouth* and *Endurance* both have their own marines and some SBS. I make it seventy-four all told; that's probably about half the Argentinian force, not enough by normal rules of warfare but they're well trained and raring to go. If we could soften them up with some frightening gunfire I think our chances are very high.'

'The problem will be getting you ashore fast enough. The Wasps are too small, which means we only have the two Lynx helicopters from *Brilliant* and our Wessex, *Humphrey*, which is now fully loaded with sonar equipment. Even they can only carry eight men each. That's only twenty-four at a time. We'll have to get you in fast before the Argies catch on,' the captain said.

Guy Sheridan spread a map onto the plotting table. 'I'd like to land the main force here on the Hestesletten Flats. It's more-or-less hidden from King Edward Point by the ridge of Brown Mountain. If you could bombard the area before we land in case they have it defended and then fire some heavy gunfire on the slopes of Brown Mountain above Grytviken, just to let them know what we can do, that should keep their heads down. From there it's only three miles for the troops to yomp over the shoulder of the mountain and around the coast to the base. Once we get

Antrim's main force down at Hestesletten the helicopters can lift the remaining troops from *Plymouth* and *Endurance* and drop them on the side of Mount Duse on the high ground above King Edward Point.'

'Nick Barker wants to run *Endurance* up onto the beach at Maiviken and put his marines ashore where they can make an attack from the rear. He's quite certain that with his ice-strengthened bow his ship will be okay but I'm not keen on the idea,' Captain Young said.

Guy Sheridan grinned. 'He's dead keen but we can get them closer with the helicopters. It's not worth the risk. What about the guns, Keith?' he asked, turning to Colonel Eve.

Lieutenant-Colonel Keith Eve was the head of training of naval gunfire for all NATO and Commonwealth forces. A trained paratrooper and commando, he had seen action in Aden and the Yemen and against *Eoka* terrorists in Cyprus.

'We can really lay it on, Brian. *Antrim* can fire in from outside Cumberland Bay and we can lob shells over the Barff Peninsula from *Plymouth*. I'll remain here in control of the guns and I have an excellent forward observer, Captain Chris Brown. If we can put him up in one of the Wasps to call the guns we'll give you accurate fire wherever you want it,' Eve said.

'Right, I'll leave that to you. We want a good fireworks show but definitely no damage to property unless with my authority,' Captain Young stated.

'*Antrim* and *Plymouth* have 4.5mm twin gun turrets. We can lob fifty-pound shells from each gun sixteen times a minute; it'll be one hell of a fireworks display,' Keith said with a wide grin on his face.

At 2 p.m. Tony Ellerbeck and David Wells took off from *Endurance* with Captain Chris Brown, Royal Artillery, crammed in the back seat and flew over the coast to the Barff Peninsula. The sky was clear but a low-lying mist and the odd cloud were obscuring the full view of Cumberland Bay. They landed just behind the ridge and Chris scrambled out and surveyed the scene through his binoculars. It wasn't very clear and he was unable to see the full panorama.

'Can you get me over to Dartmouth Point, Tony?' he asked.

The pilot and David Wells looked at each other doubtfully but after a moment Ellerbeck shrugged and nodded. The helicopter flew back behind the peninsula and slipped through the Sorlings Valley, crossed the Nordenskjold Glacier and, flying low along the beach, landed behind Dartmouth Point. With the blades still turning, Chris jumped out and clambered up to a perfect viewpoint overlooking King Edward Cove and little more than a mile from Hestesletten Flats. The submarine was sitting ominously alongside the jetty and he could see men moving about the base. He ran back to the helicopter.

'It's perfect, Tony. How much fuel do you have?'

'About forty-five minutes if we idle, less if we're flying,' the pilot said.

'That's not enough: can you shut down for a while?'

I hope this'll be all right, Chris thought as once again the two airmen looked at each other in consternation. They were very close to the Argentinian position and would be unable to take off in a hurry once the engine was turned off. Finally Ellerbeck nodded and shut down. The silence was deafening as all three men scrambled up to the crest of the ridge.

Antrim was in position just off Sappho Point, with the *Plymouth* three miles north-west of the Barff Peninsula. Chris switched his radio on and began to read out his instructions to the gunners aboard the two ships. The two airmen watched quietly.

'Ready,' he said, realising that he was about to launch the first naval barrage of the Falkland Island War.

'Fire!' *Plymouth*'s first shell erupted from her guns and sailed over the Barff Peninsula, reaching a height of six thousand feet before it curved over and exploded in the centre of Hestesletten Flats thirty seconds later. As the first shell landed another four shells were in the air screaming in from the guns of *Antrim*. Already airborne, the three helicopters were flying in with Major

Cedric Delves and the SAS mountain troops. The beautiful, sunny Antarctic day was shattered by the thunderous roar of exploding shells echoing around the mountains.

51

In the hut behind the beach in Antarctic Bay it was as normal a Sunday morning as was possible under the circumstances. It was fine for a change after the light snowfall during the night. Sebastian came in, stamping the snow off his boots. The women already had a brew on the stove and Alison was taking her turn at cooking breakfast. It was the same most days: porridge, hard tack biscuits with jam and as much tea as you could drink, but today as on most Sundays they opened a tin of bacon from the fids' food boxes. Alison had mixed up some potato powder and was in the middle of a fry-up. A pleasant bacon fug filled the small hut.

'I could smell that out in the tent, it just about has me dribbling,' Sebastian said, with a wide smile. He was more unkempt than ever. His black, greasy and matted beard made him appear like a scruffy Indian yogi; his clothing was filthy and in tatters. Nevertheless, he had lost weight and was probably fitter than he had ever been in his life and he admitted that the enforced isolation suited him.

'What's keeping David?' Alison asked, as she handed Seb a mug of tea.

'He's just coming back along the beach; he got up early and walked out to Tornquist Point to see if there's any sign of a ship. It's a lovely morning. Anything on the news?'

'Nothing about us. The Task Force is still heading down to the Falklands and General Haig's peace initiative seems to have fizzled out,' Anna said. 'There are riots at the Maze prison in Northern Ireland and Yasser Arafat is upsetting the Israelis.'

270

'Situation normal then, though those helicopters must have been up to something. I can't believe they've just left us here to rot,' Seb said cheerily.

David Asquith came into the hut. 'Morning all, just been down for the papers. That bacon smells fantastic,' he said, grinning at Alison. In contrast to Sebastian he had trimmed his beard and Alison had cut his hair. His clothes were repaired and serviceable and he looked almost identical to when Alison had first met him.

'I vote we have a day off. It's much too nice a day for geophysics. I fancy a walk up to the col over Possession Bay – those helicopters came from that direction. It's worth a look. How about you, Alison?' David asked.

Alison looked over to Anna. 'That's OK with me, I could do with a rest and I need to write up some notes,' Anna said.

'Suits me too, I'll hang around here and take life easy,' Seb said lazily.

They both knew that their two assistants needed some time off together, and there was plenty for them to do around the hut. David switched on the Racal Squad Call radio set and tuned in to Bird Island. Paul Goodall-Copestake was already speaking to David Roots on Signy Island.

'Your signal is very poor, David, reading you strength three. We're all still okay. Do you have any news?'

'Our aerial was damaged during the last storm, we've made some temporary repairs but things will improve now that we can get outside. We still have no news other than yesterday's aircraft sightings. How's everybody making out?'

Cindy Buxton came on the air. 'Everything is fine here, and we're still managing to do some filming,' she said. Alison always admired the air of quiet confidence that came from the women at St Andrews Bay; their situation was very similar to her own and not once had she heard a word of concern or complaint. She hoped that she sounded just as confident as they did.

Things were not so good at the Lyell Glacier hut. 'It's very serious here, the hut is providing very little shelter in these storms,'

Damian Saunders said. 'We'll try to last for another week but that will have to be it. We'll have to walk over to King Edward Point and hand ourselves in.'

'Try to hang on if you can, Damian, I'm still getting signals from the director to try to keep you there. There must be some reason,' David Roots answered.

They switched off. Nothing seemed to be happening. David was agitated. 'You know, we could make it over to the Lyell Glacier hut,' he said, looking at Alison. 'We left a small supply of food hidden on the beach at Fortuna Bay. We could retrace our route back there and then sneak round the back of the whaling stations. It's only an easy ten-mile walk from there.'

'It's not sensible, David, we'd have to leave Anna and Seb here, the snow on the Fortuna Glacier must be much deeper now than when you came over, and the way the weather is we could be stuck over there for weeks waiting for a fine spell to get back. We'd probably use more of their food than we could take.'

David nodded. 'I guess you're right but I just hate this waiting and hanging around. I know just how they feel in that hut.'

Sebastian had been sitting quietly listening. 'It's an odd thing, I keep thinking I hear thunder – that's twice I've heard it but it's such a fine morning, I wonder where it's coming from?' They all waited, listening, but heard nothing.

David and Alison set out along the beach towards the back of Antarctic Bay. The great rookery of king penguins was unusually noisy this morning. The water's edge was filled with wildlife. A small colony of fur seals played in the shallows and a large leopard seal lay on the beach. They gave it a wide berth but it ignored them as they passed. They scrambled up snow-covered scree for about a thousand feet to the low col overlooking Possession Bay where they had seen the helicopters pass through. It was a spectacular sight. Just below them was a small tarn, partly frozen over, and way beyond they could see right through the Shackleton Gap to King Haakon Bay on the southern side of the island, a low, snow-covered pass not much higher than where they were standing.

'That's where Shackleton landed in the *James Caird*; you can almost see Peggotty Bluff where they rested for a few days. Seb and I worked over there earlier in the season. It seems years ago. Shackleton must have crossed over to Possession Bay and then climbed that slope up to the Murray Snowfield.'

They sat quietly, looking across the mountains. It was a beautiful, peaceful day. Large icebergs gleamed in the sunshine over at King Haakon Bay and below them lay the sheltered waters of Possession Bay with the silhouette of the huge cliffs of Cape Constance dropping into the sea.

'What now, David? We can't stay here indefinitely. Although I almost wish we could,' Alison said.

'I'm certain that David Roots at Signy knows more than he's admitting over the radio. He's really putting the pressure on for the Lyell Glacier party to stay where they are and the women at St Andrews Bay sound very buoyant. Those helicopters must have come from somewhere and the Schlieper Bay fids saw ships and aircraft a couple of days ago. I think something's going to happen in the next few days.

'What happens when we get rescued, David?' Alison found she had a lump in her throat. For all the apprehension this had been a very happy time for her. So much had happened since the *Endurance* had landed them at Antarctic Bay. Theirs had been a strange affair. All of them had come to rely on the tall New Zealander and she wondered what he would do when they were no longer marooned together. There had been little chance to be together by themselves and he didn't seem the type to be tied down, but she thought she would be heartbroken to lose him.

There was a long silence; the same thoughts were going through his mind. 'I've not given it a lot of thought, Alison, I guess once we get back to Britain I'll be heading home to New Zealand.'

Her heart sank and there was another long silence, both of them staring blindly out to sea.

He stirred and turned to look at her. 'Will you come with me?

It's not like England but it's got a lot going for it,' he asked, quietly.

A great flood of relief surged over her. 'Of course I will, I thought you were never going to ask!' She put her arms around him and hugged him.

They were still sitting like this when the first roll of thunder echoed around the mountains. Moments later another, and then another, until the distant roar became almost constant, great waves of sound echoing through the valleys and glaciers.

'That's not thunder,' David said, 'it's gunfire.'

52

Hestesletten Flats, Sunday 25 April 1982

They switched the gunfire target from Hestesletten to Brown Mountain two minutes before *Humphrey*, flanked by two Lynx helicopters, came skimming fifteen feet above the water through the Merton Channel, crossed Cumberland Bay and landed the first group of SAS mountain troops on the flats. Jammed in the hold among the sonar and anti-submarine hardware, Captain John Hamilton and seven of the SAS troops scrambled awkwardly out while Fitz Fitzgerald handed out their usual large supply of weapons through the side window.

'It's a bloody good job that there doesn't seem to be any opposition here, it's taking ages to get those choppers away,' Christian shouted as they dashed for cover. The noise from the shells falling on Brown Mountain was deafening. Everybody was keyed up and very excited.

'There's something moving over there at ten o'clock,' Lofty shouted. One of the men opened up with his general purpose machinegun.

'You big buffoon, you've just shot a company of elephant seals!' somebody shouted. Everybody was grinning. The small group spread out and began to advance towards Brown Mountain ridge, urged on by Major Delves.

A message came over the radios. 'There's a machinegun site just below the ridge – there's some light-coloured rock and a post sticking up above the horizon.' Everybody dived for cover.

David Hamilton was carrying a Milan missile launcher, a French-made portable anti-tank weapon with a range of two kilometres.

'Give me a hand, Chris,' he shouted. The two men lay in the snow-covered grass and Christian fed the large missile into the firing posts. Hamilton had used the weapon before but it was the first time that Christian had seen one in action. There was a muffled *woomff* and the wire-guided missile streaked off and exploded spot on target. They all charged forward only to find some light-coloured rocks and a marker post left by the whalers. Feeling sheepish they spread out again and continued advancing up the ridge. Behind them the second batch of troops was landing with Major Guy Sheridan, noticeably angry at their slow progress.

Looking out from his perfect vantage site at Dartmouth Point, Chris Brown watched the troops across the flats. The 4.5mm shells were falling every few seconds, with terrific explosions amplified and echoing around the mountains. A large cloud of rock dust was drifting above the scree. As Chris called out the coordinates the shells were moving slowly across the hillside towards Grytviken. The two airmen, crouched alongside him, watched, mesmerised.

'I think *Antrim* should come out into the open, sir,' Chris radioed to Keith Eve. 'We'll be able to put accurate fire onto the mountainside above King Edward Point.'

'I'll see what can be done; we're concerned about missiles from Hope Point.'

'I can't see any movement over there, sir, it seems safe enough.'

A few moments later *Antrim* moved out of the shelter of the peninsula into the open fjord and began to shell still closer to Grytviken.

'That'll rattle their best china,' Chris shouted to Tony Ellerbeck.

On board *Antrim* Lieutenant-Colonel Eve was directing the first real naval barrage he had ever seen. This is what men must have faced at the Somme every day, he thought. The gun crew were stripped to the waist, struggling to feed shells at a rate they had never dreamed of in practice. The paint had long ago burned off the red-hot gun barrels.

Chris Brown's voice crackled onto the radio. 'Can I lob a few shells into the whaling station, sir? There may be snipers hidden in there.'

Eve glanced at Captain Young, who shook his head angrily. 'For God's sake, no! What's the matter with your spotters, don't they understand English? No damage to property.'

The SAS mountain troops had now reached the crest of Brown Mountain ridge and were at last looking down into King Edward Cove. The dark silhouette of the *Santa Fe* could be seen on the jetty in front of the base. Down below them in the tussock grass the Puma helicopter, wrecked by Keith Mills and his marines, lay on its side. From his vantage point it looked, to Chris Brown, like a fortified gun position and he called its coordinates to *Antrim*. Almost immediately a salvo of shells burst around the hulk.

'You're shelling a dead helicopter,' Christian radioed back to the ship. The shelling moved back to Brown Mountain. *Plymouth* was now lobbing shells over the top of *Antrim* and they were screaming across the base onto the scree of Mount Duse. It must be terrifying in that building, he thought.

They were now over the ridge and heading down the hillside towards the whaling station. There was still no sign of opposition. 'Let's have a go at the *Santa Fe* with a Milan missile, we're just about within range now,' David Hamilton called to Christian. The two men set up the firing posts and Christian began to load the missile.

53

Shackleton House, King Edward Point, Sunday 25 April 1982

While Captain Horacio Bicain organised the evacuation of the *Santa Fe*, Hugo and Tono Cassin ran up to the radio shack. Luciano Lagos, the commando captain, was speaking to his men over the radio. He looked tired and frustrated.

'I've done as much as I can, sir. We have the jetty and helicopter pad booby-trapped and I've set mines alongside the tracks to Hope Point and Grytviken,' he said.

'Have you got enough weapons for the submarine crew?' Hugo asked.

'Not really. We have some rifles and ammunition but most of the men are untrained in this kind of fighting. We'll use them to defend the base. There isn't enough winter clothing to go round anyway, so they won't be able to go outside for long. My own men have set up a number of machine-gun sites and we have an anti-tank battery at Hope Point. The garrison troops aren't up to much, most of them want to throw in the towel. To be honest, I don't think we can hold out for long but we may be able to give them a bloody nose before we're done.'

The radio crackled into life and the cultured voice of Alfredo Astiz came on the air. 'What's happening, Capitan Lagos?' he asked.

'Nothing much at the moment, Teniente, the submarine crew is still arriving at the base. There have been no further attacks by the British helicopters.'

'We have our orders, Capitan; we must fight to the last man. Argentinian soldiers do not surrender.'

Hugo took over the microphone. 'We'll do what we can, Alfredo. It's impossible at the moment to know what we're up against and we're short of weapons and have injured men here. This is not a suicide mission as far as I'm concerned.'

Captain Bicain had just entered the shack and was listening intently to the exchange.

'You know your orders, Corti,' Astiz snarled. 'You must defend the island to the last drop of your blood.' The radio went dead.

'Ignore him, Hugo, he'll be the first to run when the bullets start to fly in his direction,' Horacio said, laying his arm on Hugo's shoulder.

They left Luciano Lagos speaking to his men and went back into Shackleton House. It was mobbed with sailors still milling about in a state of shock. Ricardo, the injured gunner, had been carried upstairs and they'd laid him on the same big table that Sergeant Leach had used when he sighted his sniper's rifle on the *Guerrico*. Ricardo still had a tourniquet around his thigh; the medics gave him another shot of morphine and stripped away his clothing. The leg was a mangled, ugly mess and they realised immediately that there was nothing they could do to save it. One of the men dashed down to Captain Bicain. He looked shaken and nervous.

'Ricardo's very bad, sir, we don't have a doctor but I think we should remove his leg. If we don't do something immediately I think he'll die.'

Horacio nodded. 'Hugo, I'm needed here to organise my men, can you help with the operation? Capitan Lagos will see to his marines.' He managed a weak smile. 'I told you today might prove interesting.'

The room upstairs was quiet compared with the chaos below. The two medics had already set up a saline drip and were cleaning down the table with disinfectant. A stove was boiling water and packs of surgical instruments were strewn along one of the benches.

Ricardo was still conscious, looking pale and frightened. 'I told you your capitan would get you back in one piece,' Hugo said.

The young gunner tried to smile. 'Are you going to take my leg off, sir?' he asked, his eyes pleading.

'Yes. It's a mess I'm afraid, and there's nothing we can do to save it, but we'll get you a brand new one as soon as we get home. You'll be up on your feet in no time.'

A feed had been set in one of the veins on his wrist and one of the medics inserted a syringe. Hugo smiled and held his hand as he watched the young man's frightened eyes close and his body relax.

'I'm going to take it off at the knee,' the medic said, pulling a mask over his face. 'I've never done anything like this before; I usually have to ask permission to dispense an aspirin.'

As he reached for the saw the first shell from HMS *Plymouth* exploded into Hestesletten Flats. The base shook and the noise increased in volume as shell after shell screamed over the building.

'Get on with it,' Hugo said hopelessly. 'There's nothing more that we can do.'

Reluctantly, the three men set about their gruesome task.

Forty minutes later they had finished. The barrage was still continuing, and the noise from the bombardment had reached a deafening crescendo. Hugo went down the stairs. His head ached and his hands were shaking. He found Horacio in the radio shack with Captain Lagos. Both officers were very agitated.

'We've decided to surrender, Hugo. There's nothing we can do – there aren't enough weapons to defend the place. They know that if they shell the base we'll be blown to bits. I've managed to contact Mar del Plata and given them a report of our situation. Officially we're instructed not to surrender and to fight to the last man but they know our situation. There are none of our ships in the area so I guess we're on our own. The admiral is going to protest to the United Nations. One of the men has put a white flag up the pole but the British either can't or won't see it. And we can't seem to get anyone on the radio.' He handed Hugo a cigarette and lit one himself.

'We can see troops coming over the ridge above the whaling

station and there are two battleships at the entrance to the cove. For some reason they've been shelling the crashed helicopter,' Captain Lagos said.

Hugo was trying not to duck each time a shell screamed over the building. 'I agree. We should put some sheets out of the windows and anywhere they can be seen – there must be spotters guiding the artillery, surely somebody will see them. If they really wanted to kill us they would have blown this place to pieces by now.'

'Tell the men what we are going to do, Luciano. I don't want any heroics – too many lives are at stake – and for God's sake make the gun crews keep away from their weapons.'

Horacio switched to channel sixteen and, speaking in English, tried again. 'This is Capitan Horacio Bicain, can anybody hear me?'

There was a short pause and then a clear polite voice came over the air. 'Reading you loud and clear, Captain, strength five, please pass your message.'

Horacio took a deep breath. 'I am senior officer on the base; I wish to announce that I and my men wish to surrender. There will be no resistance. I have a serious casualty requiring urgent medical attention.'

'I understand, Captain, please stand by.' There was a short pause and then another voice came on the air. 'This is Captain Young, HMS *Antrim*; it will take a few minutes to stop the bombardment. When it does your men must come out into the open and stack their weapons on the beach. You will be treated correctly under the rules of war.'

Horacio acknowledged and a few minutes later the shelling stopped abruptly. An eerie silence settled over the cove after the deafening roar of the last hour. Horacio went back on air and spoke to *Antrim's* radio operator. 'The helicopter pad, jetty and both tracks to the base are mined; your men must take great care as they approach.' There was little else he could do. He and Hugo sat glumly down to await their fate.

The call to cease fire crackled over the radio as John Hamilton and Christian were still in the process of launching the Milan missile. The temptation to go ahead anyway was almost overpowering. Shells continued to explode on the mountainside for a few minutes before they came to an abrupt stop. The troops were spread in a wide line descending the steep slope above Grytviken. Everybody stopped and waited. They were all very fired up. It was almost 5 p.m. and dusk was already spreading over the South Georgia mountains.

Major Delves, ahead of the main force, was almost at the whaling station with a warrant officer from the Royal Signals and two of the SAS mountain troops. He could see the white flag flying below the Argentinian pennant and white sheets were visible from most of the windows.

'They've chucked it in, it's all over bar the shouting,' Delves said.

Instructions for all troops to stay where they were came over the radio. 'Bugger that, my set's not working properly, let's go and sort them out,' Delves said.

The others grinned. 'We're with you, sir.' They walked out into the open and began to march quickly along the track through Grytviken, past the old whale catcher, *Petrel*, still floating alongside the flensing platform, and a couple of half-sunken hulks along the front of the factory buildings.

'What about mines, sir?' one of the men asked, nervously.

'The ground will be disturbed, keep a careful eye; it should be easy to see where they are,' Delves said.

A hundred yards up the track they came to the first machinegun post. The nervous crew were standing well away from the trench with their hands held high in the air.

'Good afternoon, how do you do?' Delves said, as he marched past without stopping.

As they approached the base the Argentinian defenders were spilling out of the buildings; they looked nervous, demoralised and dirty. Delves said, 'Good afternoon' to everyone as he passed.

Three officers stood by the flagpole in front of Shackleton house, looking awkward and uncertain. Major Delves walked up and saluted smartly. 'Good afternoon, do any of you speak English?' he asked.

'Good afternoon, sir, I'm Capitan de Navio Hugo Corti and these are Capitan Horacio Bicain and Capitan de Corbeta Luciano Lagos. Capitan Bicain of the submarine *Santa Fe* is the senior officer here. We all speak some English.'

Major Delves shook the hand of the three captains awkwardly; he was at a loss for what to do. A large crowd of nervous-looking Argentinian soldiers were milling around them.

'Please ask your men to go down to the beach and await instructions.'

A Wasp helicopter was slowly approaching the base. 'The beach and helicopter pad are mined,' Captain Bicain said urgently. 'Capitan Lagos will show where it is safe for the men and we must signal the helicopter away from the landing place.'

Tony Ellerbeck landed Guy Sheridan alongside the flagpole a few moments later. By now British troops were arriving in single file along the footpath from the whaling station. The temperature was falling, there was a rising wind and there were a hundred and twenty Argentinians now milling around the buildings like an unwieldy crowd at a football match.

SAS Sergeant-Major Lofty Gallagher arrived with his team and removed the Argentinian flag, replacing it with a Union Jack, a family heirloom he had saved for just such an occasion. Looking very pleased with himself, he set his men about the search for booby traps and weapons but it seemed clear that the Argentinians were simply pleased to be alive and there was little likelihood of last-minute resistance.

'Sir, one of our seamen is badly wounded and needs urgent medical care. Can you help?' Hugo asked Guy Sheridan.

Sheridan spoke rapidly into his radio to Tony Ellerbeck. 'Bring him out on a stretcher, we'll fly him out to the sickbay on *Antrim*,' he said.

Antrim had entered the cove and dropped anchor close to the base. *Endurance* and *Plymouth* moved in and blocked the entrance while *Brilliant* stood guard out at sea, the warships standing out, dark and dwarfed against the stark contrast of the surrounding snow-clad mountains. A tired and very relieved Guy Sheridan had a busy night ahead. As darkness fell it was too late to transfer any of the prisoners to the ships and they would have to spend another uncomfortable night in the base. It was built to house thirty or so fids and there were now a hundred and twenty prisoners and eighty Royal Marines.

Captain Brian Young took stock: Leith Harbour was still in Argentinian hands, though Tim's SAS team were giving a running report of their every movement and were confident it should be dealt with by tomorrow. Three of his men were missing in one of the Gemini assault craft and nobody was very hopeful of their survival. All this could be sorted out in the morning. It was twenty-three days since the Argentinians had invaded the Falkland Islands: three weeks of bad news, national humiliation for the government and frustration for the British navy. It was time to be optimistic – with the exception of one injured seaman there were no Argentinian casualties and very little damage. So far, so good.

In classic naval jargon Captain Young signalled Admiral Woodward, his immediate superior officer on board HMS *Hermes*, who was leading the Task Force slowly south:

Be pleased to inform Her Majesty that the White Ensign flies alongside the Union Jack in Grytviken, South Georgia. God save the Queen.

54

The signal was passed on immediately. It was 8 p.m. in London when Commander Denis Davies and Peter Bacon-Smith became fully aware of the situation. It had been a long and worrying day at the *Paraquat* cell, deep below the ground in the bunker at Northwood. Denis was exhausted, having hardly left the room during the past week. The men shook hands with an overwhelming sense of relief.

Peter made an immediate telephone call to the prime minister's office and after a few moments' wait Mrs Thatcher came on the line herself. 'For a change I have good news, Prime Minister,' he said.

An hour later a jubilant Margaret Thatcher stood with John Nott on the steps of 10 Downing Street facing a barrage of the world's press.

'Rejoice! Just rejoice!' she told them.

Shock and relief was very evident on both their faces. She was clearly overwhelmed by the success of the mission after being informed, only hours earlier, of the SAS disaster on the Fortuna Glacier.

In retrospect these were strange and inappropriate words to signal the opening of hostilities between Britain and Argentina but such are the fortunes of war, and disaster had been averted by the narrowest of margins. The prime minister had been totally clear and determined in her objectives and her support for the navy was much appreciated by the officers and men in a service that had suffered under political masters whose sole interest had been to reduce costs. Perhaps she could be allowed her moment of glory.

The Task Force now changed gear as it approached the total exclusion zone around the Falklands. The diplomats had failed to find a political solution and the hovering about was over. Aboard his flagship, the aircraft-carrier *Hermes*, Admiral Sandy Woodward gave a rare interview to the detachment of war correspondents accompanying the ships.

'South Georgia is the appetiser. Now it's the heavy punch coming up behind. My battle group is properly formed and ready to strike. This is the run up to the big match, which, in my view, should be a walkover,' he said.

How wrong can you be!

55

Grytviken, Sunday 25 April 1982

Nick Barker and Guy Sheridan tapped politely and entered the untidy, smoke-filled room used by the Argentinian officers in Shackleton House. The three captains sitting inside jumped uneasily to their feet.

'Hello, Horacio. The last time we met was under much better circumstances,' Nick Barker said. *Endurance* had moored alongside the *Santa Fe* earlier in the summer at Mar del Plata and the officers and men had socialised together.

Captain Bicain shook hands awkwardly. He was still uncertain how they were to be treated and the dreadful events of the day weighed heavily upon him. Hugo, though, was amazed at Bicain's composure: he was still functioning and clear headed.

Guy Sheridan came straight to the point. 'We have no wish to use unnecessary force against Teniente Astiz and his men, Captain. He is hugely outnumbered and there will be no dishonour in surrendering his command. We understand that there are still some civilian scrap-metal workers at Leith – all your people will be treated well. As the most senior officer on the island will you use your authority to convince him that it will only cost lives if he attempts to put up a fight?'

Horacio thought for a moment. 'Teniente de Navio Astiz is the legal military governor of this island. He has the full authority of the Argentinian Government and I have no authority over him. He has said that he is prepared to fight to the death.'

'What about the civilian workers? They should have no part in this,' Nick Barker said.

Horacio glanced at Hugo and nodded his head. 'I'll see what I can do. Capitan Corti knows him better than I, and perhaps he can help convince him.'

The whole party walked to the radio shack and after a short call Astiz's voice came on air. He spoke politely in perfect English and Nick Barker formally asked him to surrender. There was a short pause and then he came back on air speaking in rapid Spanish. None of the British officers could understand a word but it was evident that the three captains were trying to convince him that the game was over.

'If I fall into British hands it will be very bad for me, I'm a wanted man in Europe. This place is well mined and booby-trapped; we can hold out for a long time, my men are very determined. Tell them I will not surrender and will fight to the death.'

'Don't be a fool, Alfredo; you will be blown to pieces and the workmen with you – there is no dishonour against these odds,' Hugo said.

'You always were spineless, Corti, tell them and be damned!'

Captain Bicain sighed and reverted back to English. 'I'm sorry, he will not surrender,' he said.

'It's all very well being heroic but this man's bloody stupid,' Nick Barker said as he and Guy Sheridan left the radio shack. He and Captain Pentreath of HMS *Plymouth* were given the job of clearing the Argentinians out of Leith. None of the troops on their ships had been involved in sorting out the base and the remaining men of the SAS and SBS were raring to go. Tim's observation team were still watching the Argentinians and confirmed that there was an ideal landing beach hidden from view at the north side of Leith Harbour. His men would open up with small-arms fire to keep the garrison's heads down while the landing took place and the two ships would bombard the hill behind the whaling station. It was going to be hard to avoid a bloodbath.

56

Through the night *Endurance* and *Plymouth* moved into position outside Stromness Bay in preparation for a dawn attack. In the early hours of the morning Nick Barker once again spoke to Alfredo Astiz.

'For goodness' sake, Teniente, we have no wish to harm you – you are totally outnumbered,' he said.

'I am a trained commando and an underwater swimmer, I will place limpet mines on your ships during the night,' Astiz shouted over the radio.

Nick grinned at this extraordinary statement; it was a pitch-black night and the Argentinian could not possibly know where the ships were, let alone swim any kind of distance in these freezing waters; the man was behaving stupidly.

It was a hectic night as they prepared for a dawn assault. Under the cover of darkness *Plymouth* entered Stromness Bay and, sailing as near to shore as she dared, lowered the ship's Avon inflatable dingy and the remaining serviceable Gemini assault craft into the water. The men had considerable problems negotiating large floating masses of kelp but within an hour Tim was able to take command of sixty well-armed members of D Squadron SAS who spread out in concealed positions along the crest of Harbour Point ridge.

Nick Barker took his ship's cutter and crossed over to *Plymouth* for a last-minute conference with Captain Pentreath. While he was away the radio sprang to life. It was Alfredo Astiz. The officer of the watch who received the call was Surgeon-Lieutenant Neil Munroe.

'I have changed my mind,' Astiz told the startled surgeon. 'I no longer intend to fight. Please accept my immediate surrender.'

The surprised surgeon managed to relay the message to his captain and a few minutes later Nick contacted the Argentinian and accepted his surrender.

It was arranged that at first light the civilian metal workers would walk out along the beach to the waiting troops, where they would be searched. Astiz suggested that he and his men should form up on the old football ground behind the whaling station and mark out a landing site for the helicopters. This was agreed. At 6 a.m. *Endurance* launched her two Wasp helicopters with the remaining SBS commandos, who landed on the beach ready to receive the workmen.

As the first light of dawn tinged the South Georgia mountains a line of torches emerged from the buildings and forty-eight civilian scrap men plodded along the beach to the waiting troops. They were filthy, unkempt and terrified, convinced that they were going to be shot, many of them old men with little understanding of what was happening to them. The soldiers searching them for hidden weapons were shocked at the state they were in.

Nick Barker was uncomfortable. 'There's something fishy going on; I don't know what it is but I don't trust that man,' he said to Tony Ellerbeck as he prepared to fly out to meet the Argentinians. 'We'll skip the football pitch. Get Astiz on the radio and tell him to take his troops down to the beach; I want him out in the open.'

They radioed the new instructions to Astiz, who reacted angrily. 'No, Captain, the football ground is a much better place, it's very open ground.'

'You and your men will leave the buildings in single file and proceed unarmed to the beach where you will be met by my men,' Nick insisted.

There was nothing Astiz could do but comply and a few minutes later the two captains watching from their ships through binoculars saw the contingent of soldiers emerge and walk along the beach to the waiting SBS where they were stripped and searched and very pleased to get back into their clothes. These were a very different calibre of men to the civilians but in comparison to the SAS and SBS troops they were facing they were a pretty poor lot and wouldn't have stood a chance against Tim's small observation party. Had they put up a fight they would have been polished off easily.

The prisoners were taken along to Stromness to await transport to the ships and Tim took his men forward and began to search Leith. A few minutes later he radioed Captain Barker. 'Sir, this place is a bloody time bomb; there are mines all around the buildings and on the beaches. It's pretty primitive stuff but very dangerous. We've just found an oil drum packed with explosives hidden under the helicopter site on the football pitch. You and Captain Pentreath would have been blown to smithereens if you'd landed there.'

'Fly Astiz out to *Plymouth*, we'll sort things out there,' Nick said, thoughtfully.

During the night a surrender document had been drawn up and that morning a formal ceremony took place in *Plymouth's* wardroom. The document was signed by Captains Nick Barker and David Pentreath on the British side and Alfredo Astiz for Argentina.

'What about the booby-trapped helicopter pad, Alfredo? You had unconditionally surrendered!' Captain Pentreath exclaimed as they completed the signing.

Astiz grinned, completely unrepentant. 'It was the only way that I could get you.'

David Pentreath was disgusted. All the Argentinian officers he had met previously had been honourable men but this was the kind of behaviour of a man with no morals whatsoever. With people like this in power it was no wonder that Argentina was behaving so outrageously. Astiz was going on board *Endurance* to be transferred to *Tidespring* for the journey back to Ascension Island. Captain Pentreath was glad to be rid of him.

Tony Ellerbeck and his aircrew were among the searchers of

the buildings occupied by the Argentinians. In Astiz's room he found a large supply of condoms.

'What on earth are you doing with this lot in South Georgia?' he asked the Argentinian incredulously.

'You never know, you have to be prepared for anything,' Astiz smiled lewdly.

Nick Barker was not so amused and breathed a sigh of relief that the women still marooned around the island had not fallen into this man's clutches.

While the surrender documents were being signed Tony Ellerbeck was handed a signal from HMS *Plymouth*. A light had been seen flashing high on one of the mountains of the Busen Peninsula, thought to be the SAS team from the missing Gemini assault craft *Delta*.

How the hell did they finish up there? he wondered, as he prepared Wasp 434 for take-off.

Four nights earlier, as the outboard motors of the five Gemini assault craft began to fail one by one, *Delta* had taken *Charlie* in tow and reached the seaward side of Grass Island just before dawn. Tom, the sergeant commanding *Delta*, was faced with a double dilemma: should he remain to spy on the Argentinians or go back in search of his missing companions? Cursing under his breath he quickly confirmed that there was no opposition on the island and, leaving the crew of *Charlie* preparing defences, set off back into the heavy sea in search of the missing boats.

The sea was rising rapidly and a strong katabatic wind was blowing off the glaciers feeding into Stromness Bay. For an hour they searched for their missing comrades when, with little warning, an exceptionally large wave crashed into the side of the little inflatable. It smashed the machine gun mounting in the bow, swamped the boat and drowned the outboard motor.

They were now in the same situation as the other SAS boats, drifting rapidly out of Stromness Bay in the strong southerly wind, along the coast of the Busen Peninsula. As the first tinge of dawn lit the skyline the shadow of Justa Peak rose out of the sea, huge thousand-foot high cliffs with crashing surf at their base. The men bailed frantically as the Gemini drifted past, very close to destruction.

'Paddle for your lives, boys; if we don't get ashore somewhere here the next landfall's Australia!' Tom yelled.

As they passed the headland of Justa Peak they could see a small bay with a beach at the foot of the cliffs. With a superhuman effort the three men fought their way into the shelter of the point and leaped into the water dragging the half-flooded Gemini onto the beach. It wasn't much of a place, just a rocky cove with a crowd of inquisitive elephant seals. There was a cave at the foot of the cliffs and they dragged the Gemini up into its cover.

In true SAS fashion they settled down to discuss their options. Tom had the last word but listened attentively to the ideas of the others. They were dressed in drysuits but had taken a terrific soaking in the time they had drifted out of Stromness Bay.

'We work on the outboard all day and then motor up to Grass Island as soon as it's dark. Joe can try to fix the machinegun mounting and Mike and I'll make the bloody outboard work if it's the last thing we do,' Tom said.

Throughout the day they tinkered with the motor and catnapped in the cave but it was cold and miserable. The outboard finally fired up and they ran it on and off successfully until nightfall when, as darkness fell, they loaded the Gemini and set off. All went well until they rounded Justa Peak and were once again in the choppy sea. The outboard failed again and they were back in the same situation as the previous night; in total exasperation they paddled frantically back to their tiny beach. They stripped the engine again and made several attempts to escape throughout the night but each time the motor failed.

'Sod it, Sarge, it's a waste of time. The only way from here is up and out. The bloody outboard's had it, I've tried everything!' Mike said.

'OK, we should be able to climb out during the night and walk over to Husvik whaling station. We may be able to link up with the others from there,' Tom said.

The thought of climbing the huge cliffs above them was outrageous but there seemed to be no other option. They deflated the boat, hid it in the back of the cave and spent Saturday 24 April trying to rest and keep their spirits up. As darkness fell they started the long climb up the cliffs of Justa Peak. Each man was carrying eighty pounds of equipment and ammunition and an armour light rifle. They had no rope or proper climbing equipment with them. It was loose ground, mostly snow-covered rocks and scree with sheer rock steps to cross. Their progress was painfully slow. In the darkness and wind things seemed extraordinarily steep. At one point they found themselves teetering along a tiny snow-covered ledge with a colossal drop into the darkness below them.

The arrival of daylight found them high on the upper slopes of the mountainous ridge of the Busen Peninsula, with a long climb still ahead of them and a day's walk out to Husvik and Stromness. They had no idea what had happened to their team or what was taking place on the island. They were now in full view of Leith Harbour and were certain that any lookout worth his salt would spot them, so they took cover, digging some shelter into a snow slope, and settled into another cold day of inactivity.

The first crack of thunder was startling. In a situation like this the last thing they needed was a storm, but the weather seemed set fair and yet the sound continued and rose to a crescendo.

'That's like no thunder I ever heard, Tom; it sounds like gunfire,' Joe said.

They listened, fascinated, as the amplified roll of gunfire began to echo around the mountains. It seemed to go on for hours and come from all directions, reverberating through the valleys and down the glaciers. They could see that nothing was happening at Leith and assumed that some kind of battle was raging at Grytviken.

Around 5 p.m. it abruptly stopped. It was dusk with a rising wind and they began to prepare for another night's ordeal. Just before it became totally dark they spotted HMS *Plymouth* slipping up the coast towards Stromness Bay.

Tom grabbed his torch and began frantically signalling into the gloom in Morse code.

... S − − − O ... S ... S . − A ... S SOS SAS...

Plymouth slid quietly on into the night.

SOS SAS

Suddenly, a light began to flash on *Plymouth*. There was a long series of flashes.

'They've seen us,' Tom said. 'I guess there isn't anything they can do tonight: it's too dark to fly and the helicopter will give their position away to the Argies.' *Plymouth* was already vanishing into the gloom.

'At least they know where we are,' Joe said. 'They're bound to send help in the morning.'

'OK, we stay where we are, and if they don't appear first thing, we'll risk going for it in daylight; at least it will be safer,' Tom said.

And so began their fourth endless night in the open, short of food and miserably cold. Dawn found them exercising stiff limbs and boxing each other to keep warm. As daylight reached the mountains one of the Wasps from HMS *Endurance* flew in from the sea. Mike let off an orange smoke flare and the helicopter circled in towards them. They recognised the grinning face of Tony Ellerbeck waving from the cockpit.

'Bacon and eggs for breakfast in ten minutes, boys,' Tom said, with a wide grin on his face as the helicopter eased its way in towards them. Suddenly, they were engulfed in cloud. Horrified, they heard the Wasp accelerate its rotors and zoom away from the mountain in the direction of the ship.

It was a bad moment. Throughout the day the cloud hung around the mountain tops; twice they heard the sound of rotors but saw nothing and then, suddenly, it cleared and Tony Ellerbeck swooped down to the mountainside. Within minutes they were sitting down to eat the long dreamed of meal in *Endurance's* plush wardroom. Later that evening they joined the rest of their team as they started the work to make Leith Harbour safe.

And so the hostilities ended, though not entirely without accident. So far there were no British casualties and only one badly wounded Argentinian. The following morning an attempt was made to remove the slowly sinking *Santa Fe* from the much-needed jetty at King Edward Point. Captain Bicain agreed that his men could help blow the tanks and manoeuvre the submarine across to the old whaling station pier at Grytviken. It was a nerve-racking job, with British and Argentinian sailors working alongside each other in the eerie and claustrophobic inside of the boat. Petty Officer Felix Artuso was in the process of blowing air to clear the ballast tanks and one of the marines mistook his action for an attempt to scuttle the submarine. In the confusion he was shot and killed. Captain Bicain, who was on the conning tower at the time, finally collapsed in tears.

Sometime later Squadron Sergeant-Major Laurence Gallagher, who had raised the Union Jack over King Edward Point, was killed in a helicopter accident. While the mopping up and clearing of mines and boobytraps was going on Guy Sheridan decided that it was better to leave the stranded fids where they were.

57

RFA *Tidespring*, South Atlantic, Wednesday 4 May 1982

Alison and David stood at the stern of *Tidespring* along with a small group of civilian seamen, watching the Argentinian Boeing 707 aircraft circling the ship. They were six decks above the waterline on this massive ship and, two decks above them on the helicopter flight deck, they could hear the encouraging shouts in Spanish from the Argentinian prisoners, who were clearly watching with a different attitude to their anxious British captors. Half a mile away they could just make out the shape of HMS *Antrim*. Everybody was wondering whether she would use her Sea Slug missiles to bring down the aircraft. In the event nothing happened and the aircraft turned away to the north. Although it was well within range, Captain Young's request to take it out had been refused. The government was still forlornly pursuing a political solution, much to the frustration of the navy, which was beginning to feel extremely exposed.

For the residents of the small hut in Antarctic Bay it had been an exciting week. They had listened to the news of the recapture of Grytviken on the BBC World Service on the night of Sunday 25 April but, having heard the heavy gunfire, were uncertain what had exactly happened. It was not until Tuesday morning that Trefor Edwards at Lyell Glacier radioed in excitedly with the full story.

'We've just had a visit from one of the *Endurance* helicopters, David. It was Tony Ellerbeck. What a relief; we were just about out of food and they've sent us loads. Better still, there's a case of beer and a bottle of Scotch. The Argies at Leith have surrendered and apparently they're still clearing the place from mines. They want us to hang on for another day or two until they get things cleared up,' Trefor said.

'Got that, Trefor, don't drink it all at once!' David Asquith said, grinning over at Seb.

'We've already started,' Trefor called back cheerfully. 'We aren't going to hang around here, though, this hut is miserable. We're planning to walk out to Grytviken tomorrow. We'll go over Echo Pass and round Mount Hodges. Anything's better than this place.'

'Too right, Trefor, I don't blame you. We're OK here for the time being.'

They spent the day packing up their equipment. Seb had been filling boxes of rock samples and Anna sorted her film and camera equipment. It seemed amazing how much they had accumulated, well over a ton, Alison reckoned, and she hoped that whoever evacuated them would be as accommodating as the crew of *Endurance* had been.

It was not until the following day that they heard the thumping sound of an approaching helicopter and one of the Wessex choppers from HMS *Brilliant* circled and landed and they were shaking hands excitedly with the crew.

'We can't get you out until tomorrow afternoon,' the pilot said, 'but we've brought some goodies for tonight.' His wingman was lifting a large box out of the hold with eggs, fresh fruit, vegetables, bread and bacon.

'We liberated a lot of this stuff from the Argies at Leith; here's a box of Argentinian cigars. There's also some beer and a bottle of Scotch,' he said, to the delight of Seb Holmes.

'Most of the fids were evacuated today: you're the last to go. We're very short of space on the ships. We're putting you on RFA *Tidespring;* she's full of Argentinian prisoners but it's the only space we have. You'll be sailing directly to Ascension Island,' the pilot said.

'What about our samples and equipment? We have about a ton of stuff,' Seb asked, anxiously.

'That's OK, you ought to see what they've taken aboard from Bird Island and Schlieper Bay: they even had a crate with two live South Georgian pintail ducks for Peter Scott's Wildlife Trust. This is a hell of a strange way to run a war!' the pilot grinned. Before leaving he filled them in, as best he could, on what had happened during the last few days.

That last afternoon Alison and David walked down the snow-covered beach towards Cape Constance. It was a vastly changed place to when the two women had first arrived two months previously. The Antarctic autumn was well advanced now and many of the seals and penguins had vanished to their winter feeding grounds, but there was still a colony of elephant seals lying at the water's edge. The bay was filled with large icebergs carved from the Crean Glacier and these were reflected in the motionless bay. It was a peaceful, unspoiled place.

'This will be something to tell your grandchildren about,' David said.

'I've loved it: you couldn't invent a trip like this if you tried. I wonder if we'll ever come back to this place?' Alison asked.

Their last night at Antarctic Bay was a cheerful affair. They cooked a feast and at last there was no more rationing. The men smoked the Argentinian cigars and they all toasted each other. It was almost over and they were glad and sad to be leaving in almost equal measure.

They flew out to *Tidespring* the following morning. She was a huge, ugly floating factory of a ship, stripped almost bare of paint and damaged in the storms. Amidships she was festooned with cranes and derricks. There was a patch of metal plates welded along her port side, a remnant of damage she had sustained when she smashed into the dockside at Gibraltar in her rush to go south. Effectively, she was an unarmed merchantman with a civilian crew, one of the workhorses of the fleet auxiliary supplying fuel and stores to the Royal Navy under the control of Northwood.

Captain Shane Redmond met the Wessex as it landed on the large flight deck. He was in a rush to get away north. A small crowd of Argentinian prisoners were sitting on the deck aimlessly watching the scene, guarded casually by a single marine. The snow-clad peaks of South Georgia glistened in the distance but they didn't seem in awe of the view; merely pleased to be alive and in one piece.

'That's Captain Horacio Bicain, the commander of the *Santa Fe*.' The pilot pointed to a lone figure standing disconsolately looking out to sea. 'I guess he doesn't have much to go home to. He and Tony Ellerbeck are good friends; it was quite an emotional meeting they had at Grytviken. He's a good man and I suspect no lover of the junta but he's a patriotic Argentinian. We let him and the senior officers free on deck most of the time; they've given their word not to cause trouble.'

Alison found herself feeling quite sorry for the solitary figure, who must realise that his career was in ruins.

'He was terribly upset about the death of Felix Artuso; it was a ghastly accident and there's a lot of bad feeling about it among the Argentinians. We moved their commander, Lieutenant Astiz, over to *Antrim* to keep him from stirring up trouble,' Captain Redmond said.

They were taken below and given cabins in the crew's quarters. 'Eat with us in the galley,' the captain said. 'You're free to wander around the ship but keep away from the forward hold; it's being converted into a prison at the moment. The Argentinian scrappies are good workers and helping us build bunks. It will be a bit rough and ready but comfortable enough.'

The two women vanished off to find the first bath they had had in over two months. It was glorious to wallow in clean, soapy water. To their surprise and delight the ship's Chinese laundryman arrived, beaming from ear to ear, having washed their clothes in double-quick time, and carrying a large box of women's clothing. This was like a story book. The two women rummaged excitedly through and found some very presentable dresses and, for the first time in months, dressed smartly for dinner. Feeling self-conscious and very feminine, they went down to the galley.

At the bar they were met by a clean-shaven man with short-cropped hair in a dark suit, who offered them a drink.

'Thanks,' Alison accepted, smiling. There was something familiar about him and she looked again. 'My God, Seb!' They hugged each other, laughing. The transformation was startling: the scruffy geophysicist who hadn't cut his hair or beard in over a year had metamorphosed into a smart young man.

'You look twenty years younger, Sebastian,' Anna said, throwing her arms around him.

There was a discreet cough from the barman, who was pouring drinks behind the counter. He handed them round, smiling, and then burst into laughter.

Alison looked at him, startled. 'David! Oh, I don't believe it.' The tall young man behind the bar was barely recognisable: gone was the mane of curly hair and smart trimmed beard.

'You look pretty startling yourself, Alison,' he said, coming round and kissing her shyly on the lips. Alison found herself looking at this strange new man who she hardly recognised and realised that he was going through much the same thing.

The evening meal was a pleasant affair. The helicopter pilot, Lieutenant-Commander Mike Tidd, introduced himself. After his crash on the Fortuna Glacier he had found himself and the rest of his flight crew jobless so they had offered their services as guards for the prisoners.

'I didn't realise that there were so many or we might not have been so keen,' he said, wryly.

He was surprised to learn that they had seen the helicopters fly up the glacier and he had not at the time realised that there were people in Antarctic Bay close to the crash site.

'We were in big trouble ourselves, almost in the same place,' David told him, and explained about his and Sebastian's epic crossing of the Fortuna Glacier.

At the end of the meal Captain Redmond tapped his glass and made an announcement. 'We have just heard that HMS *Conqueror* torpedoed and sank the Argentinian battle cruiser *General Belgrano*.

It seems that it went down quickly and there is thought to be significant loss of life.'

There was a stunned silence. 'The *Belgrano* has been a constant worry. It happened not far north of here, less than three days' steaming from South Georgia. With her heavy armour, six-inch guns and Sea Cat missiles she's been a grave threat to both us and the main Task Force, and she's been able to vector aircraft flying, from the mainland, onto us,' the captain continued. 'News is out on the World Service and there's an international outcry. I guess we can say that, if not before, Britain and Argentina are now officially at war.'

There was consternation around the room. Up until now it had been an almost gentlemanly confrontation. After the almost bloodless recapture of South Georgia it seemed as if some diplomatic solution might be found to end the conflict. What had happened to the battleship was too horrible to contemplate. The party spirit melted away and it was a sombre end to a pleasant evening. Everything had changed.

Later that evening, Alison wandered up on deck for some fresh air and made her way curiously forward, crossing the main holds to where much of the cargo from the forward decks had been moved in order to make room for the prisoners. She clambered up to where racks of the ship's lifeboats hung on their gantries. In this vast ocean the little open boats would be very vulnerable and she prayed that they would never have to use them.

A small man dressed in a long military greatcoat was standing at the rail looking out to sea, and she realised that this must be one of the Argentinian officers. He looked tired and ill.

'Are you all right?' she asked politely. 'I don't want to disturb you.'

The man jumped nervously and then steadied himself. Alison saw that there were tears on his face.

He clicked his heels, straightened his back and reached out a hand shyly. 'I am Capitan Hugo Corti,' he said, speaking in almost faultless English.

'I'm Alison Shackleton; I'm one of the field personnel who were stranded on the island,' she said, taking his hand.

'Ah, my apologies. I was the officer in charge of the garrison at Grytviken: we had no means of coming out to rescue you. It seemed better to leave you where you were.' He made no mention that Astiz had suggested that the scientists might well be used as a human shield.

'We expected that you'd collect us very early on and couldn't understand why you just seemed to ignore us?'

'You were safer where you were,' he said, without explanation. 'We did not think that your government was interested in South Georgia and would retaliate, and we were woefully undermanned. Most of the reinforcements that we expected were sent to the Malvinas.'

They stared out to sea for some time, watching the sky darken.

'I understand that you will be going home once we get to Ascension Island,' she said, breaking the silence.

There was a long pause. 'I'm not sure what kind of reception we'll have when we get home,' he said, pensively.

'I expect your family will be pleased to see you,' Alison said, tentatively.

There was another long pause and then he offered her a cigarette. She shook her head and he lit one himself, his hands shaking.

'My son, Raul, was on-board the *General Belgrano*. I have no idea what has become of him,' he said quietly.

Alison was shocked at the enormity of this man's situation. He was leaning against the rail, drawing heavily on his cigarette, trying desperately to control his emotions. She rested an arm on his shoulder for a while and they stared out into the falling darkness.

'Oh, Argentina, however did we get into this situation?' he asked, shaking his head.

She had no idea how to comfort him and after a while she left him in the darkness; a small, solitary man staring blankly into the night.

Aftermath

London, April 2007

On Monday 2 April 2007 it was twenty-five years since the Argentinian invasion of the Falkland Islands, and a day later the anniversary of the first battle of Grytviken, where Keith Mills' small party of marines had defended King Edward Point. The details of the short but bloody war that followed are common knowledge, but what fate awaited those who had been involved in this earlier skirmish?

During his short time as a prisoner of war, Mills was never sure what kind of reception he would receive on his release. His orders had been vague to say the least and he had the underlying concern that he might return home to face a court martial. He knew he had acted on impulse when he ordered his men to open fire on the Puma helicopter, but felt that his action had been common sense and that he had done his best under the circumstances. During his confinement he was questioned civilly by his captors and congratulated on his defence of King Edward Point.

One admiral shook his hand and said, 'Remember, when you get back to England tell your people you have been treated well here. In the war that will soon come, we shall expect the same hospitality.' Perhaps he had a premonition of the future.

Mills, the contingent of marines and the captured fids were released and flown to Uruguay, where at Montevideo Airport they were amazed to be greeted by a battery of the world's press. Everybody wanted to buy them a drink and they were flown back to Britain via Ascension Island to a hero's welcome. After a short leave, at their own request, they returned south to rejoin HMS

Endurance. At their stopover on Ascension Island they had the satisfaction of guarding Alfredo Astiz before he was shipped to England. After the war a grateful government concluded that they had done as much and more than could be expected. Lieutenant Mills received the DSC and Sergeant Peter Leach a DSM.

HMS *Antrim* headed back to the Falkland Islands and was involved in much of the fighting. During the San Carlos water landings she was hit by a thousand-pound bomb, which ripped through her deck and landed in her Sea Slug missile store, but fortunately it did not explode. She had the luck of the Irish on that day. Both Lieutenant-Commander Ian Stanley and Petty Officer Fitz Fitzgerald received shrapnel wounds in the same attack.

After the war, *Humphrey,* Antrim's famous old Wessex 406, became a permanent exhibit at the Fleet Air Arm Museum at RNAS Yeovilton. Looking into her small hold it's hard to imagine how this old machine managed to lift sixteen very thankful SAS men off the Fortuna Glacier. A letter of thanks from their leader, Major Cedric Delves, to Ian Stanley likened the whole escapade to something out of a boy's adventure annual.

Our indebtedness to you is great. There is no doubt that, without you, the successful outcome of the operation would have been soured by particularly high losses amongst the squadron. You were so successful that 406 was coming to be viewed by us as a cure-all!

Ian Stanley and Captain Brian Young both received DSOs and Lieutenant Chris Parry and Fitz Fitzgerald were mentioned in Dispatches. *Antrim* sailed home to a hero's welcome and was decommissioned two years later and sold to Chile, where she is now renamed *Almirante Cochrane.*

HMS *Plymouth* also went north to the Falklands and was the first ship to enter San Carlos water during the landings, where she was one of the few to be undamaged in the attack. A few days later she was attacked by five Mirage aircraft. She shot down two with her Sea Cat missiles and damaged two others but was hit by four bombs and numerous shells. One hit her flight deck and detonated a depth charge and another entered her funnel, though failed to explode. Nonetheless, she underwent emergency repairs and rejoined the fleet to provide gunfire during the mopping-up operation off Port Stanley. Her captain, David Pentreath, received a DSO. She was the last Type 12 frigate in service and was decommissioned in 1988.

As for the Red Plum, HMS *Endurance*, she remained in the Southern Ocean throughout the war. She once more went into action on *Operation Keyhole* when, in the depth of the Antarctic winter, they overran the illegal Argentinian base on Southern Thule in the South Sandwich Islands. Grytviken became the safe harbour for the fleet to a far greater degree than the naval planners had originally anticipated; it was used for the cross-decking of thousands of men and hundreds of thousands of tons of stores, ammunition and food. King Edward Cove was at times filled with ships: on one occasion the two luxury liners *Queen Elizabeth II* and *Canberra* transferred 5 Infantry Brigade before they went into action. The two giant liners almost filled the cove.

Endurance, with her sophisticated listening gear, acted as guard and maintenance vessel. She was the first and only ship in the South Atlantic at the outbreak of hostilities and the last home at the end. She arrived at her home port of Gillingham after almost a year to a tumultuous welcome. Some twenty-thousand people turned out to meet the little red ship that the Argentinians couldn't sink. Relatives and dockworkers screamed themselves hoarse as a veritable armada of small boats escorted her up the Medway into the dockyard. Fire hoses sprayed multicoloured rainbows in the sunshine; there were balloons, hooters and sirens blaring. Among the dignitaries awaiting the Plum and to shake Nick Barker's hand was Lord Shackleton.

In defence of his intention to scrap *Endurance* without replacement, John Nott, the defence secretary, said, 'She possesses only limited military capacity.' This may well be true but she was one hell of a ship. In the spring of 1982 Britain was still carrying a proportionally heavier defence burden than the rest of her NATO allies, the cold war was waging and the Soviet Union seemed the only perceivable threat. Of the services, the Royal Navy was the least involved in European defence and was more associated with global reach. If cuts had to come it seemed to Nott that the navy could most readily be shrunk; hence his decision to sell one of the navy's aircraft-carriers to Australia and drastically cut a number of other types of ships, of which *Endurance* was one.

Captain Nick Barker had lobbied Whitehall that Argentina was making warlike preparations but the Ministry of Defence had ignored him. 'Barker is only trying to save his ship,' was the general opinion; ironically this was the same opinion held by Ambassador Anthony Williams in Buenos Aires. Nick's only ally was Governor Rex Hunt in Port Stanley. On the journey home he spoke out angrily to the press that his warnings regarding Argentinian intent had been unheeded. This did not bode well with his superiors or the politicians in Whitehall and he was effectively silenced. His unwelcome warnings had been proved right by events and, although he received an OBE for his part in the war, he was shunted into a career backwater and later took early retirement. Nick Barker died in April 1997 aged 63, a disappointed and angry man. Anthony Williams and Rex Hunt both received knighthoods.

HMS *Endurance* got her reprieve and a refit and continued her yearly lone voyages to Antarctica. Seven years later in 1989 she struck an iceberg and, although she was repaired, a survey in 1991 decided that her hull was not sound enough for the Antarctic seas and she was finally scrapped. Her replacement, the MV *Polar Circle*, was later renamed *Endurance*. Her Wasp pilot, Lieutenant-Commander Tony Ellerbeck, received a DSC and his observer, Lieutenant David Wells was 'Mentioned in Dispatches'.

None of the fids involved on South Georgia received any recognition for their part in the war, although at great personal risk, particularly at Lyell Glacier and St Andrews Bay, they had patrolled and spied on the Argentinians. The parties at Bird Island and Schlieper Bay monitored shipping and aircraft and kept constant lookout. The British Antarctic Survey gained much from the war: its budget was increased as the government realised that if Britain was to have a serious role to play in Antarctica they needed to be properly equipped and there are now large modern bases at Halley Bay and Rothera. In the 1970s and 80s most of these men and women went south on a two-year contract; these days with improved air transport most scientists are flown in for the summer and only a few overwinter. It was BAS scientists who first alerted the world to the hole in the ozone layer, the first major indicator of global warming. Field personnel such as David Asquith and Alison Shackleton still look after scientists and are working in isolated places deep in the Antarctic continent.

At the time of the Falkland invasion the vast majority of the British people were behind the government's decision to send the Task Force to the South Atlantic. There have subsequently been many political attacks on the prime minister for her bombastic attitude and general disregard for world opinion. Whatever happened in the future this was clearly not the case at the beginning of the Falklands conflict. Buenos Aires was excessively impatient to start the war, London curiously reluctant to accept what was staring them in the face. The desire for a bloodless resolution is very clear in the events of *Operation Paraquat*: Captain Brian Young could easily have pounded King Edward Point and Leith with overwhelming gunfire and there would have been little need to put the SAS and Fleet Air Arm helicopters at risk had the navy just sailed in and done its job. The more difficult 'gently, gently' policy was clearly chosen to leave a way open for the junta to withdraw without losing face; this the military regime of Generals Galtieri, Anaya and Lami Dozo studiously chose to ignore.

Buenos Aires, April 2007

The one hundred and fifty-one soldiers and thirty-nine civilians captured in South Georgia were taken by RFA *Tidespring* to

Ascension Island. After three weeks they were handed over to the International Red Cross and flown home to Argentina, with the exception of Alfredo Astiz. He now became an embarrassment to the British Government.

The 'Blond Angel' was sought in Italy for his role in the kidnapping of Angela Maria Aieta, and Giovani Pegoraro and his daughter, Susana. They had been held in the Naval Mechanics College but were never seen again. In France he was wanted for the abduction and murder of two French nuns, Alice Domon and Leonie Duquet, members of a support group for relatives of the 'Disappeared', which was infiltrated by Astiz posing as a student searching for his brother. The Swedish Government also asked for his extradition. In 1977 he had shot and wounded a seventeen-year-old Swedish tourist, Dagmar Hagelin, as she tried to evade a kidnap. Witnesses saw her later in the Navy Mechanics College and claimed that it was Astiz who interrogated her. She was never seen again. These foreign nationals were to cause him far more problems than the hundreds of his own people he was suspected of murdering.

In Argentina his most infamous coup during the dirty war was the successful kidnapping of Azucena Villaflor de Vicenti, the founder member of the 'Mothers of Plaza de Mayo', a non-violent group of mothers protesting at the disappearance of their children. Neither she nor any other mothers taken that night were ever seen again.

As the rest of the prisoners were repatriated the British Government came under intense diplomatic pressure from the French and Swedish Governments for his extradition. To buy time he was taken by ship back to London and the Foreign Office announced that he would be made available for questioning by their representatives. The questioning took place twice but on both occasions Astiz remained silent. As this was happening the Argentinian Government arrested three British journalists and accused them of spying, and indicated that their release would be linked to that of Astiz.

Much to the anger of her allies, Britain chose to interpret the third Geneva Convention as protecting him from criminal prosecution in the UK or from extradition, and he was repatriated to Argentina on 10 June, just before the start of the battle for Port Stanley and the Argentinian capitulation on the 14th.

After the surrender, the military junta was forced to resign and Argentina returned to democratic rule under the popular leadership of President Raul Alfonsin. In an attempt to reunite the country he set up a commission to discover the fate of the 'Disappeared'. Estimates varied that between twelve and thirty thousand people had vanished during the dirty war. The commission report, entitled 'Never Again', found that the armed services responded to terrorist crimes with a terror far outweighing the one they were combating. They used the impunity of an absolute state to abduct, torture and murder thousands of their own citizens.

The generals were put on trial. President Leopoldo Galtieri was indicted for numerous human rights violations. In December 1985 he was acquitted but recharged with incompetence concerning the Falkland Island invasion. He was stripped of his rank and sentenced to twelve years in prison. His sentence was later reduced by President Carlos Menem, and various amnesty laws made it almost impossible to bring the military to justice. In 2002 these laws were deemed unconstitutional and therefore null and void and he was rearrested. He died in January 2003 before it was possible to put him on trial.

Admiral Jorge Anaya was tried and acquitted; various attempts have been made to rearrest him. General Jorge Videla and Admiral Massera were both sentenced to life imprisonment for crimes of assassination, illegal confinement and torture. They were pardoned and freed in President Menem's general amnesty.

Various attempts have been made to extradite Alfredo Astiz but under Argentinian amnesty laws he remained a free man and well-known face in Buenos Aires. In 1987 he was promoted to captain in the navy. During the same period he was tried in absence by a French court and sentenced to life imprisonment. Two international arrest warrants have been issued for him by Italy and Sweden.

Like the psychopath he is, he has shown no remorse for what occurred during the dirty war. 'I regret nothing,' he bragged to outraged reporters during an interview. 'The military chose the only option open to them to save the country from communism. I was the man best prepared to kill politicians and journalists.'

For this outburst President Menem discharged him from the navy and he received a three-month suspended jail sentence.

In 1995 Adolfo Scilingo became the first Argentinian military officer to be tried in Spain as a foreign national, charged with crimes against humanity committed in an outside country. He spoke openly about the abuses of the junta. According to him up to two thousand people were thrown, fifteen to twenty at a time, into the sea from aircraft during 'flights of death', run every Wednesday for over two years.

In July 2003 Argentina repealed the decree prohibiting extradition and on the same day Astiz was arrested from his house in Mar del Plata. The following day France requested his extradition. During the next two weeks he was released and rearrested but the French request was refused and he was once again, and still remains, a free man.

After the war Constantino Davidoff contacted Salvesen and, to Sir Gerald Elliott's amazement, asked if he could continue with the contract to retrieve the scrap from Leith. He was politely refused. 'What about the money I paid for the scrap metal?' he asked. 'No Argentinian is going to get within sight of the island for a very long time: you are in breach of the contract,' he was told. Salvesen kept the money.

In 2004, President Nestor Kirchner announced that the Naval Mechanics College in Buenos Aires was to be converted to a 'Museum of Memory' to the 'Disappeared' of the dirty war. It would be nice to think that Captain (Retired) Hugo Corti, his wife, Maria, and son, Raul, a survivor of the sinking of the *Belgrano*, were present at the inauguration.

The situation between Britain and Argentina is little changed. The old war cry '*Las Malvinas son Argentina's*' (The Falkland Islands are Argentina's) has resurfaced in graffiti and posters all over the country. The Islands are a matter of wounded pride. At 2006's service of remembrance to the dead in the Falkland War President Kirchner said, 'The Malvinas must be a national objective of all Argentinians and with dialogue, diplomacy and peace we must reclaim them for our fatherland.'

In Britain, little has changed. The war drifts from people's memory as other, more recent events, take the centre stage. A garrison of some twelve hundred troops protects two thousand six hundred islanders at an estimated cost of a hundred and ten million pounds per year.

On South Georgia little has changed on the beautiful island. At Grytviken the old whaling station rots slowly away and the whale catcher *Petrel* now rests on her side, no longer floating. The British Antarctic Survey has a brand new scientific base where the old Shackleton house once stood at King Edward Point.

A recent article in the *Guardian* said, 'The three most basic truths self-evident to any Argentinian are: Evita is a saint, the footballer Maradona is God and the Malvinas belong to Argentina.' To them this may seem so: the Maradona claim may not require third-party corroboration but the Vatican has yet to be convinced about Evita, and the Union Jack still flies over South Georgia and the Falkland Islands.

Postscript

In 2005 Argentina's Supreme Court decided that the amnesty implemented during the transition to democracy was unconstitutional and legal action against Astiz was renewed. His defence that he was a military officer under orders was followed by the unrepentant statement that he had been persecuted by a government that 'won't forgive us for having successfully battled subversion'.

Alfredo Asdiz, now 59, was tried with seventeen other former military and police officials and found guilty of crimes against humanity inside the Navy Mechanics School. He was sentenced to life imprisonment by the Supreme Court in 2011.

Under the same court decision Spain attempted to extradite General Jorge Anaya. While awaiting trial he suffered a heart attack and was rushed to a naval hospital where he was deemed unfit to stand trial. He died on 9 January 2008, still under house arrest on charges of human rights violations.

Bibliography

Barker, Nick, *Beyond Endurance*, Trowbridge, Redwood Books, 1997

Buxton, Cindy & Price, Annie, *Survival South Atlantic*, Book Club Associates, 1983

Carr, Tim & Carr, Pauline, *Antarctic Oasis*, London, W. W. Norton & Co. Ltd., 1998

Elliott, Gerald, *A Whaling Enterprise (Salvesen in the Antarctic)*, Norwich, Michael Russell (Publishing) Ltd., 1998

Hastings, Max & Jenkins, Simon, *The Battle for the Falklands*, Michael Joseph Ltd., 1983

Perkins, Roger, *Operation Paraquat (The Battle for South Georgia)*, Chippenham, Picton Publishing Ltd., 1986

West, Nigel, *The Secret War of the Falklands*, Little, Brown & Co., 1997

Woodward, Admiral Sandy, *One Hundred Days*, Harper Collins, 1992

Worsley, Commander F. A., *Shackleton's Boat Journey*, The Folio Society, 1974